Dry Stone Walling

BTCV is the UK's largest practical
conservation charity annually involving 130,000
volunteers in project to protect and improve
the environment – in the UK and worldwide.
BTCV runs a programme of training courses,
many of which are designed to help people put
the theory contained in the Practical Handbook
series into practice. For information about any
of BTCV's volunteering opportunities, please
contact us at the address below:

Other titles in BTCV's
Practical Handbook series:

Fencing

Footpaths

Hedging

Sand Dunes

Toolcare

Tree Planting and Aftercare

The Urban Handbook

Waterways and Wetlands

Woodlands

To order any of these, or for details of other
BTCV
publications and merchandise, please contact:

BTCV, Sedum House, Mallard Way,
Doncaster DN4 8DB
Tel: 01302 388883

www.btcv.org/shop

Dry Stone Walling

a practical handbook

Alan Brooks
Sean Adcock

edited by Elizabeth Agate

BTCV

ACKNOWLEDGEMENTS

In addition to those individuals and organisations acknowledged in the first edition of Dry Stone Walling (published 1977), BTCV acknowledges with thanks the advice received from the following individuals during the research for this second edition of Dry Stone Walling:

Nick Aitken; Steven Allen; John Bown; John Butler; Seamus Campbell; Roger Clemens; Philip Clark; Daryl Craig-Elliot; Philip Davies; Jeremy Gavins; Dave Goulder; Norman Haddow; Stephen Harrison; Garth Heinrich; Ivan Hewitt; Kathryn Hewitt; Sally Hodgson; Vic Hollings; Brian Hough; Richard Ingles; Gary Knipe; Richard Leishman; Roger Lewis; Richard Love; Simon Lund; Alistair MacDonald; Grant McFarlane; John Pengelly; Shaun Seaman; Jimmy Scott; Mick Sharp; Jacqui Simkins; Andy Stokes; Peter Tennant; Kirsty Thornber; Alex Turner; Trevor Wragg.

The staff and members of BTCV who have contributed their advice and experience.

Many thanks to The Esmée Fairbairn Charitable Trust
for generously supporting the development of *Dry Stone Walling*.

DISCLAIMER: The information given in this publication on behalf of BTCV is believed to be correct, but accuracy is not guaranteed and the information does not obviate the need to make further enquiries as appropriate. This publication is not a comprehensive statement on all safety procedures and the reader must take all reasonable steps to ensure the health and safety of all users and to take all necessary steps to implement a health and safety policy. This publication is issued without responsibility on the part of BTCV for accidents or damage as a result of its use.

ISBN 0 946752 19 2

Written by Alan Brooks and Sean Adcock, edited by Elizabeth Agate

Illustrations by Elizabeth Agate and Linda Francis

First published 1977

Revised and newly illustrated, August 1999

Appendices revised September 2002 and June 2004

5 7 9 8 6 4

BTCV acknowledges support from the Department
of the Environment, Transport and the Regions.

Produced in-house by BTCV Publications. Typeset in 9.5/12pt Palatino

Printed by Wrightsons Limited, Earls Barton, on recycled paper.

Published by BTCV, Sedum House, Mallard Way, Doncaster DN4 8DB
Registered Charity 261009

Contents

Introduction   vii

1 Walls in the landscape   1
    Characteristic regional walls....................... 1
    Walls in history.. 8
    Wall dating.. 10

2 Dry stone walls and conservation   13
    The loss of walls and banks........................ 13
    The condition of walls 13
    The wildlife value of walls.......................... 13
    The future of the walling craft.................... 15

3 Walls and the law   17
    Wall ownership 17
    Boundary wall maintenance 17
    Obligation to fence 18
    Tenant and landlord 18
    Rights of use.. 18
    Treasure trove 19

4 Safety, equipment and organisation   21
    Site risk assessment 21
    General safety considerations 22
    Work season and weather precautions........ 26
    Clothing 28
    Tools and accessories................................ 28
    Organising group work 34

5 Know your stone   35
    Building for durability................................. 35
    Characteristic walling stones..................... 36
    Sources of stone and amounts required............. 37
    Breaking and shaping stone 40

6 Rebuilding a free standing wall   45
    General features... 45
    Walling procedure...................................... 46
    Dismantling.. 47
    The foundation 48
    Use of batter frames.................................. 49
    Building 51
    Throughs.. 55
    Coping.. 56
    Gapping 57
    New walls.. 58
    The use and abuse of concrete and mortar 59

7 Technical walling   61
    Walls on slopes 61
    Coping on slopes.. 64
    Walls on undulating ground 65

    Walls across slopes 66
    Curves 67
    Obstacles.. 68

8 Retaining walls and stone hedges   73
    Retaining walls 73
    Stone hedges.. 76
    Cloddiau 77
    Cornish hedges 81
    Turf tops 84
    Galloway hedges 85
    Stone hedge furniture 86
    Protection, maintenance and repair.................... 88

9 Standard wall furniture   89
    Wall heads 89
    Changes in direction 92
    Cripple holes and smoots.................................... 93
    Stiles 97
    Gates... 101
    Walls with fences.. 104

10 Dry stone features   107
    Pillars 107
    Cairns 112
    Arches 114
    Niches and boles 117
    Holes and apertures 118
    Seats... 120
    Steps... 121
    Pens 121
    Butts 122

11 Variations in walling   125
    Dimensions... 125
    Specialist building techniques 128
    Throughstones... 130
    Types of coping 132
    Single walls or dykes 139
    Galloway dykes.. 141
    Stone fences... 144

Appendices   147
    A Conservation and the volunteer worker........ 147
    B Contacts.. 148
    C Associations, training and grants 150
    D Site studies and surveys............................. 152

    Bibliography 154
    Glossary.. 156

Index   159

Introduction

This handbook describes how to construct and repair dry stone walls, stone-faced earth banks, retaining walls and other dry stone features. It is intended to be used by conservation volunteers and others interested in learning the skills of dry stone walling.

Building with dry stone is one of the earliest skills developed by man, used for building shelters, fortifications, burial mounds, ceremonial structures and animal enclosures. The Neolithic village of Skara Brae, in Orkney, built in about 3000 BC and buried in sand for thousands of years until rediscovered, demonstrates the early development of skills in dry stonework. The magnificent Iron Age fortified buildings of Scotland, called brochs, which have stood for thousands of years, are proof of the durability of this ancient craft.

Dry stone walling is so durable because it contains no mortar to crack and fail, but is held together merely by the weight of stone, and by the skill of the builder who selected and fitted the stones together. Dry stone structures are constructed in such a way that as they slowly settle with time, they become stronger and more closely bound. A correctly built structure of durable stone contains nothing which can deteriorate or fail. Dry stone structures use only natural material, with many walls and other structures built of stone gathered at the surface or by quarrying outcrops. Dry stone is infinitely recyclable.

Dry stone walls dominate the rural landscape wherever stone is near the surface. The thin soils and exposed conditions limit tree growth, and so the characteristic landscape of fields and dry stone walls has developed. In most of these areas stone provided a fortuitous building material in the absence of timber for fencing or bushes for hedging, but where surface stone was over-abundant, walls were an essential way of clearing the ground for grazing and cultivation.

In areas such as parts of Wales and the South West, where soils are deeper and surface stone less abundant, stone-faced earth banks are the traditional method of enclosure. These banks provide shelter from the wind for both animals and crops, as well as using up surface stone. Sometimes a hedge is planted along the top to provide additional shelter. Various combinations of stonework, bank, ditch, hedge or fence are used according to the site and the circumstance.

The skill of dry stone walling has a fairly continuous history, being practised by farmers wherever land needed enclosing or walls repairing. At times of agricultural change, notably during the enclosure era, there was an expansion in the amount of walling, with a large number of skilled workers employed during the late 18th and early 19th century. By 1820 the walled landscape was largely complete, and was kept in good repair for about a hundred years until the mechanisation of agriculture brought the next wave of change. The latter part of the 20th century has been characterised by a huge reduction of the numbers of people working on the land, and the demise of the multi-skilled farm labourer. Craftsmen wallers had only been needed in times of agricultural expansion, and by the 1960s walling as a full-time occupation had virtually disappeared. It was then that the conservation movement gained momentum, in time to learn the skills from those who remained.

The Dry Stone Walling Association started in 1968, and is a thriving organisation with about twenty local branches, a recognised Craftsman Certification Scheme, and a register of qualified, skilled wallers throughout Great Britain. BTCV continues to play an active part in introducing volunteers of all ages to the craft of walling, in developing skills, and in helping to rebuild this important part of our upland landscape. There is a still a huge amount to be done. A survey in 1994 revealed that of a total estimated length in England of 70,000 miles (113,00km), only 4% are categorised to be in excellent condition. 50% are no longer stockproof, with most of these remaining only as derelict or remnant walls. At current prices, it is estimated that it would cost £3 billion to restore them all to excellent condition.

Dry stone walling is not just a skill to be used in the rural uplands. In the last few years, dry stone wallers have become involved in designing and building garden features, sculptures and other structures, bringing the skill of dry stone walling into community gardens and other urban sites. Wherever it is built, dry stone work can be useful, aesthetically pleasing and a valuable wildlife habitat.

1   Walls in the landscape

Characteristic regional walls

Dry stone walls reflect the bedrock or glacial drift material which lies beneath them. Originally built with what came to hand during field clearance, few field walls were important enough to warrant the transport of stones over any great distance. The Enclosure Era blurred the lines slightly, as for example on the borders of the Craven district of Yorkshire, where sandstone 'throughs' were sometimes transported several miles across country to use in the limestone walls. In the Cotswolds, much walling stone was produced as a by-product of building-stone quarries located some miles away. On the whole though, even during the most intensive period of new walling, most stone was quarried very close to the lines of the walls. Stones were carted, carried or sledged downslope to the work site, with small quarries being constantly opened and abandoned as the wall progressed.

With modern transport, some walls, particularly new or rebuilt roadside walls have lost their distinctive local identity as stone is transported over greater distances. In the Lake District, for example, there has been much rebuilding in cut slate supplied by a few big quarries. Although cheaper and quicker to build, these walls can look quite foreign to those of different types of stone or local slate. Generally though, the policy is to try and blend new work with old, so that the two can hardly be distinguished once the harsher angles and different colour of new stone have weathered and aged. There are often unavoidable differences with new stone, as modern quarries may have stone of a slightly different character from older quarries in similar stone.

Despite these qualifications, dry stone walls provide an excellent introduction to local geology. At the same time, geology reveals why the walls are there in the first place, and why they take on rather different forms in different areas. This connection between local geology and dry stone walling is developed in the following section.

The simplified geological column below helps put into perspective the approximate ages of the various types of walling stone mentioned in this handbook.

Virtually all stone used in this country for dry walling dates from the Jurassic Period or earlier, although Cretaceous materials such as flints are found in mortared walls in southern England, where more suitable stone is generally lacking. The most important types of stone for dry walling include Jurassic and Carboniferous limestones, Triassic,

Permian, Carboniferous and Devonian sandstones, Silurian, Ordovician and Cambrian slates and shales, Precambrian metamorphic rocks, and volcanic and granitic and other intrusive rocks of various ages.

Era	Period or System	Start of Period (millions of years ago)
Cenozoic	Quarternary	2
	Tertiary	63
Mesozoic	Cretaceous	135
	Jurassic	180
	Triassic	230
Palaeozoic	Permian	280
	Carboniferous	345
	Devonian	405
	Silurian	425
	Ordovician	500
	Cambrian	600

Precambrian

One can get a rough idea of where walls are likely to be found in Britain by looking at a geological map. Bear in mind though, the complicating effects of glaciation throughout large parts of Britain. In some areas, notably much of Ireland, glacial drift has covered up the useful walling stone. In other areas, poor underlying stone has been augmented by glacially transported boulders, so that walls have been built where, by the map, none would be expected.

The design of a typical dry stone wall is shown below, with the parts named in accordance with widespread north-of-England usage. The ways in which regional and local styles differ from this general pattern are described further below, and in Chapter 11.

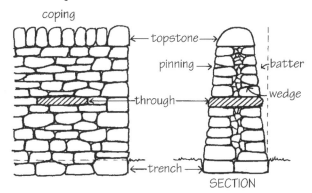

SECTION

SOUTHERN AND CENTRAL ENGLAND

If one thinks of walling in southern or central England, it is the landscape of the Cotswolds which probably springs to mind. Stone walls and buildings of warm russet-brown or golden grey which, according to J B Priestley, know 'the trick of keeping the lost sunlight of centuries glimmering upon them'. The stone is Jurassic limestone. The thicker oolitic beds supply freestone for building purposes while the shelly limestones, which break irregularly, provide ragstone for the walls. Most Cotswold walling stone is quarried from a layer about a foot below the subsoil, under which lies the more regularly jointed building stone. In the past, large areas of quarry land would be scalped of their overburden to expose the wall stone layer, which would be allowed to weather and break up naturally with the winter frosts. In some places, as at the top of Bredon Hill, the walling stone is fairly hard and rings when hit, but elsewhere it is soft or grades into sandstone and sounds dead when tapped. The harder the stone the better it lasts, and experienced Cotswold wallers can tell at a glance where their supply has been quarried and what its qualities are.

The Cotswolds form only one part of the Jurassic limestone belt which runs right across southern and central England from the Isle of Purbeck north-northeast to the Cleveland Hills. Each district shows the influence of local variations in its stone. The belt is quite narrow, trailing off into clay vales along the southern or eastern dip slopes. This is the country where, as Hawkes (1951) puts it, 'the sudden appearance of walls instead of hedges catches the eye'. Nowhere is the change more dramatic than in Lincolnshire, where the limestone of Lincoln Edge is only a few miles wide, and there is an abrupt change from hedges with brick and timber buildings, to the geometrical austerity of dry stone walling.

There are other areas of walls in central and southern England. In northwest Leicestershire, the hills of Charnwood Forest, rising unexpectedly from the Midlands plain, and representing an island of Precambrian granitic, volcanic and slaty rocks, possess rough and intractable boulder walls which seem more in keeping with the mountainous West than with the fertile and gentle country around.

The rocks of the Mendips, while not nearly as ancient as those of Charnwood Forest, form an equally interesting inlier among the more recent deposits of this region. The Mendips consist largely of a plateau of Carboniferous limestone, the oldest widely occurring limestone in Britain, out of which protrude a few higher hills of the older and more resistant Old Red Sandstone. Limestone dominates the walls, although sections built of sandstone or breccia occur where these rocks form the uppermost strata. The breccia is known locally as 'pudding-stone', a term also used locally to describe any round stone, in order to

distinguish it from the more angular 'ploughshare' stones. Many of the fields are large, with the north-south walls often higher than those orientated east-west.

At first glance the walls look very much like those of the Craven district of Yorkshire, but on close inspection their stones are rougher and more irregular, and they lack throughs and topstones.

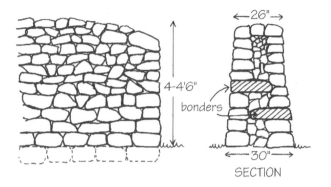

SECTION

'Bonders' are used instead of throughs, extending part way through the wall. These are important because Mendip wallers tend to place many of the face stones with their long edges running along rather into the wall, known elsewhere as 'traced' stones. Short stones used with their long edges into the wall are known as 'key stones'. Mendip walls are built with little batter; only about 2" (50mm) for a 4-4'6" (1.2-1.37m) high wall.

In general, walls throughout southern and central England lack the variety of openings and other structures which are such a feature of Pennine, Lakeland and Scottish walls.

THE PENNINES

The Pennines represent the single greatest expanse of walled country in England. Rising from the Midlands plain on the Staffordshire-Derbyshire border, the moors run northward for about 140 miles (220km) to the Tyne Gap. Immediately beyond, the Cheviots continue the uplands to the Border Country, while to the west the Howgill Fells create a link with the Lake District. The bedrock geology of this area is fairly simple, but contains striking contrasts. In the Craven district of northwest Yorkshire and in the central Peak District of Derbyshire, Carboniferous limestone forms the surface cover. Here, over the ages, water and ice have carved a landscape of glaring white crags and scars where underground watercourses abound but there are few surface streams and pools. Farther south and east, through most of South and West Yorkshire and Derbyshire, the relatively acid and impervious shales and sandstones of the Millstone Grit and Coal Measures cap the geological series. Here, and over wide areas throughout the Pennines where glacial deposits obscure the solid geology, drainage is poor, and surface waterlogging has encouraged the formation of sombre heather moors or blanket peat bogs.

The limestone pavements of North Yorkshire and Lancashire are of particular interest, both for their geological and botanical importance, and as unique landscape features. These pavements, along with those of Cumbria and elsewhere in the British Isles comprise the world's most important areas of limestone pavement, so there are also international responsibilities to protect them. Throughout history they have formed tempting sources of stone supply, with widespread damage in Victorian and more recent times for walling and building, and for ornamental and rockery stone. While the importance of limestone pavements is now recognised, damage by deliberate removal of stone or inappropriate management is still taking place.

Most limestone pavements are now protected by Limestone Pavement Orders, which have the effect of prohibiting the removal or disturbance of limestone. Many important pavements are also included within Special Areas for Conservation (SACs) under the EU Habitats Directive, and these and other pavements will also have been notified as Sites of Special Scientific Interest. However, statutory protection needs to be accompanied by a reduction in demand for limestone pavement stone, which is sold as 'water-worn stone', 'Cumberland limestone' or 'Westmorland limestone'. Local authorities are being urged not to specify such stone in their landscaping schemes, and to ensure that it is not used in any development which requires planning permission. For further information see the advice leaflet *Limestone Pavement* (Countryside Commission, 1998)

The walls of the Pennines reflect the geological contrasts in their colouration: clean grey-white in the limestone districts, dappled at their border with other formations, and sooty grey or dark brown elsewhere. The colour alone is enough to tell you when you have crossed the Craven Fault near Stockdale or along the Settle-Malham road, revealing the alternating grits and limestones in the Yoredale series as the walls change from dark to light to dark again as they mount the upper slopes of Wensleydale.

In the northern Pennines the rocks are mostly of Carboniferous age, as in the Craven and Peak district, but here the strata are more mixed than further south and the walls are more often of varied sandstones and shales than of limestone. Of quite different origin are the walls of the Whin Sill, a dark blue-grey dolerite which was injected into the Carboniferous beds at a later date. The most famous of these walls is Hadrian's, which takes advantage of the craggy scarp formed by the Whin Sill along most of its north side. Parts of the Roman structure can be seen among the rough rubble of the farm walls which run back from its line. Also distinct from the main mass of sedimentary rocks of this region are the Cheviots: a granitic core surrounded by a dissected dome of lavas of Devonian age, from above which the Carboniferous rocks have eroded.

THE LAKE DISTRICT

The Lake District, a compact area only about 30 miles (48km) across, contains a surprising number of different rock types and corresponding styles of walling. Starting with the oldest formations in the district, the Skiddaw Slates of the northern peaks, one finds walls of dark or occasionally greenish fissile slates and flags. The wall shown has only one row of throughs, but two rows may be used depending on the height.

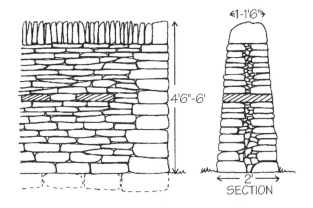

Between Keswick and Ambleside, in a broad zone which includes the most rugged part of the district, the Borrowdale Volcanics form a varied group of erosion-resistant massive lavas and tuffs. The granite and granophytes of Ennerdale and Eskdale produce walls of similar type but a warm mottled pink. The volcanic walls are generally similar in design to those of slate but are generally coarser and more massive.

The Lake District is full of historically fascinating examples of stonework, such as the clearance walls (p126), and the 'cyclopean' walls of huge boulders found in several locations. The most impressive of these, about 9' (2.7m) high on the downhill side with enormous footings, runs beside the road near Far Kiln Bank above the Duddon Valley.

The southern part of the Lake District is made up of Silurian slates, which includes shales and flags as well as true slates. These resemble the Skiddaw slates in their well-marked cleavage which produces slabs for walling.

Where the Coniston and Brathay Flags occur at the boundary of the Silurian slates and Borrowdale Volcanics, roughly quarried slates are sometimes used upright to make stone fences (p144). Many examples can be found around Coniston, Hawkshead and Ambleside.

Around the edges of the Cumbrian dome other newer rocks occur which connect Lake District walls with those of the Pennines and the Carlisle area. Carboniferous limestone around Furness, in the area south of Kendal and elsewhere is used to build silvery-grey walls, quite similar to those found farther east in Yorkshire. New Red Sandstones occur on the coast around St. Bees and in the long tongue of the Eden Valley, where the walls are rusty red and often of shaped and well-bedded blocks, while between here and the limestone area is a narrow belt of Coal Measure gritstone walls.

WALES

Gwynedd contains most of the oldest rocks in Wales, and has a complex geology, reflected in the range of wall types. Slates, granite and volcanic rocks, Carboniferous limestone and Precambrian schists and gneisses lie in a series of roughly parallel bands broken by intrusive dykes and sills. The topography is determined by many factors. Most of Anglesey belies the diversity of its bedrock, as it is a fairly uniform, low plateau which represents an old wave-cut platform. Around Snowdonia, volcanic rocks play a significant part in the strong relief. The area is a syncline of resistant rocks, sculpted by glaciation. Similar rocks occur also in Cader Idris to the south, while the intervening Harlech Dome consists of more highly eroded Cambrian grits and slates.

Volcanic rocks dominate the walled farmsteads of the western foothills of Snowdonia and parts of the passes of Llanberis, Nant Ffrancon and their surroundings. The stone is tough and coarse, the walls rough and grey. Along the roadside in this area every sort of combination can be seen: rough volcanic copings on slate walls, slate copings on slate walls, slate copings on rubble walls, and slate fences.

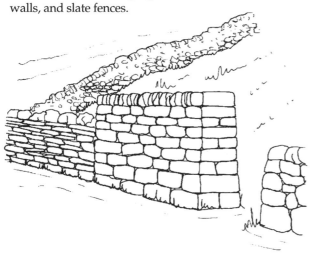

Moving south, the wide expanse of central Wales with its rounded hills of mudstones, shales and slates, is mainly hedged or fenced, although quite often a wall separates the rough grazing of the highest land from the better fields below. The South Wales valleys present a scene more like that of the southern Pennines than of the rest of Wales, with grits and flags predominating

THE SOUTH WEST

All linear enclosing features which are not regular masonry are termed 'hedges' in mid and west Cornwall. Through much of this area the hedges are earth banks faced with stone or turf, but on the high downs and moors, especially in the far west, dry stone hedges are common. The distinction between dry and mortared walls and earth banks is sometimes blurred. On the moors and country around Camelford some dry stonework is found, but most of the hedges are of earth capped with stone or brushwood. A type of hedge found occasionally in the Boscastle-Tintagel district consists of stonework only one stone thick. Similar walls are common on the Isles of Scilly, and it's said by islanders on the 'off' islands that such walls were built so that gaps could easily be made as necessary to take boats across the fields to the sea, when sea conditions prevented boats being launched from their usual landing.

It is the stone- or turf-faced bank which is most commonly called a hedge in other parts of the South West, and this forms the dominant type of fence whether or not it is crowned with a row of living shrubs. Turf hedges are described in *Hedging* (BTCV, 1998). The design and construction of stone-faced banks is described in chapter 8 of this handbook.

The 'standard' Cornwall County Council stone hedge is shown on page 81, and is the type specified in county road-widening schemes. It may be built in two forms, depending mainly on whether the stone used is slate or granite. The use of quarried slate from north Cornish mines has been extended into the western granite areas, although this is unpopular with local craftsmen who prefer the traditional material, however expensive. For farm hedges the source of stone is normally the land being cleared. The stone is mainly fragments cleared from the surface or within a plough's depth. 'Pop' or decomposed granite is favoured because it has flat surfaces. Blue elvan, which is also found, is harder to handle because it is smooth and splinters into wedge-shaped pieces. Around Truro most of the stone used is spar, supplemented by waste stone from the tin and copper mines, and by quarried granite. The latter is an expensive material which is usually laid in even courses of smooth blocks to produce a neat, masonry-like finish. Unfortunately these blocks bind poorly with each other and with the earth packing and tend to slump, especially when placed with their long edges along rather than into the bank.

The last two rows of slate hedges are normally built in the herringbone pattern, also called 'Jack and Jill' or 'Darby and Joan'. This helps to use up the small pieces which are cracked from the 'raisers' or face stones during building, and provide a good rooting medium for the turf capping. Herringbone work is usually found wherever thin, splintery stone must be used which would otherwise be hard to manage.

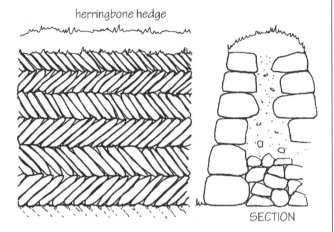

herringbone hedge

SECTION

Many stone hedgers prefer to use rough horizontal coursing of largely untrimmed material, which some claim is stronger, as well as being easier and faster to build. The Devon 'chip and block' style is similar, being roughly graded from biggest at the bottom to smallest at the top, but there is a mixture of small stones (chips) and large stones (blocks) within each layer. Great emphasis is given to placing the stones tightly together and to wedging them from behind so that they sit well and bond with the earth packing. Cornish work often shows considerably more earth between the stones on the face of the wall.

The diagram shows different sides of the same gate end, near Dartington, South Devon. One side was built in 'chip and block' by a local worker, the other by a Cornishman. Both sides use mainly river-washed boulders, but the Devonian has knocked off most of the rounded faces to bring them into line with the overall batter. In chip and block the stones can be placed either vertically or horizontally, and

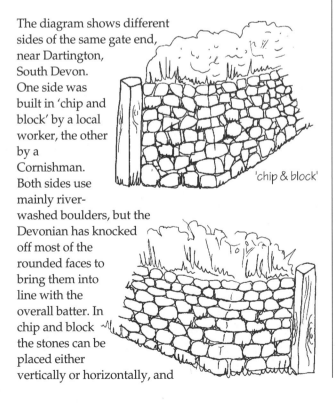

'chip & block'

the joints are broken depending on the alignment of the stones.

In the South West, free-standing dry stone walls are mainly limited to the edges of the granite moorlands: Dartmoor, Bodmin Moor, the Land's End area and the Isles of Scilly especially. They are of rough horizontal courses, sometimes topped with turf. In a few places granite walls give way to more geologically diverse structures, such as at Sticklepath on the north edge of Dartmoor, where there is a remarkable range of rock types, colours and textures in the local walls. Free-standing walls and stone hedges are sometimes intermixed in a boundary, and derelict free-standing walls tend to be rebuilt as stone hedges.

One sort of wall which is unlikely to ever need repair is that found in a few places on Dartmoor, but most spectacularly near Zennor, in the far west of Cornwall. Some of the tiny fields are enclosed with single rows of enormous granite boulders or 'grounders', rising up to 7' (2.1m) from the ground. These are relics of ancient enclosure, and may be 2,000 years old or more.

Although such walls seem primitive, the clever granite cattle grid (p87) is part of the same enclosure system.

SCOTLAND AND THE ISLE OF MAN

The 'drystane dykes' or dry stone walls of Scotland are found in various forms which reflect the type and size of stone in the locality, as well as particular walling techniques, both local and more widely adopted.

The typical dry stone wall is called a 'double dyke', because it has two faces, which are packed with hearting and joined with throughstones as in other areas. Almost any type of stone can be used, but whinstone double dykes are more common through central Scotland, with sandstone dykes found in certain districts in Southern Scotland and the west coast. The dimensions given below were as specified by the Stewartry Drystane Dyking Committee (Rainsford-

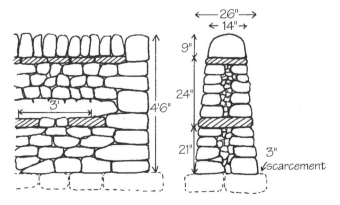

Hannay, 1972). The subdivision dyke is the normal height wall for field enclosure, with the higher march dyke used as a boundary to the great estates.

Whinstone is rough and makes a varied and irregular dyke such as that shown, containing ordinary 'doubling' stones, big face stones called 'blonks', and wedge- shaped stones called 'nickers', which help bring the course up to level. Pinnings are used in the face. Sandstone dykes are often cut and trimmed and built up in evenly graded courses. Face stones are placed with long edges into rather than along the wall. A feature is the use of the 'locked top' (p133) using heavy wedged topstones. One third of the wall's weight is supposed to be in the coverband and coping. The throughstones and coverband project about 2" (50mm), to help dissuade sheep from jumping the wall.

As with north of England walls, Scottish double dykes are well supplied with openings for the use of the shepherd and trapper. Construction methods are the same as in England for 'pen holes' (rabbit smoots) and 'double water pens' (water smoots). 'Lunkies' or 'lunky holes' (cripple holes) are made narrower at the bottom than the top, rather than being rectangular (p94).

More common in Scotland than elsewhere in Britain is the single dyke, built of stonework one stone thick. This developed as a way of using large stones, and is particularly suited to coarse textured stone, such as granite, which have less tendency to slide than does smoother stone. Single dyking is quick to build and repair, and it's said that sheep are discouraged from trying to climb anything which they can see through.

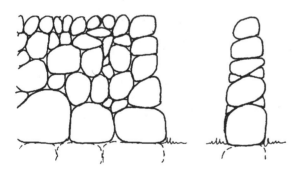

The half-dyke or Galloway dyke is a style found only in Scotland, and was developed in order to use a variety of medium and large shaped stones, with little hearting available. The larger stones are too large to use as the lower part of a double wall, as they would make a wall which would be too wide to fill with the hearting available. Instead,

in reverse to the normal procedure, the smaller stones are used in the lower part of the wall as a double dyke, and the large stones are used above as single stonework.

Further information on single dykes, half dykes and Galloway dykes is given on pages 139-144.

Galloway seems to have long been a centre for innovations in dyking methods, and for the export of men and ideas to other areas. The walls of the Isle of Man, mostly about 220 years old, were extensively rebuilt and improved in the 1880s by a pair of Galloway dykers with the help of local labour (Rainsford-Hannay, 1972). Slate-faced banks are prevalent but there are granite walls on the high ground and sandstone elsewhere. The sandstone outcrops in good-sized slabs, 2-3" (50-75mm) thick, which are used both in free-standing walls and in stone-faced banks. Some of the banking takes advantage of the slightly wedged shape of these slabs, where they are placed in vertical courses (p82) with their thick and thin ends alternating. The weight of the bank drives the stones tightly together. The banks are up to 7' (2.1m) high, about 6' (1.8m) wide at the base and 4' (1.2m) wide at the top, and topped with turf.

In the north of the Isle of Man, the easiest stone to find is water-worn beach cobbles. These are too smooth to use in the ordinary way, but are placed edgeways-in to face earth banks. The Manx free-standing walls are coped with very big slabs, tilted at about 15° from the horizontal.

The dykes of Aberdeenshire are designed primarily to fence cattle, and are found in two forms. The rough rubble or 'dump and hole' dyke uses field stones, mostly untrimmed, or with just their corners knocked off. The 'course dyke' uses trimmed quarry stones in neat courses.

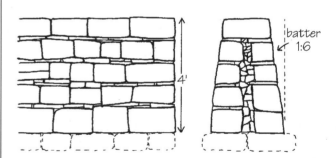

The stones are massive, about 1' (300mm) thick, and usually of granite. The dykes need not be as tall as sheep fences, but they are carefully built with no projections which cattle could rub against. Normally no throughstones are used, as stones which could span the wall would be too heavy to lift. The preferred topstones cross the full width of the dyke, and are trimmed so they don't project.

As well as fully dressed boundary walls, the Dunecht area has many rough rubble walls which appear at first glance to be ill considered heaps of boulders, until one examines the care with which individual stones are placed. A few miles to the north and west, the Cluny style takes over, which features low walls of small stones backed by post and wire fences. Still farther west, near Grantown-on-Spey, Morayshire, the dykes have a mixture of large and small stones in the courses, and are topped by rough upright boulders.

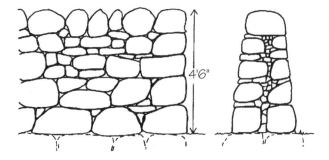

Whatever the local variation, these walls often require considerable work with the hammer and stone drill. More skill and patience are required to split granite, even roughly, than are demanded by most other stones.

IRELAND

Evans (1957) characterises Irish walls as untidy and cyclopean, mainly of rough glacial boulders and 'lacking the precision of those of north England or the Cotswold country'. This may be due to the absence of easily-shaped material, such as Jurassic limestone, as well as to the glacial drift covering so much of the country. Although a few walls or 'ditches', as all dykes or raised banks are termed in Ireland, are of Iron Age origin, most are from the comparatively recent enclosures of the 18th and early 19th centuries. Throughout the lowland farming country, the hedged ditch is common, sometimes with a 'sheugh' or open drain running alongside it.

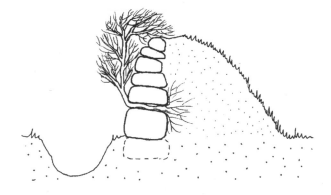

Throughout the south and central part of the country dry stone ditches, where they occur, are usually built with far less batter and far more stones than their Scottish counterparts, according to Rainsford-Hannay (1972), who goes on to list their typical dimensions as 6' (1.8m) high and 4' (1.2m) wide at the base. Throughstones are scarce but are sometimes used, and the coping may be of mortar, sod or small stones placed haphazardly on top.

In the west of County Clare and Galway, especially in the Burren district with its tiny fields and its outcrops of Carboniferous limestone, single-thickness walls are built which closely resemble the Galloway single dyke in style and function. Sheep are said not to attempt to climb these unsteady-looking structures. Single walls are also found around fields on stony moraines and drift-boulder hillsides. In east Galway the limestone ditches are built double to a height of about 2' (600mm), carefully levelled off and finished with a lacework of single boulders to a total height of 4-5' (1.2-1.5m). It would seem that this similarity between Galway and Galloway walls may not be coincidental, and that the Irish version may well have been introduced by incoming landlords and their agents. Mortar or cement is used in the coping of many Irish walls, and is sometimes used as a facing. The Irish language has no word for dry stone waller, but wallers are referred to as masons. This may also indicate the relatively recent importation of the craft into most parts of the country.

On Rathlin Island off the coast of Antrim, the idea of the unsteady-looking wall has been taken to the extreme. It's said that animals give them a wide berth once having learnt that they collapse almost at a touch. At the other extreme are the 10' (3m) high demesne walls running for miles around the big estates which, according to Evans (1957), are 'famine walls' built by destitute labourers in return for a pittance from the landowner.

Londonderry has examples of ancient head-walls, built to separate early farm enclosures from the rough outfields. These are known locally as 'Danish fences' and consist of irregularly piled stone slabs with standing stones set at intervals. Similar walls, and walls with many stones set vertically or diagonally are found elsewhere in Ulster and Munster. Often only the standing stones remain today, buried in the peat which has overwhelmed the ancient fields. Elsewhere in Ireland there are walls of almost indeterminate age: the wide granite accretion or clearance walls of the Mourne Mountains, for instance, which closely resemble those of the Lake District and Aberdeenshire.

Some of the walls of the Aran Islands have 'phantom gates', which had to be taken down every time cattle were herded through a field, and grazing plots four fields in from the road were not unknown. The reason for this laborious design was, apparently, less the lack of wood and metal but more the need to keep the wind from getting into the fields (Evans, 1957). Similar structures were also used in Connemara and County Clare.

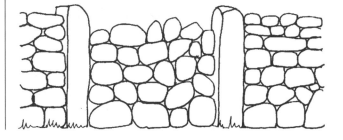

Irish walls generally lack stiles because there are very few footpaths among the tiny fields, while narrow wall-lined lanes are plentiful, with short-cuts seldom worthwhile. The acreage under stone is very great in some areas, with up to one quarter of the land taken up with stone ditches.

Walls in history

This history describes the field boundaries and enclosures built by farmers, husbandmen and labourers, which are such an important feature of the countryside they traverse, and which remain mostly in use today. It does not include the dry stone buildings and fortifications of earlier times, such as the Iron Age brochs of Scotland or the village of Skara Brae in the Orkneys, many of which exhibit advanced craftsmanship in dry stonework.

The enclosing of the rocky uplands of Britain began well back in prehistory, during the period when a nomadic pastoral and hunting life gradually gave way to settled farming. This left a permanent if faint mark on the land in the form of stone circles and surrounding irregular patchwork of ditches and dykes, which is the trademark of the 'Celtic' field system. These early settlements were concentrated on the drier terraces and hillsides where woods and scrublands were most easily cleared. They now remain, often far above the present limits of cultivation, as evidence of a milder climate. In Ireland the earliest traces of walled fields have been discovered incorporated into megalithic tombs of late Neolithic age. Here the pattern of small, apparently random-shaped fields may still be found around the scattered farmsteads which replaced the old 'clachans' or tribal hamlets.

In Britain, the remains of settlements around the South Western moors, in the Lake District and on the limestone and gritstone terraces of the western Pennines are usually assigned to the Romano-British period, although occasional findings have been dated as far back as 2000 BC. Certainly it was around the time of the Roman invasions when fairly cohesive tribal federations developed, capable of erecting extensive fortifications and defensive earthworks.

The next main period of wall building began in the early Middle Ages and continued, slowly and with many changes of pace depending on the economic conditions of the time, into the post-medieval period. It has been traced most thoroughly in Yorkshire where it is associated with the Anglo-Saxon and Scandinavian settlements of the 6th century AD onward (Raistrick, 1966). It was then that the open field system so characteristic of medieval English agriculture really developed. Typically, settlements divided their holdings into three sections. On the fertile, flat and seasonally flooded bottomlands the 'leys' or 'ings' were located, divided from the drier ground by a permanent ditch and fence, hedge or dry stone wall. The two or three common fields were similarly fenced off from each other, and from the third section, which was the common pasture

or waste which extended to the borders of the next settlement. There were no permanent divisions within the water meadows or the common field. Where medieval walls remain, they are of huge clearance boulders with little coursing of the stones, and no throughs or topstones, but with some batter. They follow fairly irregular alignments, in response to immovable obstacles or the waller's whim.

Although open-field walls can still be traced in some of the Yorkshire Dales villages, notably Linton in Wharfedale, the total impact of these enclosures was limited. Most land remained as waste, outside the bounds, although from the 12th century onward grazing disputes led in a few cases to the erection of walls between large holdings. These moorland walls or ditches are seldom traceable today, but they remain among the earliest fences for which written documents are available (p10).

Meanwhile in the 'Celtic fringe', the older infield-outfield system persisted, even where the earlier settlements were abandoned. In the granite areas of Cornwall and Devon, in parts of Wales and Scotland, and through much of Ireland, the story is one of continued nibbling away at the open land. Tiny garden-like plots fenced by massive clearance walls surrounded each farmstead, but these islands of cultivation remained virtually swamped in the vast expanse of open moor.

The next definable walling period, which particularly affected the Pennine region, started in the 14th and 15th centuries, and continued until the 18th. It was at its height in the Elizabethan period when cottagers and householders for the first time were legally permitted to enclose small 'crofts' or private holdings. The fertility of arable land was nearly exhausted by this period. To revitalize the land, it was necessary for individual householders to use their own stock to manure and improve their holdings. Crofts were small, about half an acre (0.2 hectare) on average, with four or five scattered crofts held by each house. Crofts were walled by the individuals concerned using stone quarried or cleared from the common waste. Although the walls were still squat and poorly coursed, their lines were rather more regular than the older piecemeal enclosures. By the 16th century, attempts were being made to breed improved types of sheep for their wool, and parts of the outlying wastes were enclosed to make this work easier. Enclosures in the north were restricted to the vicinity of the villages, while more extensive fencing took place in the south and Midlands. In the Pennines this period brought the completion of that 'maze of small enclosures, crofts and tiny fields, with scarcely a straight wall among them' which still surrounds many Dales villages (Raistrick, 1966).

The population continued to grow during the 17th and 18th centuries, putting pressure on the old open-field system. In the Pennines, this early industrial period saw the enclosing of 'intakes', which were rectangular fields of 1-3 acres (0.4-1.2 hectares), located beyond the old common fields. The moorland soil was unsuitable for crops, but could be limed and drained to support sheep. These intakes provided the mining and textile labourers who farmed them with a source of protein, as well as with the outdoor work which their employers considered beneficial.

This period also saw far more extensive enclosures to form the principal pastures of the community, often several hundred acres in extent, and divided adjoining townships from one another. They were made by common consent, and involved all the shareholders in the construction and, frequently, the repair of the walls. Usually a shepherd was paid to tend the pastures, and sometimes he had the duty of repairing walls and gates. Outside wallers or masons were seldom required, either for building or maintenance.

About 1780, the situation changed drastically. From this time, enclosures were promoted by large landowners or one or two private individuals in each area for their own benefit. These people had the means and influence to engineer private Acts of Parliament which effectively stripped the smaller farmers of their common rights. Each Act appointed commissioners to survey the area in question, and to allot portions to every claimant, along with proportional responsibility for fencing the holdings. Since the set limit for walling the bounds was only a year or two, the specifications were very exacting and the length required was often many miles, the commissioners had to hire wallers or men free from the land to do the work. Only the wealthiest parties could pay for this labour; the others had to forfeit their shares to the commissioners. As Raistrick (1966) concludes:

'The enclosures were a tragedy for the small man; he lost his right of pasturage on the common, lost his bit of land, and was compelled to become a wage labourer in a time of falling wages and rising cost of living. It secured the enslavement of the labouring classes.'

In 1801 the situation was further rationalised by a general Act of Parliament, and by 1820 most of the work was done. The old common field had been subdivided into small straight-walled rectangular plots. In the Pennines these enclosure walls are visually unmistakable, with their precisely placed throughs and topstones, uniform batter and unvarying height. These walls were planned by city surveyors and built by professionals, who worked in gangs all through the clement months to finish the job.

Taking England as a whole, much land was in its modern form even before the Enclosure Acts. In the Midlands, perhaps the heart of the open-field system, at least 30% of the land was enclosed by 1700. In many counties, including Kent, Sussex, Devon, Herefordshire, Worcestershire, Cheshire, Lancashire, Staffordshire, Northumberland, Durham, Suffolk and Essex the open-field system had never had a strong hold, and piecemeal enclosure had taken place more or less continuously from the 12th century onwards.

In the south west of England and much of Wales, the old Celtic field system had evolved gradually into one of separate farmsteads surrounded by small fields, with large areas remaining as common moorland. In Wales, walling remained a matter for the small farmer, even after he became tenant to an absentee landlord. A Royal Commission report of 1894 states that 'the stone walls in the neighbourhood were generally built by the tenant, except near the mountains, where sometimes the walls were long ones, and these were built by the landlord.' The Commission noted many complaints from tenants that landlords 'exhausted' the compensation for their work over a period of only fourteen or fifteen years, whereas the walls were as good as new for twenty or thirty years or more.

According to Rainsford-Hannay (1972), enclosures started in Scotland with an Enclosure Act of 1710, relating to some land in west Kircudbrightshire. Pieces of land were leased free to people who would move to them in spring, set up huts reminiscent of the Highlanders' sheilings, work their plots and in return build enclosure walls. Within a year or two many miles of dykes had been raised, greatly increasing the value of the land. This example was quickly followed, but not without opposition from bands of people who tried to break down the walls and injure the enclosed animals. The ringleaders were executed, and thereafter the enclosures proceeded virtually unhindered.

Many Scottish dykes were built to standard specifications, the best and tallest being the march dykes which bounded the great estates. In some places, special problems resulted in unusual walls, such as Monymusk clearance or 'consumption' dykes northwest of Aberdeen. Rainsford-Hannay (1972) quotes from contracts of 1736 and 1741 in which the tenant was required to wall a certain area to a height of one ell, or 3'1" (940mm), using stones 'taken from within, as long as there are any, both great and small' and 'not to leave a stone in the enclosure, which three men cannot roll or four men carry in a hand barrow'. The first contract specified a coping of 'faile' or peat sods, but the later contract omitted this, probably because it robbed the land of important topsoil. Instead the tenant was paid to bring the wall up to a height of 4'7" (1.4m) as and when he wished, using stones which arose after ploughing. The biggest consumption dyke is Kingswell West Dyke (p126).

Lake District enclosures were on the whole rather late. Until the Union of 1603, raids across the border from Scotland kept the area so insecure that the land continued to be communally farmed, which made it easier for some men to leave the land at short notice for temporary military service. After the cessation of border troubles many of the common township fields were enclosed and improved by private agreement, but farming remained generally backward compared to elsewhere in the country. Most Lakeland walls were built after the Parliamentary Enclosure Act of 1801.

Most Irish walls are also fairly recent. From the mid-18th century enclosure was advocated by land reformers, but there was much local resistance to permanent walls. Instead, one-year sod barriers were constructed, which were then thrown down after the harvest so they could replenish the soil. This practice continued into the 18th century in many areas. The ancient megaliths of Ireland have remained mainly untouched, even during periods of walling activity, as there was a strong superstition against the splitting of large stones.

The history of dry stone enclosure walls does not quite end with the 19th century, even though little land remained to be subdivided. Mining activities brought temporary bursts of walling in certain areas, such as some of the Yorkshire Dales. In the 20th century, road widening and building has brought the need for construction of many miles of walls. During the 1930s, rebuilding of roadside walls in the West Riding of Yorkshire was used to ease local unemployment. In recent times, the National Parks and other authorities concerned with the conservation of the countryside have been active in promoting dry stone walling through grants and other schemes (chapter 2). From there being very few full-time wallers working during the mid part of the 20th century, numbers are now rising again, as the importance of conserving the walled landscape has become apparent. As detailed in chapter 2, many walls are in a poor condition, and it would need an investment similar to that of the enclosure era to rebuild them. The walled landscape of upland Britain is a monument to centuries of patient labour, and it is too important to be left to decay.

Wall dating

The age of a dry stone wall is taken to be from the date of its original building, disregarding repairs and reconstructions which have not changed the basic design. A wall may therefore be very ancient, even if all its stones have just recently been repositioned.

By understanding a wall's geological make-up and design it's possible to make an intelligent guess as to its history, and the part it has played in the agricultural life of the locality. However, putting a date on its construction is not easy, except where documents such as the Enclosure awards give precise details.

A combined approach of documentation plus observation is essential in the historical study of walls. A few Saxon land charters, such as Grundy, are of assistance in wall dating. Other than these, the oldest documents referring to walls are medieval monastic cartularies. These occasionally note boundary disputes which resulted in the erection of some sort of barrier, although the type of fence is seldom specified. According to Rollinson (1972), the Rydale fence of 1277 is one of the earliest documented, but it was probably a ditch and bank rather than a dry stone wall.

Similarly, the Furness Abbey enclosures of the late 13th century in the Esk Valley headland consisted of a bank, probably topped by a wattle fence, since the aim was to restrict the movement of sheep, but not of deer and fawns. The bank in this case can still be traced and it provides a convenient causeway for walkers through this boggy area. Some of the early Pennine enclosures can be located from other monastic records of about the same period. Later documents include a number of important 16th century maps, more recent estate deeds and maps, tithe maps from the 1840s, Parliamentary enclosure surveys and awards and the first Ordnance Survey maps. The 18th and 19th century maps are especially valuable, not only because in many cases they are accurate enough to pinpoint existing walls, but also because they sometimes mark out what were then considered 'ancient enclosures' which are probably of Elizabethan date or earlier (Rollinson, 1962).

Walls which can be dated and tracked down from the written evidence may reveal general characteristics of the walls of their period. Such 'type' walls can then be used to evaluate others for which no documents exist.

Although written documents are essential to decide exactly when the different phases of enclosure took place in any given area, the relative age of walls within a district can often be assessed purely from the shape and pattern of the walls themselves. There are a few generalisations which can be made, as follows.

In the 'Celtic fringe' of western Britain and Ireland the oldest walls are likely to be clearance walls forming small fields around farmsteads. In areas where the Anglo-Danish open-field system predominated, the oldest walls are those which separate the wet meadows from the common fields, and the common fields from the original wasteland. A continuous wall, unbroken except for gates, is older than all the walls which come to a head against it.

The oldest walls usually use unsorted clearance boulders, sometimes including very large ones. There is little distinct coursing and no throughs or topstones. These walls are more pyramidal in section and in general thicker than later walls built of the same type of stone.

The oldest walls are haphazardly aligned and often change direction to take in large boulders or to avoid streams or other obstacles. Sections between obstacles tend to be curved, not straight. Old walls may have rounded or enlarged corners, like swollen joints, indicating accretion from field clearance over many years. Some 'consumption dykes' though were built to order during the Enclosure Era.

Walls closer to a village or farmstead, or to habitation sites which are now abandoned, are likely to be older than walls farther away from the habitation. An exception are the few medieval boundary walls built by monasteries to restrict the movement of sheep, and these, unless they have been rebuilt, are likely to stand out from later enclosure walls by their much cruder style.

Walls built to strict specifications, unvarying over long distances and showing a consistency of style and craftsmanship, were probably built after 1750 as a result of a Parliamentary Enclosure Act. Throughstones were not used in walls until the 18th century. Slate throughs were not used in Yorkshire until the 19th century. Dressed stone was used in dry stone walls by the Romans, but then not again until the 17th century.

Occasionally the shape of the field bounded by a wall may reveal its relative age. Medieval 'reversed S' field strips are thought invariably to predate the year 1400. Walls dividing such fields were clearly constructed at some later date. Examples from the 16th century can be seen between Grassington and Hebden in upper Wharfedale.

Sometimes the material of which the wall is built may be correlated with datable industrial, quarrying or mining activity. For example, the slate fences of North Wales are associated with 19th century mining. Railway ties used as cripple holes suggest that a wall was built since the coming of the railway to a particular area.

Occasionally, objects found within a wall may indicate a date by which it had been built. The bowls of broken clay pipes are found fairly frequently, and these can usually be dated with some exactitude.

Wall dating is most productive when it combines a detailed field knowledge with documentary research of the local historian. Raistrick (1966) has done this brilliantly for the village of Linton in Wharfedale. Volunteers making detailed notes of finds made during repair work may help provide new information for interpretation by local experts.

2   Dry stone walls and conservation

The loss of walls and banks

Walls are left derelict or pulled down for many of the same reasons that have contributed to the demise of hedgerows. These include the mechanisation of agriculture, the decline of the rural work force and rising wages. Farming patterns have changed, so that many fields once under permanent pasture have been cultivated. Many walls are no longer required for stock control, and even where they are needed for this purpose, can be replaced more cheaply by fences. Other walls have been lost to urban development and other non-agricultural uses. It's estimated that 4,500 miles (7,000km) of walls disappeared between 1947 and 1985.

It is the farmer who has the greatest burden of wall maintenance, but local authorities also have responsibility for many roadside walls.

The condition of walls

In 1994, the Countryside Commission (now the Countryside Agency) contracted the Agricultural Development and Advisory Service to survey the condition of dry stone walls in England. The details below are from the outline report of the survey *The condition of England's dry stone walls*, CCP 482, (Countryside Commission 1996).

As most dry stone walling is in upland areas, the survey considered only land more than 100 metres above sea level. From this, 700 one-kilometre National Grid Squares were randomly selected for surveying.

All the walls in each sample square were individually examined, and assessed as being in one of six condition categories, which were devised for the survey in conjunction with the Dry Stone Walling Association of Great Britain. The survey also recorded predominant land use and the frequency and condition of footpath crossings through and over walls.

The survey found that overall, the condition of walls is generally poor, with about half falling in the bottom three categories, and over one third in category C, with 'major signs of advancing or potential deterioration'. Only 13% are in good condition.

Walls associated with woodland tend to be in the poorest condition, presumably because they are associated with a land use of a century or more earlier, and there is little need to repair them. There is little difference in quality between the walls in grassland and walls in arable land.

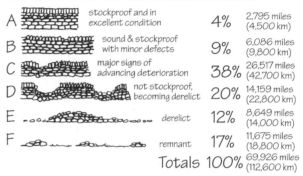

THE CONDITION OF DRY STONE WALLS IN ENGLAND

A	stockproof and in excellent condition	4%	2,795 miles (4,500 km)
B	sound & stockproof with minor defects	9%	6,086 miles (9,800 km)
C	major signs of advancing deterioration	38%	26,517 miles (42,700 km)
D	not stockproof, becoming derelict	20%	14,159 miles (22,800 km)
E	derelict	12%	8,649 miles (14,000 km)
F	remnant	17%	11,675 miles (18,800 km)
	Totals	100%	69,926 miles (112,600 km)

from CCP482 (Countryside Commission 1996)

Less Favoured Areas (LFAs) have been designated by the Ministry of Agriculture, Fisheries and Food (MAFF) as hill and upland areas of relatively poor agricultural potential. Within LFAs, the network of walls is estimated to be three times that of other upland areas, but the condition of walls is similar to that outside LFAs. Farmers in Environmentally Sensitive Areas (ESAs), are offered annual payments to enter into 10 year agreements to conserve the character of the area, which can include work on dry stone walls. At the time of the survey, there was no noticeable difference in wall condition between LFAs, ESAs and other areas, although this was early days in the ESA scheme. The survey also indicated that there was no difference between the quality of walls within and outside National Parks.

The survey estimated the total length of walls in England to be 68,204 miles (109,830 km), which is about 26% greater than previously estimated. Four counties, North Yorkshire, Cumbria, Cornwall and Derbyshire, account for over half of England's walls. Those in County Durham appear to be in the best condition, while counties with a low total length and density tend to have the worst condition walls.

As a theoretical exercise, ADAS drew up estimates for the total cost of restoring to category A, all walls in category B to F. With costs of restoring walls (1996 prices) varying from £16 per metre in Northumberland, to £35 per metre in Somerset, a total of £3,000 million was estimated! This gives an indication of the scale of the problem which remains to be tackled, if the walled landscape is to be conserved.

The wildlife value of walls

It might appear that dry stone walls are a barren, hostile environment for wildlife, but this is not the case. Although the range of plants and animals which make use of walls is fairly limited, walls have considerable habitat value for those species, and often provide an important habitat in otherwise inhospitable upland areas. Stone faced banks are even more valuable, because the soil core increases the range of plants and animals which can be supported.

WALL FLORA

Walls of all types, including retaining walls and those with a soil core, are well-drained habitats. However, the particular community of plants which develops depends very much on the aspect of the wall face. The south face of a wall may present virtual desert conditions in summer, and support true xerophytes, which are plants that thrive in dry conditions. Meantime the north face will remain cool and relatively moist, colonised by species normally associated with the surrounding area.

Local sources of moisture play an important part in determining the point-by-point variation in wall flora. Slight changes in slope, small ledges or crumbling stone tend to retard runoff and allow plants a foothold. Unmortared copings which retain more moisture than mortared or flat copings tend to support more plant growth. Any damp spots or drip lines have more luxuriant plant growth than elsewhere on the same wall.

Stone walls of all types are particularly important habitats for lichens, mosses and ferns, and allow these plants to thrive in areas where there are few or no natural rock exposures. In many parts of Britain, walls extend or substitute for natural scree, cliff and open stone face habitats for many species of both lower and higher plants. For example, navelwort or wall pennywort (*Umbilicus rupestris*), which is common on non-limestone rocks and banks in western Britain, is found on walls as far east as Kent. Walls provide the main habitat for the rusty-back fern (*Ceterach officinarum*).

The type of stone is a major determinant of the type of plant community. Gritstone and other hard acid rocks support a completely different flora from limestone. The species of acid situations are fairly limited, especially in dry lowland districts, but are richer in wetter areas. Limestone walls tend to have a far richer flora, from the orange lichens (*Caloplaca*), through mosses, spleenworts and ferns to the higher plants. In the Mendips, two rarities, the brittle bladder fern (*Cystopteris fragilis*) and the limestone polypody (*Thelypteris robertiana*), thrive on derelict walls in the area, which resemble a scree.

Walls are rather like hedges in supporting the maximum amount of wildlife at the stage when the wall is mature or beginning to deteriorate, but before it becomes derelict. Rebuilding a wall, like laying a hedge, is initially destructive, but within a few years the wall starts to be recolonised. If a wall is left to become derelict through not wanting to disturb the wildlife it supports, there will eventually be

little wall left. Walls decrease significantly in the species they can support when they drop below 2' (600mm) in height. Although a pile of stones is a valuable habitat, it tends to eventually become grown over with grasses, brambles, ivy and other plants, and the stones themselves become buried in the ground. Such a mound in no way compares to the specialised habitats provided by a dry stone wall, of mature age, but in good condition.

Before restoring a wall, it may be worth arranging for an expert to check for any rarities, as it may be possible to avoid disturbing a particular section, or to transplant individual plants. When restoring a wall, destructive effects can be lessened by replacing stones 'green side out' if they are colonised with lichens or mosses, although this should not be done at the expense of good construction. A well-constructed wall should be neat and tight, with few nooks and crannies, and so may be slower to become colonised than a poorer quality repair with larger gaps and holes. However, the better-constructed wall is likely to remain in good repair for much longer, and provide the continuity of habitat which many slow growing species require.

In practice, there is such a huge length of deteriorating and derelict wall in all walling areas, that any repairs have a very minor effect on the total picture. What is important for wildlife is the mosaic of different habitats, and apart from the unlikely event of all walls being simultaneously rebuilt, there will always be a range of habitats from new walls to remnants.

The value of dry stone walls and earth banks for mosses and liverworts is also very dependent on the level of environmental pollution. Although the situation has greatly improved, industrial towns tend to be more polluted than elsewhere, and the wall flora is relatively impoverished. Roadside walls, especially on major routes with heavy traffic, tend to be so polluted with grime, salt and fumes that little survives. The side away from the traffic is usually better colonised with plants. The most luxuriant walls are those found in sheltered rural valleys and woodlands, where the stones may be completely covered with lichens, mosses, ferns and liverworts, as well as some higher plants.

A large proportion of the higher plants characteristic of walls are introductions, many of them from Mediterranean countries, which have escaped from gardens. They flourish in the well-drained, warm conditions on walls. Examples include ivy-leaved toadflax (*Cymbalaria muralis*), Oxford ragwort (*Senecio squalidis*) and mind-your-own-business (*Soleirolia soleirolii*), a close relative of the native pellitory-of-the-wall (*Parietaria judaica*). The species name muralis indicates that the plant is usually found on walls. Native species which favour wall habitats include many members of the stonecrop (*Crassulaceae*), saxifrage (*Saxifragaceae*) and cabbage (*Cruciferae*) families.

While some wall plants such as Oxford ragwort grow also along disturbed ground or on waste and barren places, quite a few are limited almost exclusively to walls and earth banks, and are at risk where walls and banks are disturbed or destroyed. In contrast to hedgerows, which although a good habitat, tend to comprise common plant species, walls and earth banks are an important refuge for less common plants.

WALL FAUNA

A variety of animals make use of walls and earth banks. Some are permanent wall-dwellers, while nocturnal animals use the crannies in dry stone walls as daytime resting places. Dry stone walls are especially valuable habitats for insects and spiders.

Limestone walls support many types of snails, and sometimes the larvae of the glow-worm (*Lampyris noctiluca*) which feed on them. Banks and walls are useful to reptiles, particularly adders, which use them for hibernation, spring feeding, autumn nesting and as migration routes between dry wintering sites and wetter feeding areas. Walls and banks provide virtually the only places in which a variety of animals can overwinter as adults. South-facing limestone walls in particularly sunny parts of the country such as the Gower peninsula and the Isle of Purbeck are valuable in this respect.

A number of bird species sometimes nest in walls, although they may normally choose other sites instead. Blue and great tits, pied and grey wagtails, house and tree sparrows, spotted flycatchers, nuthatches and wheatears all use walls, while a few species such as redstart actually favour walls for nesting. Our smallest seabird, the storm petrel, is famous for its use of wall nesting sites in addition to rocky storm beaches and creviced cliff faces. It prefers the walls of the ruined field systems and abandoned dwellings of small and now uninhabited islands; sizeable colonies nest in the great broch of Mousa in the Shetlands and in the monastic beehive cells of Great Skellig, County Kerry.

Small mammals which make good use of earth banks and hedgerows often also inhabit dry stone walls. Field voles, house mice, rats, rabbits and hares may all seek safety in walls, while red squirrels have been known to store nuts under the stones. Bank voles seem particularly to favour old ivy-covered walls for dwelling. Rabbits may burrow below very shallow foundations, and rabbits and rats wreak havoc by tunnelling into earth banks. Voles and squirrels do not dig below foundation level, and so cause little damage. Weasels and stoats hide and hunt among the stones, and polecats sometimes winter in walls. Foxes take advantage of whatever prey presents itself and may dig into a wall or bank for dinner. Larger mammals, including on occasion man himself, use walls for temporary shelter.

Walls and banks, like hedgerows, provide protected 'corridors' for small animals to move between areas of favourable habitat. This corridor effect is most beneficial when walls are bordered by strips and unmown and ungrazed grasses and herbs. This, plus the direct use of walls as habitat means that, while no animal species appears to be directly threatened by wall removal, many will find their habitat further restricted. Dereliction is less of a problem, as a low wide heap of stones still has some habitat value, although this decreases as the stones become overgrown, buried or dispersed.

The future of the walling craft

In addition to the major phases of walling (p8), walls have needed repair and rebuilding through the centuries, which kept a certain level of skill alive in the farming community. The amount of activity would have closely reflected the cycles of agricultural prosperity and decline, with walls falling into disrepair in times of farming depression. At certain times, such as during the Enclosure Era, gangs of wallers were required to carry out the volume of work required.

Through much of the 20th century the number of full-time craftsmen wallers was low, but there has been an upsurge of interest since the 1970s. In addition to a large number of volunteers becoming skilled in walling, there are now a good number of full-time professional wallers operating through most of the walling areas of Britain. This increase has been due to many factors, of which the most important is the value now placed on the maintenance of the traditional British farming landscape. Increased leisure time and tourism, which brings more people into the countryside, together with changing values in farming have meant that the traditional features of the countryside, walls included, are now given a value far above their straight economic importance. Funding through National Parks, country parks, local authorities and other bodies, as well as through employment schemes has meant money invested in the craft of walling.

The Dry Stone Walling Association is very active in promoting the craft of dry stone walling, through working with professionals, volunteers and the stone industry. Each year they publish a list of certificated wallers/dykers and sources of stone, which lists all professional members who hold DSWA craft skills certification, plus corporate members who supply stone or walling services. In 1999 the Association had 19 local groups, who organise competitions, practice meets and other activities. For more information on the DSWA, see page 150.

3   Walls and the law

Many of the legal considerations applying to the ownership of walls and responsibility for their maintenance are common to earth banks, ditches and fences of all types. Problems posed by shrubs or trees growing along a bank or hedgerow are covered in *Hedging* (BTCV, 1998).

The guidelines given below are general and may be subject to varying interpretations. Professional legal advice should be sought in any ambiguous or disputed cases.

Wall ownership

a   Where a wall or bank has a ditch on one side, the wall is presumed to belong to the owner of the field on whose side of the wall there is no ditch, unless deeds state otherwise. The boundary is the side of the ditch farthest from the wall.

b   If the ditch exists but has been so damaged or neglected that the exact edge cannot be determined, the distance can sometimes be settled by reference to local custom. The usual width allowed is 4'6" (1.3m) from the base of the wall or bank to the far side of the ditch. However, this 'custom of the country' may not necessarily be followed by a court of law.

c   Where the wall or bank is ditched on both sides or on neither side, ownership is usually mentioned in the deeds. If the wall or bank is ditched on both sides, it usually belongs to both parties.

   If the wall or bank is right on the boundary, half belongs to one person and the other half to his/her neighbour. The dividing line is taken vertically from the boundary line.

d   Ownership and responsibility for the maintenance of enclosure walls may be indicated by the maps accompanying Parliamentary Enclosure Acts or by evidence built into the walls themselves:

   - Enclosure Award maps often set out the portion to be walled by each party, and show this by a small T mark placed with its foot on the wall line and its head into the field whose owner is to build and maintain the section of wall.

   - Long enclosure walls often have heads built in at intervals, indicating the boundaries of the sections for which adjacent landowners are responsible. To show

this, two heads are built immediately adjacent to one another with the coping carried across the gap to reduce weakness at this point, as shown in the diagram on page 89.

   - If throughstones, the coverband or topstones overhang one face only of the wall, this may or may not indicate ownership, depending on the area and the situation. In some locales the 'face side' refers to the side without protruding stones and this is the owner's side. Elsewhere it is the side with projecting stones that faces the owner's land because the throughs, coverband or topstones have been placed to keep his sheep from jumping over. Local custom may indicate which is the case in the vicinity in question. However, garden walls are usually left smooth on the outside (the side away from the owner's land) for appearance. Roadside walls are almost always left smooth on the side facing the road, irrespective of who is responsible for the wall's upkeep, in order to lessen damage to vehicles hitting the wall and to keep passers-by from climbing the wall.

e   If a wall is built on a boundary line, any piers or strengthening buttresses must be built on the owner's side; otherwise his/her neighbour may claim ownership on the basis of this evidence.

f   If there is a ditch on both sides or on neither side, and ownership is not clear in the deeds, it can be claimed by one party on the basis of 'acts of ownership', such as maintaining or rebuilding the wall or bank. In such cases it seems necessary to prove that the neighbour knew of or acquiesced in these acts and raised no objection to them. Twenty years of continual use is usually looked upon as an 'immemorial custom' conferring right of ownership.

g   Where the origin of a wall or bank cannot be determined and there are no acts of ownership, the wall or bank belongs to both owners in equal parts.

h   When land is sold the boundary may be based on Ordnance Survey field lines. These indicate the centre of a wall or bank rather than the true legal boundary, and to avoid later dispute the actual boundary should be determined before purchase.

Boundary wall maintenance

a   The owner is responsible for repairing the wall or bank and clearing the ditch.

b If the wall or bank exists on the boundary line, the owner of each half is responsible for maintaining his/her half and can do what he/she likes with it.

c When a wall or bank belongs to both parties jointly, it is assumed to be divided down the middle and each party is responsible for maintaining his/her half.

d If a wall or fence falls on the neighbour's land and damages plants or property, the owner is liable for compensation except to any things which grow or rest upon the wall by sufferance (see Rights of use, point 'a', below).

e When digging or clearing out a ditch along a wall or bank, the owner must not cut into his/her neighbour's land. He/she must throw all topsoil upon his own land.

f The owner of a ditch can erect a fence at its edge, along the boundary line, to protect his/her ditch. He/she is then responsible for repair and maintenance of the fence.

g Many secondary rural roads are owned by the landowners along either side, with the boundary line taken as the middle of the road, even where the road is controlled and maintained by the county council. If the council widens or realigns the road it must replace the wall or bank, although not necessarily with a barrier of the same type. In all other ways, including maintenance after replacement, the wall is the landowner's responsibility.

The Department of Environment, Transport and Regions is responsible for fences, hedges or walls alongside motorways.

Obligation to fence

a There is no law to compel a landowner to wall or fence his land, but if he/she fails to do so, he/she cannot claim for any damage from the owner of straying stock.

b Railways, however, must be fenced against stock belonging to owners or occupiers of land adjoining the railway, to prevent them from straying on the line. The railway company is liable for damages to stock due to improperly maintained fences.

c Each person is responsible for his/her own trespass and that of his/her stock. So while a landowner is under no obligation to fence in order to keep out his neighbour's stock, he/she must prevent his/her own stock from straying on another's land. An owner cannot claim for damages if his/her stock stray and injure themselves on a neighbour's fence.

d If the wall or bank between two neighbours is defective and only belongs to one occupier, the other neighbour must fence in order to control his/her stock. He/she can put up any sort of fence, but it must be on his/her own land.

e Where a wall or bank is owned jointly and it is defective, the owner of stock can place the fence in the wall or bank itself, along the boundary line.

f An owner or rent-paying tenant can claim damage done to his fences or gates by any trespasser, including a hunt.

Tenant and landlord

a The upkeep, maintenance and repair of walls, banks, ditches and gates is usually the tenant's obligation. In many cases the landlord must provide the necessary materials for the work. This should be stated clearly in the tenancy agreement. At the beginning or end of a tenancy the condition of the fences may be assessed and compensation is usually paid or claimed for improvements and depreciations to them all.

b In most cases the tenant cannot remove walls or banks or fill in ditches without the consent of his landlord.

c Any other fencing put upon a holding by a tenant, not necessary to the fulfilment of some obligation, is the tenant's property. He may remove it before or within a reasonable time after his tenancy ends, unless he has not paid his rent, but he must give his landlord one month's notice before removing the structure, during which time the landlord has the option of buying it. The tenant must make good any damage done in removing the fence.

Rights of use

a A neighbour has no right to attach to his/her side of another's wall or fence any creeping, climbing plant or trained tree, or to fasten anything to the wall by nails. Nor may he/she lean any loose timbers or heavy articles against the wall which may tend to damage it. If creepers or trained trees have been allowed to grow with no disturbance for a number of years, the owner's consent is presumed, but the owner is not responsible for any unavoidable damage to plants when the structure is repaired.

b When a wall or bank belongs to both parties jointly, each owner is considered to have 'rights of support and user'. This means that each can build upon his/

her own side of the wall for support, but he/she has no right to go beyond the boundary line with any portion of his/her building.

c Where a wall or bank crosses a public right of way, the owner or tenant is usually responsible for maintaining any stile or gate in a safe condition, and to a standard which does not make an unreasonable interference to the rights of users. A grant towards erection or maintenance may be available from the local authority, from whom advice should be sought.

d The owner of a roadside wall or bank or one beside a public footpath is responsible for seeing that the structure does not become a nuisance. 'Nuisance' is defined as something that may cause injury, damage or inconvenience to others.

Treasure trove

Occasionally, objects of intrinsic or historical or archaeological value may be found within walls or banks when they are under repair. The law regarding ownership of field antiquities is complex. In England, Wales and Northern Ireland, 'treasure trove' is deemed to be gold and silver that has been hidden in the soil or in a building and of which the owner cannot be traced, and is claimed by the Crown. If there is no element of hiding, the items most probably belong not to the Crown, but to the owner of the land. In Scotland, however, all finds are deemed to be treasure trove, whatever their apparent mode of deposition, and whether or not they are of gold or silver. In all cases, the most sensible course of action is to report any finds to the police, who can then inform you of any further procedure required.

4 Safety, equipment and organisation

Site risk assessment

The Construction (Design and Management) Regulations 1994 place certain requirements on employers on projects where:

- there are five or more employees;
- and/or the projects lasts 30 or more days;
- and/or the project exceeds 500 man-days.

The regulations relate to the management of health and safety at all levels, setting out requirements for those commissioning works, those organising the work and to all those carrying out the works on the ground. These regulations are aimed primarily at the building and construction industries, but may apply to dry stone walling projects. Generally speaking, all work on new walls which fit the above criteria are likely to be subject to regulation, whilst work on existing walls remains a grey area. If in doubt, consult your local health and safety inspector.

The relevant sections of the regulations normally applying to BTCV and other project leaders or self employed wallers are those relating to 'principal contractors', which requires a health and safety file to be made for relevant projects. This will comprise safety plans, written risk assessments and recording of any accidents, all of which are basic good practice for any job. For further information, refer to the leaflet *Construction (Design and Management) Regulations 1994: How the regulations affect you* (HSE 1996).

RISK ASSESSMENT

The Health and Safety Executive identify five stages in risk assessment. The following section outlines how this might be applied to dry stone walling projects, but this information should not be regarded as comprehensive or definitive. For further details on risk assessment see the BTCV learning resource pack available from BTCV Enterprises.

A hazard is defined as something with the potential to cause harm, and covers ill health, injury and damage to property. A risk is the likelihood of that harm actually taking place. Risk assessment is about identifying hazards and the level of risk associated with them, and then prescribing measures to control or reduce those risks.

Look for hazards

Look around the work site to assess possible hazards. The manual handling of stone will always present some risk, and hazards such as slippery ground conditions or slopes should be noted. Consider the hazards presented by machinery used to transport material onto the site. Many old walls and those in need of repair are liable to collapse, especially once dismantling work begins.

Who might be harmed?

Workers will vary in their work experience and awareness of risk, and may include inexperienced workers, young, old or disabled. The work itself may pose a threat to people other than the workers. Visitors to the site or the general public in the vicinity may be at risk from falling stone, uneven ground and so on. When working alongside a public right of way, temporary barriers and an alternative route may be needed, together with signing of hazards.

Evaluate the hazards

The first step is always to try and remove the hazard. If this is not possible, the next step is to control the hazard as far as possible. For example, a hazard which is impossible to eliminate is that of wallers trapping their fingers. The risk of this happening can be reduced by giving training on safe handling of stone and good working practice, together with the provision of safety gloves. Actions to reduce risk may produce other hazards. For example, the provision of winches or other mechanical aids to move stone will themselves present a hazard, which must be met with proper training and checking of equipment.

Recording

The HSE show a simple way of recording information in four columns:

1 Risk/ hazard

2 Those at risk

3 Controls or provisions to reduce risk

4 Subsequent measures for further risk reduction as necessary

Review

Review your assessment and revise it as necessary. Legal requirements may change. Note that risk assessment needs to be considered individually for each walling project, as sites and conditions will vary.

General safety considerations

a   A sufficient number of suitable first aid kits should be supplied (p28). There should be one Basic Trained First Aider on all practical courses, training courses or any other event. There should be one Qualified First Aider on all projects with significant levels of risk. Volunteers must be briefed at the start of each project as to the provision and location of First Aid kits and trained First Aiders.

b   Be careful at all times when working with and among stones. Keep the work area as clear as possible, leaving a clear space of 2-3' (600-900mm) alongside the wall. Watch out for loose stones under foot, and keep all stone within a well defined area.

c   Take particular care when working on a slope not to overbalance or to let stones roll away.

d   Bear in mind that grass is slippery, especially when wet or on a slope.

e   When dismantling a wall be aware of a possible collapse. Work carefully to avoid this happening, and ensure you have a clear area in which to make your escape.

f   Take great care when removing large stones and heavy coping from the wall, when there is a high risk of back strain. Also be aware that other stones may be dragged off the wall along with the large stone, or a more general collapse may be initiated.

g   Avoid bending more than is necessary. Work from the downhill side on a slope.

h   Carry as little as possible uphill. Collect stones from higher up and carry or roll them down to the wall.

i   When climbing a wall, press down on the stones rather than pulling up or out. Put your feet as low as possible, on a solid ledge, not a projecting stone. Don't put your feet on the coverband or coping. If you can get over without touching the coping at all, so much the better.

j   Keep tools within easy reach, but not where you may trip on them. Lean tools against the base of the wall when not in use.

k   Work far enough away from other people that you won't get in their way, and won't hurt anyone else if you drop a stone.

l   Some types of stone are more difficult to handle than others, and require extra care. Granite is particularly bad because it is coarse grained, readily cuts the skin and tends to leave flakes of mica in the wound, which then goes septic. Clean even minor scratches and abrasions well.

MANUAL HANDLING AND LIFTING OF STONE

When moving stone, always think of the dangers involved and choose methods appropriate to the size of the task.

Remember that injury can be caused by the repetitive movements involved in handling large amounts of smaller stone, as well as in moving single, heavy stones. People who are unused to manual handling work should work at a sensible speed and take rests as necessary, and even experienced workers should be wary of repetitive strain injury. The total weight lifted by one person during a day of dismantling or building a wall can be considerable.

Assess the stone and how it is likely to balance. You will want to position yourself so that any uneven weight distribution is towards your body. You will also need to determine how good a grip you can get, and where to hold the stone. Note that it is easier to lift a straight edged or regular stone of a given weight than a rounded or lumpy one of the same weight.

Stance affects your balance, which in turn affects the possibility of muscle strain. A good stance is important during all operations involving handling of stone, from the lifting of heavy boulders to the placing of smaller stone on the wall. You can equally strain your back through repetitive incorrect bending as through trying to lift a heavy stone. Work with your feet slightly apart, one slightly in front of the other and on as level ground as possible. Always stand on stone free ground, not on a pile of rubble.

This stance provides a solid 'platform' to work from, transfers stress and reduces the amount by which the back is constantly compensating for lifting and movement.

Having assessed the stone and positioned your feet, you now have to lift the stone. Keep your shoulders back and tilt your head back to straighten the upper part of the body.

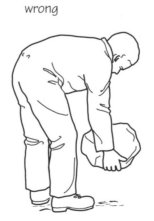

wrong

right

The tilting of the head is very important, as where the head goes the trunk will follow, and your spine will be straightened as your head goes back. Lift the stone in one fluid movement, with your elbows locked and keeping the stone as close to your body as possible. The locking of the elbows coupled with the straight back ensures that your thighs, which have the strongest muscles in your body, do most of the work. Fluidity of movement evens out the sudden forces and strains from making jerky movements.

Keeping the stone close to the body reduces leverage on the spine, as you are holding the stone as close as possible to your centre of gravity. You are also less likely to topple, stagger or drop the stone.

Take care in particular when removing large coping stones from a wall. Some leverage on the spine is inevitable, but it is often possible to 'strengthen' your back by leaning on the wall for support.

CARRYING AND PLACING STONE

To reduce the risks involved with carrying, the largest stones should be manoeuvred over the ground until they are alongside the wall, and then lifted directly into position. However, some large stones will have to be carried, if only a few feet.

a Be careful where you tread, as uneven ground and stones will affect your balance. Be ready to compensate for unavoidable hazards such as slopes, or find an alternative method of moving the stone.

b As with lifting, keep your elbows tucked into your side and your head up, to ensure that your legs do most of the work.

c If you need to pause for a moment before placing the stone, slightly rest large stones on your thigh.

d Avoid twisting from the waist, but instead move your feet to change the orientation of your body. Twisting places enormous strain on the spine, and it is repetitive or sudden twisting which is the most common cause of back problems in wallers.

e To place a big stone, stand sideways to the wall and swing the stone most of the way over it. To avoid pinching your hand, lower the outer end first so that the stone rests on its midsection. If necessary, support the stone in this position while you place a temporary wedge under it, which will allow you to manoeuvre the stone without catching your hand.

SUMMARY

1 Assess the stone

2 Stand with correct stance

3 Use secure hand holds

4 Keep your back straight

5 Keep your head upright

6 Think about rhythm and timing

7 Do not twist your body

8 Know your own capacity and do not try to exceed it

Co-operation

The same lifting and placing techniques are used with two people working as with one, with a few refinements:

a Wedge the stone underneath before trying to lift it, so that both workers can safely get a grip without risking trapping their fingers. Lever the stone up at one end with a crowbar, and use smaller stone or blocks of wood to chock it up. Repeat the process at the other end. Take care that the stone is resting stably on the chocks.

b Lay the stone on the wall at an angle, keeping the outer end down, so that the person at the other end doesn't get pinched.

c Where the stone is so large that subsequent positioning may damage the wall, it can be useful to place a 48" (1.2m) crowbar or similar across the wall first, so that the stone can be 'skidded' into position over it. This method is suitable for large flat slabs, for example of slate, schist or sandstone. Take particular care that no-one spears themselves on the crowbar, or traps their fingers when removing the crowbar. This should be done by twisting the bar, rather than pulling it.

d When working with another person you must co-operate, or you are both likely to get injured. Co-operation involves co-ordination, timing and communication. Talk through the procedure first, so you both know how and where you are going to lift, move and place the stone. Co-ordinate your actions – for example, "1,2,3 LIFT!", and likewise for putting down. Whatever you do, don't drop it without some form of warning to your partner.

e With irregular or rounded stone which is difficult to grip, a sack can be used to lift the stone. Lay the sack on the ground near the wall, roll the stone onto it, and then one person each takes two corners to lift the stone into place. To aid grip, small stones can be set into each of the four corners of the sack, which is then twisted around them.

f For some large stones to be placed above waist level, three people can work together. Carry out the same procedures as above, with a pair lifting the stone to their waist, and the third person acting as a boost getting 'under' the stone to help lift it the last foot or so.

g Whenever you place a bigger stone on a smaller one, take care that the smaller one doesn't rise up and 'chock' your finger.

Manoeuvring large stones

a Big, partly-buried stones can be levered out of the ground with a crowbar. Use a small stone as a fulcrum, placed as near to the end of the bar as possible for maximum leverage.

It is safest to use just one bar. Often, however, two are required, each one alternately worked as a lever and then held steady to keep the stone in position while the other bar lifts. In any case, restrict the workforce to one person per crowbar, since the risk of someone being injured is much greater if extra people are around when the bar or stone slips.

b Don't use a pick to lever up a stone unless you are sure the stone is reasonably flat underneath. Otherwise the pick is likely to slip off it and throw you off balance. It is safer to lift it using a broad-bladed mattock and then, as soon as there is sufficient space underneath, to wedge the stone and finish lifting it with a crowbar.

c To shift a large stone across the ground, tilt it up on its end or side, straddle it and roll it along between your legs. With a long rectangular slab, you can 'walk' it by pivoting it on alternate corners, aligned either horizontally or vertically depending on its shape.

d Shift a really big slab or boulder with the aid of boards and rollers. First use a crowbar and blocks or wedges to get the stone level and off the ground. Clear any obstructions from underneath with the crowbar. Lay solid planks, 2 x 8" (50 x 200mm), from the stone to the wall. The planks must be level, or the whole enterprise may get out of control. Put the near end of the second plank a few inches under the far end of the first plank to anchor it. Place wooden or metal rollers on the plank and nudge the stone along slowly, in turn moving the rollers to the front.

An even heavier slab can be moved by first manoeuvring the stone onto a short plank, and then rolling stone and plank together towards the wall. Instead of rollers, you can use a trolley, such as the base of an old supermarket cage.

e Planks can be used as ramps to get large stones onto the wall and avoid lifting. They should be about 2 x 8" (50 x 200mm) and about 8' (2.4m) long, and set against the wall to make a ramp no steeper than about 30°. Blocky stone can be rolled up the plank, and less blocky stone lifted and moved in short stages up the plank. A heavier slab can be moved by means of rollers or a short plank plus rollers, pushed up a pair of suitably supported planks.

f To move boulders on a slope where rollers are impractical, use a Tirfor winch with the hook-and-line chain described below.

g The easiest way to move really heavy rocks is with a tractor or four-wheel drive vehicle. Use a chain or nylon slings and webbing as supplied for use with winches and other lifting equipment. The chain should have a flattened hook at the

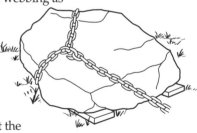

end which can fit around any of the links of the chain to secure. First prop up the front end of the stone several inches, wrap the chain around it and pull the stone out onto level ground.

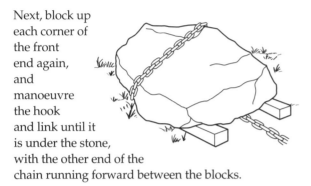

Next, block up each corner of the front end again, and manoeuvre the hook and link until it is under the stone, with the other end of the chain running forward between the blocks.

Back up the vehicle until it is almost over the end of the rock and secure the chain as tightly as possible to the trailer hitch. Knock the blocks out from under the stone, leaving the slab raised at its front end so that it won't plough up the ground as you drag it away. On soft ground you can slide a plank under the stone to ease its journey.

Manual handling regulations

The Manual Handling Operations Regulations 1992 require employers to include manual handling where appropriate within their general requirements to carry out risk assessment procedures. The HSE give details in Manual Handling Regulations 1992, *Guidance on Regulations (HMSO 1992)*, and in a short leaflet *Getting to grips with manual handling: a short guide for employers (HMSO)*.

The following points indicate how some of the regulations could apply to dry stone walling.

a Wherever practical, use a mechanical device such as a winch for the manoeuvring of oversize stones.

b Provide suitable equipment, such as ramps and sacks, for lifting large stones onto the wall.

c Ensure that everyone involved in the work has had suitable instruction in manual handling and is fully acquainted with the risks involved to themselves and others.

d Do not move or use stones which present an unacceptably high risk of injury.

The HSE has set out guideline figures for lifting and lowering materials, which in walling terms includes building and dismantling walls. The figures are only guidelines, and not limits, and experienced wallers would be expected to handle stones heavier than suggested by the guidelines. They do provide a useful guideline for novices. As shown in the diagram, the capacity to lift or

lower is reduced significantly if, for example, the load is held at arm's length or the hands pass above shoulder height.

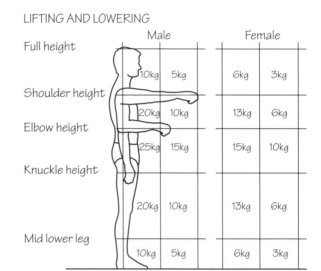

LIFTING AND LOWERING

	Male		Female	
Full height				
	10kg	5kg	6kg	3kg
Shoulder height				
	20kg	10kg	13kg	6kg
Elbow height				
	25kg	15kg	15kg	10kg
Knuckle height				
	20kg	10kg	13kg	6kg
Mid lower leg				
	10kg	5kg	6kg	3kg

These figures need careful interpretation. They assume the handler is well trained, using the correct procedures and working in reasonable conditions with a stable body position, or in other words, on level ground. They also assume that the load distribution is stable, which requires good hand holds on regular shaped stones. While people who are fit, well trained and experienced could be reasonably expected to exceed these limits, the HSE state that 'any operations which would exceed the guideline figures by more than a factor of about two should come under very close scrutiny', (HSE, 1992, p43).

HAMMERING STONE

a When breaking stones with a hammer, work away from other people so they are not in danger if the hammer head flies off the handle, or if stone chips shower their way. Wear goggles when breaking or drilling stone.

b Hit the stone with the hammer head flat to it, not angled. This makes the chips fly out in front of you, and lessens the chance of the shaft breaking. It also gives the most effective blow. Try to stand so that you can hit the stone with the hammer central to your body, neither to your left nor right, but in line with your nose. This way the hammer head itself prevents chips flying upwards into your eyes.

c Don't hold small stones in your hand to break them. Even if you don't smash your fingers, your wrist will get sore after a while.

d Don't push stones which stick too far out of the wall into place by hand. Tap them in with a hammer instead.

CEMENT AND LIME

Cement, lime and some additives such as waterproofer, frostproofer and and hardener contain irritants. They should be supplied clearly labelled with a black X on an orange background, with full instructions and safety precautions, with which users should familiarise themselves before use.

The irritants in dry dust react with body fluids such as sweat and eye fluid and cause irritation, dermatitis or burns. In wet mixes the presence of water results in similar irritation if there is skin contact. Contact with the eyes is particularly dangerous, and the eyes should be rinsed with clean water immediately and medical advice sought. The packet listing the chemicals involved should be shown to the doctor.

Take the following steps to minimise risk:

a Work in a way which minimises the amount of dust produced.

b Wear PVC gloves or preferably gauntlets, which also cover the wrists, at all times when handling or mixing mortar.

c Wear clothing in such a way that it cannot trap mortar against the skin. Sleeves should be tucked into gloves, and trouser legs worn over boots.

d Wash contaminated skin in clean water immediately.

e Wash hands after using any of the listed products, and before meal breaks.

f In breezy conditions, wear a dust mask. When the wind is stronger, and splashing might occur during mixing, also wear goggles and mix in the shelter of the wall.

ROADSIDE WORKING

If you are responsible for, or supervising work alongside a road or footway you should initially contact the highway authority for advice. There are various requirements for major and minor works, which may involve signing and coning, vehicle and pedestrian barriers, safe working buffer zones, stop/go signs and traffic lights. High visibility jackets or waistcoats should be worn at all times.

Advice is given in the booklet *Safety at street works and road works: a code of practice* (HMSO).

Work season and weather precautions

a Walling can be carried out in any season, but is best done when it is not too cold or wet. If possible, avoid working in frosty weather, as foundations are hard to dig, stones stick to the ground and split in unexpected ways. Walling in cold weather is very hard on the hands, and serious back problems are most likely to develop when you are cold and stiff.

b Avoid working when the stones are wet, since they are slippery and dangerous to handle. If you work in heavy rain you get soaked directly, and if you work in waterproofs, you get almost as wet with sweat. Either way, you quickly become tired and careless.

c Gapping is best done as soon as possible after finding a break, although a temporary repair may have to suffice until there is time to do the work. On farms, late spring is usually a good time for routine repairs.

d The summer is the best time for major walling jobs because the days are longest and the weather most likely to be settled.

SUNBURN

Sunburn is caused by ultraviolet radiation from the sun, which is categorised as either UVA or UVB. Outdoor workers are at considerable risk from skin cancer.

UV levels depend on various factors:

a Time of day, with UV levels highest around noon.

b Time of year, with UV levels highest during the summer, but still significant in early spring.

c Height above sea level, as UV levels increase with altitude.

d Weather conditions. UV levels are highest when skies are clear, even if temperatures are low. Do not be misled by the cooling effect of the wind, as it does not reduce UV. Even on an overcast day, around 80% of the UV radiation can still reach exposed skin.

Skin colour is a major factor in the risk of skin cancer, with three levels of risk identified:

High risk   - pale freckled skin, blue eyes, fair or red hair.

Medium risk - medium colour skin and hair.

Low risk   - black or brown skin.

Precautions

a Wear clothing of tightly woven material, a wide brimmed hat and sunglasses. It is possible to burn through a T-shirt or other thin clothing, and various types of UV protective clothing are becoming available. Don't remove your shirt!

b Avoid working around noon during the summer.

c Always use a sunscreen on exposed skin.

d Moles and freckles are not unusual, but if they become inflamed or itchy, weep or bleed, or change shape or colour, consult your doctor.

Sunscreens

Sunscreens are categorised by their Sun Protection Factor (SPF), which is the factor of protection offered. For example, if you normally burn in ten minutes of exposure at midday, then an SPF of 2 would double this to twenty minutes. Weather bulletins now include sunburn forecasts when the risk is significant, and this information can be used as a guide to the precautions you should take. Always err on the side of caution, bearing in mind your skin type. The Health Education Authority recommend SPF of 15, and even then advise against prolonged exposure.

As a general guide apply sunscreen before you start work, and at each subsequent meal break. Put enough on, and note that putting on double the amount of SPF 8 is not equivalent to SPF 16, but is still SPF 8. Sunblocks with high SPF ratings generally also block perspiration, so they should not be used as an alternative to protective clothing, but reserved for sensitive exposed areas such as the nose.

DEHYDRATION AND HYPERTHERMIA

Other problems with summer working, particularly on sunny days with little breeze, are dehydration and hyperthermia (heat exhaustion).

Dehydration can be a serious problem when working all day in direct sunlight and high temperatures. Sufferers may not realise, because feeling thirsty is not one of the early symptoms. You may not realise that you are sweating, and thus losing body liquid, in conditions where sweat is evaporating quickly. It may be convenient not to have to pass urine during a working day, but it can also be an indication that you are becoming dehydrated! Common symptoms are headache, tiredness and malaise, with muscle cramps, normally in the lower limbs and abdomen, possibly indicating more severe dehydration.

Prevent dehydration by taking rest periods in the shade, wearing appropriate clothing, and having plenty of suitable drinks. Fruit drinks are best for replenishing body fluid. Plain water, carbonated drinks, and tea and coffee which have a diuretic effect, are less effective. It can also be important to replenish body salt with tablets or electrolyte solutions, or just to increase the level of salt in your general diet during hot weather. Bottled mineral water can help maintain the intake of salts.

Hyperthermia can be caused by over strenuous activity in hot and humid weather, and is exacerbated by wearing unsuitable clothing, overeating and drinking alcohol. It has similar symptoms to dehydration, together with nausea, dizziness, fast and shallow breathing, and possible fainting. Mild cases can be treated by moving into the shade, splashing with cold water, fanning, and taking plenty of fluids. More severe cases should be treated as follows.

a Lay the victim down in a cool shady place, with the feet raised about a foot (300mm).

b Give continual sips of a weak salt solution, made up of quarter level teaspoon of salt to half a litre of cold water.

c If the victim is unconscious, they should be placed in the recovery position and medical assistance sought.

EXPOSURE AND HYPOTHERMIA

Exposure is severe chilling of the body surface, which if left unchecked, can lead to hypothermia. This occurs when the body temperature falls below 35° C. While the risks of exposure and hypothermia are much lower than the risk of sunburn and heat exhaustion for most outdoor workers in the UK, anyone who works in cold and/or wet weather may be at risk.

Exposure and hypothermia are caused by exposure to the cold, which can be exacerbated by rain, wind chill and fatigue.

Prevention

If possible, avoid working when weather conditions are very bad.

Wear suitable clothing (see below). Take a thermos flask with hot drinks or soup, and include some high energy foods to eat during the day.

If weather conditions suddenly worsen, you will have to decide between taking shelter or calling it a day. Stoically taking shelter may not be the better option, as inactivity can accentuate heat loss.

Symptoms and treatment

There are a number of physical symptoms, any two of which can normally be regarded as indicative:

- feeling very cold

- becoming irritable and unreasonable

- resisting help

- poor balance

- sluggish physical and mental responses

- slurred speech and impaired vision

- unconsciousness

If a person appears to be suffering from hypothermia, they should be moved to the nearest sheltered position, and wet clothing removed if it can be replaced with dry clothing. Insulate them from the ground with any available material such as sacking or clothing, and keep the body, head and neck covered. A warm companion lying beside the patient is warming and comforting. Warm, sweet drinks can be given, but do not give alcohol. Do not rub the patient, or allow them to exert themselves as this will use up their already depleted energy levels.

Clothing

The aim is always safety and comfort first.

a Wear comfortable work clothes, tough enough to withstand abrasion from rough stones. Scottish wallers used to wear aprons cut to knee length in front, with bibs designed to protect their waistcoats, and rolled up at the back so as to tie at the waist. These are sometimes still worn at demonstrations, but overalls or a boiler suit are more convenient substitutes.

b Boots with steel toe-caps are essential to protect the toes. Heavy leather work boots with spiked or deep moulded soles are safest. If you have an old but serviceable pair, work in them, since new boots quickly become much the worse for wear when walling. Wellingtons with toe caps are adequate, but their soles do not grip as well as boots on wet grassy slopes.

c Gloves will save much discomfort later for workers not used to handling stone. They are especially important when handling coarse stone such as gritstone, corrosive stone such as limestone, and sharp slate. Gloves also protect your wrists when handling large stones.

Many people prefer to work bare handed because they find it easier to then judge the shape of the stone, and because hammers slip more readily from a gloved hand. You can toughen your hands up gradually by wearing gloves less as you become used to the work. The hammering hand should harden up fairly quickly. However, it's always worth wearing gloves for dismantling walls, as unseen broken glass can be a hazard. Dismantling accounts for half the stone handling in rebuilding a wall, and is a fairly continuous activity and thus hard on the hands.

If you only wall occasionally and for short periods, wear sturdy, flexible, leather work gloves. For more intensive periods of work, PVC gloves are harder wearing, and are waterproof for working in wet weather. Wear thermal liners inside for protection from the cold.

Some Cotswold craftsmen used to wear pads rather than full gloves. These were cut from leather or rubber, such as old inner tubing, with holes for the wrist, fingers and thumb. With these, a good waller could pick up and place stones with each hand, keeping the palms down, thereby working more quickly with less strain. This technique was probably restricted to the Cotswolds, where walling stone is small enough to be lifted with one hand.

d Goggles or eyeshields to protect your eyes when breaking and drilling stone. Eye protectors should be manufactured to BS 2092.

Tools and accessories

It is possible to build dry stone walls without any tools at all, especially if rebuilding from an existing foundation. In most cases however, a few tools are useful, and may be essential for working with some types of stone.

On group projects enough hammers should be supplied so that one is within easy borrowing distance of every worker. Common sense should suggest the number of other tools needed for each situation. It is worth applying a strip of brightly coloured paint to the handles of hammers and other inconspicuous tools, to make them easier to locate when laid down among stones. Don't paint the grip part of the handle, as the paint may flake and affect the grip.

FOR ALL PROJECTS

First aid

First Aid boxes should contain a sufficient quantity of First Aid materials and a guidance card. The number of First Aid boxes should meet the risks identified in the risk assessment. In most cases in the field, one standard kit (for 10-12 people) will be sufficient, but if work is taking place at several locations, each one will need a kit.

Pinched or crushed fingers present the most frequent problem. Stubbed toes and sprained ankles are also possible, as are sore eyes from dust and stone chips.

BTCV Enterprises can supply standard First Aid kits which comply with Health and Safety Regulations. The recommended contents for a work party are:

1 guidance card
20 individually wrapped sterile adhesive dressings appropriate to the work
2 sterile eye pads with attachments

6   individually wrapped triangular bandages

6   safety pins

6   medium sized individually wrapped unmedicated wound dressings, approx. 12 x 12cm

2   large sterile individually wrapped wound dressings, approx. 18 x 18cm

3   extra large sterile individually wrapped wound dressings, approx. 28 x 17cm

2   pairs of disposable fine plastic gloves to prevent bodily fluid contact

1   pair blunt-ended steel scissors at least 12cm long

Where clean mains water is not available, at least 1 litre of sterile water or normal saline in sealed disposable containers should be provided. Eye baths should not be used for eye irrigation. The first aid kit must be kept in a suitably marked container which will protect the contents from dust and damp.

The following 'welfare kit' is also found to be useful:

1   pair of tweezers
1   pair of scissors
10 safety pins
    needle and thread
    pencil
    sanitary towels
    whistle
    toilet roll
    cotton wool
30 plasters
3   finger pouches
    rubber gloves
    insect repellent
    sun cream
    barrier cream
2   10 pence pieces

A list of local hospitals with casualty departments should also be to hand.

Some wallers also carry home-made leather tube patches which can be slid over sore, chapped or scratched fingers, and strapped around the wrist with a thong. The leather should be supple enough to bend easily.

An eye sweep is another useful item. This consists of a thin metal stem, about the size of a match stick, with a long soft elongated loop of platinum wire clamped to the end. Use it to sweep stone fragments from the eye without any danger of scratching the eye's surface. Eye sweeps are available from welding suppliers.

Tools

a   One or more walling hammers, the type depending on the stone (p30).

b   Sledge hammer, 14lb (6.3kg)

c   Lump (mash or club) hammer, 4lb (1.8kg)

d   Heavy-duty garden spade, Devon shovel or small round-mouthed shovel, for digging foundations, cleaning around the base of an existing wall or a retaining wall or stone-faced bank. This can also be used for mixing mortar or concrete as required.

e   Pick or pick-ended mattock, to supplement the spade or shovel, and for digging up field stones. In the south west, the 'digger', which is a mattock with a single broad blade, is sometimes used instead.

A useful variant of the normal pick is the 'tramp pick', once common in Aberdeenshire but now available only through sources of second-hand tools. This has an all-steel shaft and single pick blade with a wooden handle and adjustable foot rest.

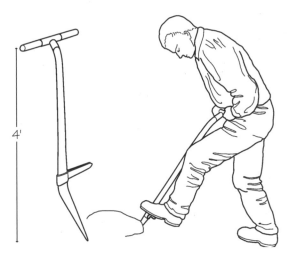

Unlike the ordinary 'shoulder pick', the tramp pick is used in the position shown, to lever and manoeuvre large, heavy stones into place, for example when positioning foundation stones in walls. The foot rest may be left on or removed as convenient. Tramp picks were made in weights of 10lb (4.5kg) to 18lb (8.1kg), depending on the work they were designed to do.

f   Batter frames or line bars (p32), with lines and pins, for setting out the dimensions of the wall.

g   Plumb bob and line, for measuring the vertical.

h   Spirit level. Most wallers level up by eye, but a spirit level is useful for beginners, to help keep courses of stonework running correctly, and for work with cut and dressed stone.

i   Steel tape measure, for setting lines and checking heights.

j   Fencing pliers, for removing or constructing temporary wire fences across gaps.

SHIFTING AND TRANSPORTING STONE

a Two crowbars

b Wooden or metal rollers, from 1" (25mm) to 4" (100mm) diameter for moving very large stones.

c Several 2 x 8" (50 x 200mm) planks, 6-8' (2m) long, to use with rollers for moving large stones.

d Wooden blocks, 2 x 2" (50 x 50mm) or more, by about 2' (600mm) long, to prop up large stones for moving and shaping.

e Buckets, barrow, sledge or trailer, depending on the amount of material to be transported to the work site and the distance involved. Buckets are useful for carrying small quantities of fillings and concrete or mortar short distances. Use heavy-duty rubber, not plastic or metal buckets which wear out quickly.

Traditionally, various forms of low, small-wheeled carts and simple sledges were used for shifting stones from local quarries down to the wall. A hand barrow, for use by two or four people, is good for moving small loads short distances over rough terrain.

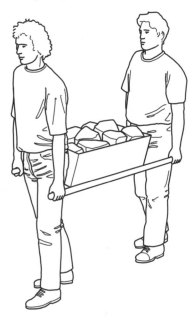

A rubber-tyred wheelbarrow is best for a single worker to move earth and stones over fairly regular ground.

f Powered transport. Trailers pulled by tractors or four wheel drive vehicles may be needed to get new stone onto the site.

A power carrier is a useful machine for carrying stone over rough ground which is not accessible to tractors or other vehicles. The power carrier is a tracked barrow, powered by a 4 or 5.5 horsepower engine, which can carry loads of up to half a ton (500kg) on level ground, equivalent to 10 times the capacity of a wheelbarrow. They have low ground pressure tracks which cause little damage to soft ground, and can climb gradients of up to 25°. They are manufactured by Honda, from whom a list of local suppliers is obtainable.

g Hand winch, for moving large stones. BTCV Enterprises can supply the Tirfor 800kg (three-quarters of a ton) capacity winch, together with accessories and spares.

HAMMERS

Hammers for use in dry stone walling were probably adapted from traditional mason's tools. Hammers are necessary for splitting, trimming or shaping of most types of stone, and for breaking large blocks down to a manageable size. The discussion which follows emphasises regional variations in the sort of hammers used, but for most purposes any single-handed shaping hammer, plus lump and sledge hammers for general use, should prove adequate.

Craftsmen show regional and individual preferences for various shapes and sizes of hammers. Whilst size and shape are determined largely by the type of stone to be worked, individual preference means that many wallers become attached to particular hammers, with which they can work most stone types sufficiently well for walling purposes.

Throughout most of northern England, especially in the Carboniferous limestone areas, hammers are carried but used sparingly, if at all. Many craftsmen of the region consider it something of a defeat to have to break their stone. Elsewhere, where well-bedded stone is abundant, wallers routinely trim it to convenient shapes and break it into smaller bits for fillings. Cotswold stone can be shaped so readily that craftsmen there use the hammer almost continuously to achieve a regular, finished appearance.

Whatever the type of hammer, it must be tempered to suit the materials. Hammers for hard stone such as granite, and general purpose lump and sledge hammers for use on metal as well as on stone, must be steel headed. Most walling hammers should not be used on metal. Cast iron hammers or mells should never be used for walling, since they may shatter or shed metal splinters when used on anything harder than wood.

Walling hammers may weigh from 1lb (0.45kg) to 25lb (11.3kg), with the heavier hammers used on harder, more massive stone. Most craftsmen carry at least two; a light hammer for splitting or trimming smaller stones, and a heavier sledge-type hammer for breaking boulders into useable pieces.

Throughout the Pennines, the usual walling or 'scabbling' hammer has one square and one pointed or blade end, with

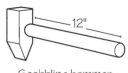

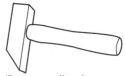

Scabbling hammer   Pennine walling hammer

its axis either parallel or perpendicular to the handle. This type, commonly referred to as the Yorkshire or Pennine walling hammer, is available from BTCV Enterprises.

The square end is for knocking pieces off stones, and the pointed end is for splitting stone along its bedding planes. The head weighs 2-3lb (0.9-1.3kg).

Many Welsh wallers also use what they describe as 'scabblers'. These can be found in a wide variety of weights and patterns covering most of the types described in this section. They have the common feature of at least one square head with a concave face, in effect giving it two cutting edges.

SECTION THROUGH HEAD

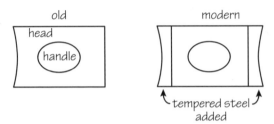

These are difficult to come by, and as with tramp picks they can only be obtained from farm sales and auctions. Modern equivalents can sometimes be found where the faces are additions to poorer quality metal heads. Whilst better steel is used for the face than the rest of the head, they are generally eschewed as not being up to the quality of older hammers. They are primarily designed for dressing harder stone such as granite, and the edges become dulled with use and need frequent maintenance. As with the maintenance of square heads (p32), it may be difficult to find a smith able to temper them correctly.

In areas of Scotland where the stone is well bedded, two types of hammer are distinguished. The usual type has both ends tapered with a square pein.

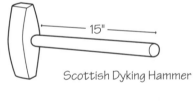

Scottish Dyking Hammer

The 'cachie' or small mason's hammer is similar to a Pennine hammer, and is sold by the Dry Stone Walling Association as the 'catchee' hammer. A blocking hammer has a symmetrical rectangular head with squared ends.

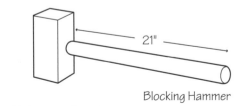

Blocking Hammer

(cachie has smaller, narrower head and 12" -14" handle)

In the Cotswolds the typical walling hammer has a symmetrical tapered head with two 'polling edges' about a quarter inch (6mm) thick for rough shaping of the stone, or one polling edge and one thinner 'dressing edge', used for fine cutting. These hammers are available in several weights, with 3.5-4lb (1.6-1.8kg) being usual.

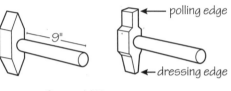

Cotswold Hammers

Some wallers use a 4-5lb (1.8-2.2kg) square-faced 'stone maul' for breaking large stones, and a bricklayer's hammer for splitting and shaping stone. The pick end is also useful for 'sculpting' the foundation trench to take awkward stones (p48), and similarly with stone hedges, for shaping the earth bank to fit the face stones, and to backfill behind them.

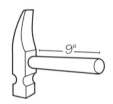

Bricklayer's Hammer

Other wallers favour a type similar to a geologist's hammer, with a spiked pick end which is particularly useful for removing awkward lumps from the bases or tops of stones.

Geologist's rock hammer

In practice, most wallers today use those hammers which are most readily available commercially, which means lump hammers, bricklayer's hammers and walling hammers. These are all available from BTCV Enterprises (pii).

Maintenance of hammers

Hammer heads tend to wear more at the front that at the rear corners, because even when trying to hit a stone squarely, one tends to swing a bit too far.

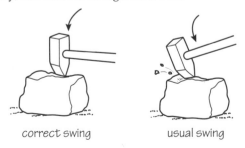

correct swing   usual swing

After the front corners have worn about quarter of an inch (6mm) they become too rounded for accurate splitting, and the head should be reversed to bring the other corners into play and promote more even wear. A badly worn hammer head can be squared by a blacksmith, but care is needed to re-temper it properly. A hammer haft should last for about 6 months of frequent use, provided you don't drop a stone on it. Once a handle becomes badly frayed or splintered it should be replaced.

The procedure for rehafting hammers is described in *Toolcare* (BTCV, 1991).

BATTER FRAMES

Batter frames are also known as walling or dyke frames, patterns, wall gauges and templates. Walls of different specifications require different frames, although within any district there are usually only one or two standard specifications. Frames are unnecessary for minor gapping work, and in the north of England they tend not to be used except on local authority and other exacting jobs. However they are very useful for beginners to ensure that the wall is built to the correct profile and that the layers are kept level. They should be constructed beforehand according to the specifications of the wall to be built, and carried to the work site.

Depending on personal preference, the frame can be made with either inside or outside measurements to give the dimensions of the wall. The frame should be made carefully, to ensure the batter is exactly the same on both sides, and that the ties are horizontal.

Outside measurements

In the example below, the outside measurements give the dimensions of the wall, and hence the lines are attached to run from the outside of the frame. The ties give the heights of throughs and top of wall without coverstones.

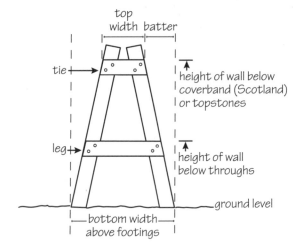

An alternative pattern uses a diagonal brace, with the heights of throughs marked by a line attached at the required height.

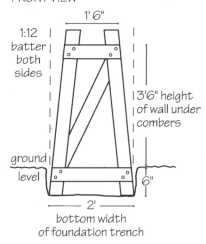

COTSWOLD WALL GUAGE
(normal dimensions showh)

FRONT VIEW

Where the frame sits on the foundation stones (footings), set it up on a pair of stones which are level and finish at ground level. If this is not possible, allowance will have to be made where, for example, the foundation stones are above ground level. An alternative arrangement is to make the frame so that it has extended legs, and sits on the base of the foundation trench, at a measured depth, as shown above.

The frame should be set carefully to the vertical, using a plumb bob as shown. Alternatively a spirit level can be used across one of the ties. If the frame is not level due to uneven foundations, level up the legs as necessary with thin stones. A wooden prop with a large nail can be used to secure the frame in the required position.

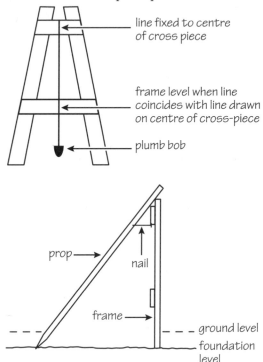

Inside measurements

The inside measurements of this type of frame give the dimensions of the wall, with the lines attached to run from the inside of the legs (p49). This type of frame can be set out before the foundation trench is excavated, and used for getting the line for 'nicking out' (p48) the edge of the foundation trench.

Stone hedges

South Western stone hedges and stone/turf hedges usually have a concave batter, which requires a more complex pattern. Two types are shown below. The one shown left is made of wood, and is held up against the side of the hedge from time to time as work progresses. The right hand pattern is made of metal tubing bent to the required shape, and secured by flat bolted metal bars and a curved tubular top section. It can be set up like a normal batter frame, propped with a pole lashed to the top cross bar.

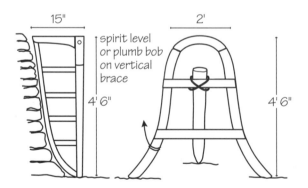

Another method is to cut a frame out of plywood to the required shape, using a jigsaw.

Lines

Guidelines should be nylon rather than hemp, which stretches and soon rots when wet. Bricklayers' pins are useful for securing lines to an existing wall, or for tightening them where they are fixed to a frame, or extended to the ground (p49). Thin wooden wedges or even bricklayers'

trowels can be substituted for these pins where they are fixed to the frame, or longer metal pins or wooden stakes can be used where they are extended to the ground.

LINE BARS

Line bars are an alternative to frames. They are adjustable, and can be set to any dimension as required, and so are useful when rebuilding a wall or gapping. They are also more portable than frames, which is useful where the site is not accessible by vehicle.

Line bars are also useful when working with groups, as a number of sets can be used to divide up the wall so that pairs or small groups have distinct sections to work on. Having several sets also lessens the chance of error caused by someone further along the wall fouling the line.

The most readily available bars are hooked fencing pins, as used to secure safety netting alongside roadworks and other worksites. Generally these are about 4' (1.3m) long with a diameter of about half an inch (10mm). They have to be driven in about a foot (300mm) to secure them in the ground, so they are not suitable for high walls. Care needs to be taken when knocking them in, and particularly when removing them, as they are fairly easy to bend. Remove by twisting and pulling, rather than by pulling back and forth to loosen.

A better choice are steel rods purchased to order from a local blacksmith or steel merchant. These should be 5/8" (16mm) diameter steel, to the length required for the height of wall, allowing for a maximum of 18" (450mm) to be driven into the ground. Lengths of 6-7' (1.8-2.1m) should cover most eventualities. Rods of 3/4" (20mm) diameter are less prone to bending, but are considerably heavier to carry. Ribbed steel reinforcing bars are a good alternative as they rarely bend, although some wallers don't like them because the ribs make it a little more awkward to adjust the lines. Some wallers have one end of the rods pointed to aid driving them into the ground, though in practice the rods are thin enough to penetrate most types of ground without being pointed.

Adding to stability

To aid stability and to stop the bars splaying apart during the building process they should be clamped together. A simple clamp can be made out of two lengths of 2 x 1" (50 x 25mm) batten, and either one or two pairs of bolts, wing nuts and washers.

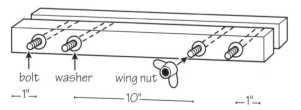

The length of the batten and position of the bolts will need to fit the local style of wall, but the dimensions shown should cope with most wider-topped walls.

The clamp is positioned so that its base corresponds with the height of the wall excluding the topstones. Ensure that it is level. If the bars are still not solid, they can be temporarily secured with large stones, as shown.

It's important to remember that it is the inside of the bars which marks the position of the face of the wall. Fasten the lines so they run from the inside of the bars. Lines are usually fastened by extending them beyond the bars and pinning them in the ground (p49).

Organising group work

Most wallers work alone or in pairs. Keep the following points in mind when working in pairs or groups:

a   Walling is one of those territorial activities in which it is easier to work on your own definite section than to work closely with another. It can be very aggravating if too many people crowd onto a section of wall, as inevitably your neighbour will use a stone you had your eye on, or place a stone where you plan to place a different one. Whatever the size of the working group, each person should have at least a yard (1m) to himself or herself, or rather more if working opposite a partner. The more skilled the worker, the greater the length they can work on their own.

b   It is best for two people to work opposite each other rather than side by side. This way each can build up one face of the wall using the stones laid out on that side, and can more easily keep out of the other's way. Paired workers can also help each other with the placing of throughs and other heavy stones. Professional wallers, especially in Scotland, often work this way since it makes for greater efficiency. It's better to have two working together on any walling project using large stones. With volunteers, experienced wallers should pair up with those of lesser skill, and give advice and help as necessary. When working in pairs, both sides should be built up at the same rate, as otherwise it is difficult to keep the centre of the wall well packed with fillings.

c   Where several people are working on adjacent sections of a wall, they should bring their sections up to the same height before placing throughs, coverbands and topstones. This allows the layers to be levelled properly before these bridging stones are placed.

d   When walling with other people be very careful not to knock or displace the guideline.

e   Extra workers can be employed collecting fillings and placing them between the positioned face stones. Swap around so that everyone has a chance to learn all aspects of wall building. Traditionally, many farm children started their walling tuition by learning how to properly position the filling stones. Extra workers can also help by bringing stones within easy reach of the wallers, although they shouldn't actually hand them the stones, as it is easier for the wallers to pick out what they want from stones on the ground.

f   From an organisational point of view, gapping is the most suitable walling work for groups of about 12 volunteers, especially where the gaps are fairly small and conveniently spaced along a length of wall. Where the task requires rebuilding a considerable length of wall, the leader must co-ordinate the work carefully. This includes ensuring that the layers are laid down at an even rate so that lines of weakness do not appear between sections, keeping the courses level and overseeing the position of throughs and topstones. Where separate lengths are started, the ends of each length must be left rough (p57) so they can be 'knitted together' when they meet.

g   Work rates are difficult to specify, as these will depend on various factors including the skill and experience of the waller, the type of stone, the type of wall and the site and weather conditions. In all situations good quality work is of much greater importance than speed. On average, a professional waller may complete about 9-15' (2.7-4.6m) per 8 hour day, with the rate likely to be slower in bad weather or poor site conditions. Amateurs and groups of volunteers can expect to complete rather less than half as much in the same time. In grand prix competitions run by the Dry Stone Walling Association, lengths are usually 6-7' (1.8-2.1m) for professionals, and 5-6' (1.5-1.8m) for amateurs. Novices in competitions are usually required to build a 3-5'(1-1.5m) length of wall.

5   Know your stone

These notes are intended as a general guide. To learn more about the stone in your locality it is worth talking to local wallers, masons and especially quarrymen, who know the stone as it comes from the ground and who take a professional interest in its strengths and weaknesses. Local terminology for various types of building stone is often complex and confusing, so it helps to be able to recognise major types and place them according to their geological features.

Building for durability

CHOICE OF STONE

Characteristic walling stones are described in the following section, but a few general points are worth bearing in mind.

a   Avoid highly fissile rock, good quality slate excepted. Fissile rock tends to split or fragment easily on weathering and so flakes away piece by piece. If it must be used, keep it in fairly thick blocks, rather than splitting it into thinner pieces which will quickly crumble.

b   For standard double walling (p45), avoid using very large stones, bigger than about 1' (300mm) on a side or 8" (200mm) high, for the face stones. Even foundation stones should be just high enough to come up to ground level from the bottom of the foundation trench, which is normally about 6" (150mm). Although large stones speed the building process, they are hard to work around and reposition, and they may settle unequally relative to smaller stones in the wall.

Larger stones may be needed for foundations, throughs and coverbands. Where the available stone supply is mainly large stones, single walling (p139) and other styles have developed. The massive stones found in many old walls are there because of the need to clear adjacent fields or to incorporate immovable boulders, and not because they add strength to the wall.

c   Avoid using water-washed stones, if possible. One occasionally comes across very beautiful walls of rounded river-bottom stones which show the work of a master craftsman. However, rounded stones are hard to use, being too smooth to grip each other properly, and often with fine cracks which cause them to break apart in frost. Normally, large rounded stones which have to be used, should be split to give flat beds and faces. Alternatively they can be broken up for fillings.

PREVENTING DECAY OF STONEWORK

Stonework, whether dry or mortared, is attacked by a number of agents including:

a   Wind-borne dust or sand which abrades the stone. This can be severe in coastal districts.

b   Fluctuating temperatures, which cause the stone to flake at the surface or split due to differential expansion and contraction within the stone.

c   Frost, which forces the stone apart along cracks as the water freezes and expands.

d   Rain, which penetrates cracks in the stone and may lead to frost damage, and which also dissolves certain types of stone directly. Limestone, which is over 90% calcium carbonate, is easily affected by the dilute acids found in rain and ground water. Industrial air pollution, which can increase the acidity of rainfall, has been responsible for the rapid deterioration not only of limestone, but of sandstone as well.

Sedimentary rock

Sedimentary rocks in the ground contain 'quarry sap', a dilute acid having silica, lime and other chemicals in solution or suspension. If the stone is allowed to dry naturally for a year or more before use, the quarry sap forms a hard protective coating on the surface. Because of this, stone which is to be worked should be shaped before curing, when it is softest.

The weather resistance of cured sedimentary stone is reduced if the surface coating is removed in building. Naturally, stone used for dry walling is not given the careful treatment of masonry stone, but it is worth remembering that limestone, and to a lesser extent sandstone, may last longer if the protective skin in left intact. This is an argument against using the hammer too actively when building with these materials.

Cotswold stone is easily damaged by frost, and the most durable stone is left in the open to weather over winter, which ensures that any bad stone breaks up before use. The topmost layer in the quarry is always the hardest, since it has been exposed to frost over millennia. Blasting out of stone may leave minute stress fractures which only show up in the first hard frost. If the stone is purchased 'green', or still moist from the earth, it should be left to dry before use. This process is also used in other limestone areas.

An important consideration when walling with most types of stone is its bedding. As used in walling, the natural 'bed' of a sedimentary stone is the plane on which it was originally laid down. In the case of metamorphic rocks, the bed follows the planes of cleavage or foliation. Since layers of rock have often been tilted or contorted by geological processes, their bedding is not necessarily horizontal when found in the quarry. However, all stones with a laminate bedding should normally be placed with the bedding horizontal in walls and other structures, which gives the stone the greatest resistance to decay. The exception are upright copings, where the bedding is placed vertically.

Stones which are quarried in large blocks with no tendency to split in any particular direction are termed freestones, and can be given any orientation when placed in a structure. Freestones include granite and other igneous rocks and a few extremely fine grained sedimentary rocks such as Portland, Bath and some of the other famous building stones.

Characteristic walling stones

The most important types of walling stones are described briefly below. Wallers often use loose generic terms to describe the rock found in their area. For example, the term 'whinstone' is used in Scotland and elsewhere to describe hard, dark stones which can include greenstone, basalt, chert or quartzose sandstone.

SANDSTONES

Sandstones consist of grains of sand, mostly quartz, cemented by silica, carbonate of lime or iron oxide. The resulting material may vary considerably in hardness. Colour ranges from white through yellow and brown to red depending on the cementing minerals. The main types of sandstone used in walling are quartzite, grits and flags. Quartzite consists mainly of quartz grains cemented by silica. Grits are hard sandstones containing small pebbles, so that the rock has a very rough surface when broken, which led in the past to their use as millstones. Flags include thin-bedded sandstones which split readily parallel to the bedding.

Sandstones of widely varying ages are found in walls in many parts of the country. Perhaps the oldest is the Precambrian Torridonian Sandstone of Sutherland and Wester Ross, but the earliest widely-used sandstone is the Old Red Sandstone of Devonian age found in many parts of eastern Scotland. The Caithness flag fences (p145) use stone of this type. Through large areas of the Pennines and the north-east of England, Millstone Grit and other coarse dark Carboniferous sandstones dominate the walls. Around Carlisle and in Dumfriesshire, the warm New Red Sandstone of Permian age is trimmed into blocks to produce masonry-like dry walls.

LIMESTONES

Limestones are calcareous rocks formed from solidified masses of whole or broken shells, from the remains of coral reefs, from chemical precipitates or evaporates, or from the redeposition of eroded materials from older limey beds. Most limestones are formed almost completely of calcium carbonate, but magnesium limestone contains a high proportion of magnesium carbonate.

All limestones are more or less readily weathered by rain and ground water containing dilute carbonic and sulphuric acids, particularly where the stone has been cracked or has developed bedding due to the pressure of overlying strata. Limestones often intergrade with sandstones and shales so that the division between calcareous sandstone and gritty or sandy limestones, for example, is not always clear.

In Britain, the oldest widespread limestone is Carboniferous limestone, which forms part of the Derbyshire Peak District and the area to both sides of the Craven Fault in the western part of North Yorkshire. This pale grey, lumpy stone is immediately recognisable wherever it occurs, not only in the walls of the north but in the Mendips and the Gower Peninsula as well. North of Wensleydale the Carboniferous limestone becomes increasingly sandy and the walls are more mixed.

Jurassic limestones of different varieties colour the buildings and most of the walls in the Cotswolds. In Oxfordshire, Stonesfield 'slate', really a sandy flaggy limestone, provided until recently an important local roofing material. The Jurassic limestone belt runs north-northeast from the Isle of Purbeck to the Cleveland Hills in North Yorkshire, and has been widely used for building. Chalk, a very fine, uniform limestone forms the downs of southern and southeastern England. It is too water soluble for building, but the flints which it contains are used alone, or banded with bricks, in mortared walls.

SHALE AND SLATE

Shale belongs to the group of argillaceous or mud rocks, made up of very fine particles of clay which have been dried and hardened by compression. Shale is distinguished from other mud rocks by its well-developed lamination, and it tends to split readily into thin slabs parallel to the original bedding. Most shale is soft and weathers readily.

Slate is mudstone or shale which has been metamorphosed under intense pressure, resulting in the flaky minerals such as mica being shifted so that their flat surfaces lie at right angles to the direction of pressure. The metamorphosed material may retain traces of the original bedding, but it most easily splits along the new cleavage planes.

Most slates or slatey shales are low grade and have little use in building, but have been widely used for field walling in much of central and north Wales, the Skiddaw slate area of the northern Lake District and elsewhere where better walling stone is not available. The common feature of these walls is the fissile nature of the slate or shale, so unless another type of stone is available to form a heavy capping, the walls often tend to flake away layer by layer, or settle sideways if on a slope. High grade slate, such as the waste from slate quarries, can be trimmed into rectangular blocks which are much more resistant to splitting, and can be used to make flag fences for example.

GRANITE AND OTHER IGNEOUS ROCKS

Granite is formed by the slow cooling of acid molten rock deep in the earth's crust. It is often, but not always, coarse grained and is made up mainly of felspar and quartz with mica and other minerals.

Granite is the toughest and most durable of the building stones. It forms the resistant bulk of many of Britain's wildest moorlands: the Cairngorms and Rannoch Moor and other parts of Northern Scotland; the Cheviots; parts of the Lake District; and in the south west of England, Dartmoor, Bodmin Moor, and much of Cornwall, including Land's End.

Detached blocks of granite have been used locally from prehistoric times for tombs and standing stones and, later, for Christian crosses. It was not until the 18th century that granite was widely quarried, so difficult was it to prise from the quarry face. The clearance walls of Zennor, Cornwall, date back to the Iron Age, while the granite walls of Aberdeenshire are of late 18th, 19th and early 20th century date.

The extrusive igneous rocks form a widely varying group, but are little used for walling. An exception are the walls of Borrowdale Volcanics in the Lake District, which are composed of varied Ordovician lavas, ashes and agglomerates, and which can be recognised by their rough surface and warm colours, compared to the dark slate walls elsewhere in the Lakes.

SCHISTS AND GNEISSES

Schists and gneisses are metamorphic rocks which represent an intermediate between sedimentary formations and granite. A distinguishing feature of both schists and gneisses is their foliation, like the tightly packed leaves of leaf-mould. Schists have the foliation closely spaced throughout the body of the rock, so that almost any part of it can be split into flakes. Schists and gneisses are of Precambrian age in Britain, occurring in the Highlands of Scotland, the Outer Hebrides, Anglesey, the Lizard in Cornwall and Start Point in Devon. While some schists produce even rectangular blocks of walling stones, gneisses tend to be rough and irregular. However, even the roughest gneisses are easier to use than granite in dry stone walls.

Sources of stone and amounts required

In general, the best stone for use in walling is the local stone. Even if other stone can be obtained more cheaply, local stone preserves the continuity between the natural landscape, the older walls in the vicinity and the new work. Occasionally local stone is not to be preferred, if it is extremely fissile and weathers poorly, or where the only local source are limestone pavements or other sites of special geological or botanical interest.

The majority of walling work involves rebuilding existing derelict, unsafe or non-stockproof walls, of which there is a huge mileage in Britain. The existing supply of stone may be sufficient, although normally there has been some loss of stone. The stone supply tends to diminish as stones get broken, become buried in the ground or dispersed. Stones are also deliberately removed for reuse elsewhere, both legitimately and illegally. Hearting tends to get buried and dispersed. In some cases new stone is not available, particularly on inaccessible sites, in which case the challenge to the waller is to make the best of what is there. In other cases, new stone must be brought in to augment the existing supply.

There are four sources of stone to consider:

a   Surface field stones, other than limestone pavements. Early farm walls were often built in part to clear the land. Often in areas of rough grazing there are still ample supplies of stone near to hand, requiring only picks and crowbars to remove. Even where bedrock does not form convenient outcrops, glacial till may supply stones large enough for walling, although these tend to be less easy to work with than quarried stone.

b   Stone from derelict walls and buildings. This stone will be weathered, and will blend in with existing stone. It will also be sorted into suitable types, which will ease the work of reusing it. Sometimes old stone is not suitable, such as some Cotswold stone and fissile shales and slates which become unsuitably soft and crumbly through weathering. Highly dressed stone is no good for dry stone walling since the faces are too smooth to bond securely. Always check with the landowner before using stone from old walls or buildings, no matter how decayed they seem. Removing an old wall will inevitably destroy the habitat, although the new wall will form a replacement habitat, but somewhat different in character.

c Stone from abandoned quarries or self-quarried stone. 'Vest pocket' quarries often dot the line of long enclosure walls, usually as near as possible to the uphill side. Sometimes these can be re-opened. Limestone faces usually produce good-sized though irregular chunks with a little pick and crowbar work, but outcrops of weathered sandstone often yield unusably big boulders. Weathered granite is very difficult to extract, but schist is less troublesome. Whinstone and slate or slatey shales can be taken from rock faces without too much difficulty. Disused quarries may have heaps of waste stone which is usable after sorting. Always check with the landowner and the local authority before removing any stone. Some sites are protected as Sites of Special Scientific Interest (SSSIs) or Regionally Important Geological/geomorphological Sites (RIGS), and stone removal may not be permitted.

d Professionally quarried stone. This is now probably the main source of supply where additional stone is needed for walling. It is expensive, but where costs of employing a skilled waller are also high, the cost of stone becomes less significant. Inquire locally as to the best source to match the existing stone. The *Register of Certificated Professional Wallers/Dykers and Sources of Stone*, published by the Dry Stone Walling Association, may also be of guidance.

AMOUNTS REQUIRED

The amount of stone required for building a wall depends on:

a The wall's dimensions.

b The regularity of shape of the stone, and the skill of the waller.

c The density of the stone.

Dimensions and amounts are given here in metric, as quarries deal in tonnes rather than tons.

The wall's dimensions

The higher or wider a wall, the more stone it will require for any given length. In order to calculate the wall's volume, calculate the following:

Length x height x average width

The height is measured from the bottom of the foundations to the top of the coping. The average width is calculated by adding the base width (below the foundations) to the top width (at the top of the topstones) and dividing by two.

For example, taking a wall 0.8m wide at the base and 0.4m wide at its top, 1.6m high and 100m long:

$$\text{Average width} = \frac{0.8m + 0.4m}{2} = 0.6m$$

Volume = 0.6m x 1.6m x 100m = 96 cubic metres

Regularity of stone and skill of waller

Not all of a wall's volume is stone, as it also contains air between the stones. As a very rough guide, allow the following:

Regular, level bedded stone will create a tight, well packed face, limiting the amount of air to as little as 10%. Sawn slate off cuts, with slate chipping hearting, is possibly the most regular stone available, and air content may be reduced to as little as 5%, but this is exceptional. Irregular and rounded stone tends to create a slacker face, and with larger stone the gaps can be quite marked. The air is likely to comprise about 20%.

The skill of the waller is also significant, with a skilled waller building a wall with perhaps 10% less air than a novice. The regularity of the stone and the skill of the waller also has implications on wastage. Less regular stone can be dressed to a certain extent to produce a tighter wall, but this becomes more difficult with larger and harder stone. There is likely to be more wastage with a novice than with a skilled waller. Estimates are difficult, but even for irregular stone used by novices, wastage should be less than 5%. With regular stone there should be no wastage.

Density of stone

Different types of stone vary in density and hence weight. In order to know how much stone is required you need to know its 'bulk density', which is measured by how much a solid cubic metre of it would weigh, and is normally expressed as tonnes per cubic metre (t/m^3). It can also be expressed as millions of grams per cubic metre (Mg/m^3).

Basalt, for example from Skye, is one of the heaviest walling materials, with a bulk density of around $2.95t/m^3$. At the other extreme, Oolitic limestone from the Cotswolds, one of the lightest stones, can have a bulk density of around $2t/m^3$.

If an allowance of 15% air is made, the 96m³ volume (from the example above) would require 82m³ of stone.

For a basalt at around $2.95t/m^3$ this would require 242 tonnes.

For an Oolitic limestone at around $2t/m^3$ this would require 164 tonnes.

Generalisations within a stone type are also problematic. Oolitic limestone provides a good example of this. Oolitic limestone from the Cotswolds is likely to fall in the range of $1.9-2.1t/m^3$, whereas Oolitic limestone from Portland is likely to fall in the range of 2.1-2.3t/m³. These variations occur because of the slight differences in the stone between quarries, and even between two faces in the same quarry.

These differences can have serious implications for cost and wastage. When combined with the difficulty of assessing air and making any allowances for wastage it can be very easy to overestimate, and to pay for stone which you do not need. This extra stone will also have to be cleared up and transported away, involving more time and expense. Equally, you can easily run out of stone. On a large job this might not be a problem, beyond the extra cost, as you can order another 16-20 tonne load. For smaller lengths a shortfall of 5 tonnes will seriously affect the price as the transport costs are likely to increase out of proportion to the amount of stone required.

There is also a problem in obtaining information about the exact bulk density from the quarry concerned, as they may not know it, or give rather inaccurate estimates. The table below gives a rough guide to the various main types of stone, but note that there will be variation between different areas and different quarries. A variation of +/- 5% should be allowed.

	t/m³
Granite	2.6
Carboniferous limestone	2.5
Sandstones:	
Old red sandstone	2.35
Coal measures sandstone	2.3
New red sandstone	2.25
Gritstone	2.2
Portland Oolitic limestone	2.15
Cotswold Oolitic limestone	2.00

It is a rather inexact science, and accurate estimates can only be made with experience. The problems of estimating can make it difficult for dry stone walling contractors involved in competitive tendering for work, and it is well worth being aware of the pitfalls before a tender is made.

Other considerations

Unless you know the quarry company well, it is always advisable to inspect the stone before it is delivered, as the interpretation of 'walling stone' can vary. With regular, level bedded stone there shouldn't be a problem with suitability, although sometimes a lot of the stone is too big and slabby and has to be reduced with a sledgehammer. The less regular the stone the greater the problem, and walling stone may tend towards being the material which the quarry can't otherwise get rid of. This will make walling work difficult, and may result in a lot of wastage.

Often it works out more cost effective to buy hearting separately, as smaller stone is usually cheaper to buy. However this will depend on the regularity of the stone, and on how individual quarries operate. Generally, the more regular the stone the less hearting occurs 'naturally' within a load. A certain amount of hearting will be generated through dressing stone, but it can be wasteful to smash up good building stone to create hearting, if the hearting can be purchased more cheaply. With larger, rounded and irregular stone it is going to be harder to 'create' sufficient hearting if it does not occur naturally in a load. Washed stone of 5"-1" (125-25mm) makes good hearting, and some of the larger pieces will make suitable face stones.

Purchasing hearting separately does not affect the total tonnage you require, but you will have to make some calculation of how much you need as a percentage of the overall mass of the wall. This will be affected by the dimensions of the wall, and the relative size of the face stones. For example, many walls built out of smaller stone can contain 30-50% of their bulk in hearting, whereas walls built of larger stones and slabs can contain as little as 10%.

Generally it is safest to slightly underestimate the percentage of hearting required, as you can always 'waste' some of the building stone by reducing it to hearting. Conversely, if you have to substitute many of the face stones with larger hearting the stability of the wall may be compromised.

If you require throughstones you may need to purchase these separately, as with many stone types they do not occur 'naturally' within a load in sufficient quantity. Some good quarries sell suitable throughstones separately, whilst with others you will need to visit the quarry and hand select the stone.

The number required can be calculated from the pattern of throughs to be used in the wall. It's advisable to order about 5% extra, to allow for any damage in transit, and to give a wider choice in use. Try to arrange a separate delivery of the throughs so they are less likely to be damaged, and can easily be kept separate on the work site for ease of use. Either deduct the weight of the throughs, as supplied, from the total walling stone required, or for smaller amounts, ignore the weight and regard the additional stone as part of wastage.

Most of the considerations for throughstones also apply to coping, but the quantities involved are much greater. If you do require a separate order you will need to calculate the volume of coping required, with allowance for air and wastage. As the coping is a significant proportion of the total volume, this needs to be deducted from the total walling stone required in order to avoid unacceptable wastage.

Breaking and shaping stone

Margaret Brooks (1973) once talked to a Yorkshire waller who said he used his hammer only:

'with something of the feeling of giving way, something of a feeling of defeat. One ought to be able to fit all the stones, make use of all the stones whatever their shape and size. One should manage with the stones as they are, especially stones from an existing wall that's fallen. They have been used before; it should be possible to use them again.'

This is a sentiment that many wallers would agree with. Nevertheless, breaking and shaping stones is often a necessity either to provide material of a more usable shape and size, or to trim it to a more regular finished product.

GENERAL POINTS

a Be careful when breaking stones, hammering or drilling. Safety goggles must be worn.

b Examine each stone before hitting it to see how it will break. Almost every stone, even granite, has some lines of weakness along bedding or cleavage planes, or in areas of frost damage and other weathering stress. It is along these planes that stones break most easily and predictably. If there is no obvious crack to work on, hammer away until one appears and then concentrate your efforts on this crack.

c To quarry slabs of bedded or cracked stone, enlarge the cracks with a pick until you can drive in wedges with a sledge hammer, or prise the rock apart with a crowbar.

d Most types of walling stone can be split with a hammer of an appropriate size and weight for the size and type of stone (p30). Hit the stone 'fair on' or you will just chip it away and round it off. If you can't split it as far in as you want, you may have to cut it in several stages, working back gradually to the correct shape. Hit with the full face of the hammer head as shown.

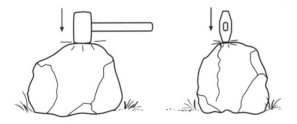

This is the most effective action, causes least wear on the hammer, and helps prevent chips from flying up into your face. Use a full, solid swing except when doing careful trimming. Hit very slightly away from the line of proposed fracture, so that the correct part of the stone breaks off. If the stone doesn't split immediately, keep hammering away at the dust which you create. The dust acts as a wedge to force the stone apart.

e Experiment with each type of stone to find the way in which it splits most readily. Sometimes it works better to hit at right angles to the grain, than to strike in the usual way along the grain.

f Break stones on the ground, not on the wall, which will be disrupted. Don't break stones in your hand, as you are likely to hurt yourself. Support the stone against another stone and hold it firmly with your left foot. It is easier to split the stone when it is positioned more or less on edge, as shown, rather than flat on the ground.

g Before you break up a big stone, make sure it won't be needed as a through, cover, topstone or gate post. Try to break it so as to produce several usable face stones, or one useful face stone plus fillings. Don't waste effort and stone trying to shape stone exactly for normal walling.

h There are various ways by which stone can be shaped more precisely when required. Cotswold and other soft stones can be chipped away using a hammer with a narrow or pointed pein. Other methods include scoring and wedging apart big slabs, drilling and wedging freestones, and splitting finely bedded or foliated stones with a hammer and chisel. Techniques are described in the following sections for slate, granite, schist and gneiss. These techniques can be adapted for use on other types of stone.

SLATE

Slate can be cut in square-cornered blocks of the desired size and split down to almost any thickness using a cold chisel and a lump hammer. A bricklayer's bolster can be used to break slate across the grain. The ideal chisels are special slate-cutting chisels, but these are hard to obtain. If you do manage to acquire second-hand slate-cutting chisels take care of them, as their flanges are easily broken of if they are misused. A typical pattern is shown below.

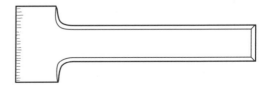

Quarrymen often work with a set of three identical chisels, allowing two to rest while the third is in use. The set should be sharpened and retempered about once a month if in constant use.

A block of good-quality slate can be split easily and precisely in two planes, but not all three. It can be cleaved, that is forced apart along a cleavage plane. It can also be split along the grain, which is the original bedding plane which lies roughly at right angles to the cleavage. However, it cannot be as easily split perpendicular to both the cleavage and the bedding. Lower-quality slate, more often encountered in rough walling, can be cleaved, but not so easily split along the grain.

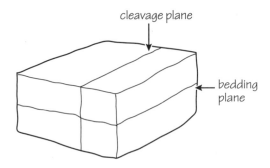

To cleave slate, place the stone on end with its cleavage planes running vertically. Hold the chisel or bolster in one hand, perpendicular to the surface as shown below, and tap it firmly but not heavily with the lump hammer. If cleaving a narrow block, hold the chisel in the centre of the line which you wish to cleave. If cleaving a wide block, start near one end and work gradually along the line.

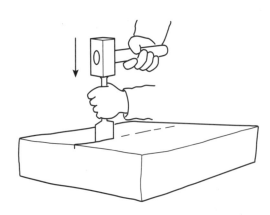

If the block is too large it may not split, but a crack should appear which you can gradually force apart with further light taps of the chisel or by gently prising with a wrecking bar.

To split slate along its grain, start with the chisel or bolster at one edge of the slab and move it along the line of the desired cut, tapping it in the same way as described above. At first you may have to go over the line of the cut more than once, but with practice you should be able to split it with two or three blows. It helps if the ground below the line of the cut is soft enough to absorb some of the shock and distribute it through the slate.

To split slate perpendicular to both the grain and the cleavage, first cut a groove with the chisel along the line which you hope to split. In quarries special chisels are used, but you can use an ordinary cold chisel to carve out a line about 1/4" (6mm) deep and wide. Now tap along this groove in the same way as when splitting along the grain.

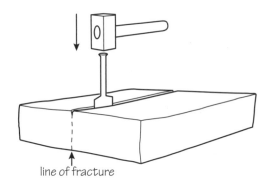

line of fracture

You may have to hit quite a bit harder than when splitting the slate in other ways, and the break will probably occur not at right angles to the end of the block, but slightly off it.

In commercial cut work, slate is sawn along this line rather than split with hammer and chisel, to achieve a more exact result, but for general walling or building purposes it doesn't matter if the cut is a bit off.

GRANITE

The following tools are suggested for use on granite:

a A 15" (375mm) grinding chisel with a three-quarters square shaft with a flat top for striking, tapering to a 3/4" (18mm) wide arrowhead grinding surface. A star drill may be used instead.

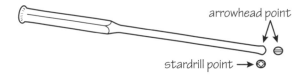

arrowhead point

stardrill point →

Drills may also have waisted shanks, which are particularly useful on wider drills to prevent them jamming in the holes.

For drilling a hole in which to set a metal post or similar, it's best to have several drills, graduated in length so that as the hole deepens you can use progressively longer drills. This is easier than using a long drill from the start. Drills for this purpose should be 1/4" (6mm) wider than the post to be set in, so that there is space around the post to pour in lead or cement for fixing. Various electric drills, including rechargeable portable drills are also available, and make the work very much quicker and easier.

b Cleaning tool to remove rock dust when drilling. This is a light metal rod, 6-7" (150-175mm) long and about 3/16" inch (5mm) in diameter, with the last 1/2" (12mm) flattened and curved as shown.

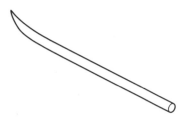

You can also use a bicycle pump to blow out debris.

c Six sets of shims and wedges. Each set consists of a pair of metal shims or 'feathers', narrow at the top and flaring outward so that you can grip them, and a metal wedge.

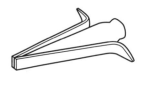

d Lump and sledge hammers.

e Steel wedges, 6" (150mm), of the sort used in tree felling.

f Crowbar and wrecking bar.

To split granite:

1 Drill a series of holes along the line to be split. Their distance apart is set mainly by the length of stone to be split with the available shims and wedges. Holes can be spaced up to 1' (300mm) or more apart, but the closer they are the more accurate the results.

To drill each hole, hold the grinding chisel or star drill in one hand, with the shaft perpendicular to the rock. Rest the drill point on the rock and hit the drill smartly with the lump hammer. Do not use very heavy blows, however, since these will not necessarily speed the work and, if attempted on other types of rock, may shatter the stone. Then turn the drill 60°. Continue hitting and rotating the drill until the hole is 4-5" (200-250mm) deep, or less for a small slab. Flick the dust out of the hole from time to time with the cleaning tool. Drilling granite by hand is a very slow, tedious job, so don't exhaust yourself by trying to rush it.

2 When all the holes are drilled, insert a pair of shims in each with a wedge between. Pound each wedge once, moving down the line in consecutive order. Return to the first wedge and repeat the operation until a thin crack forms between the wedges.

3 Insert one or more large steel wedges into the crack. Retrieve the shims and small wedges. Then hammer the big wedges a few times until the split is wide enough to

insert the crowbar or wrecking bar. Remove these wedges and lever the slab apart.

SCHIST AND GNEISS

Schist has definite planes of foliation and along these it splits much more readily than granite. Mica schist is the easiest type to split. Gneiss can be split using the same tools and methods but the results are less easy and predictable. Extremely irregular and tenacious gneiss may require drilling before it is split.

To split small slabs of these rocks all you need is a lump hammer and a cold chisel. To split and trim big slabs you need:

a Two heavy sledge hammers, one square peined and one with one square and one bevelled pein. The latter should be as heavy as possible, up to about 25lb (11.3kg).

b Lump hammer

c Hand hammer with one square and one bevelled pein, about the same size and weight as the lump hammer.

d Thin steel wedge. An old discarded axe blade is ideal.

e Crowbar and wrecking bar.

It is easiest if two people work together:

1 Prop the slab up on edge using wooden blocks or stones.

2 Mark out a straight line parallel to the grain of foliation.

3 While one person holds the bevel-pein sledgehammer with its edge along the line to be split, the other pounds it with the square-pein sledge. Starting at one end of the slab, move along it striking one solid blow in each position. Repeat the sequence until a crack shows along the line which has been marked out.

4 Tap the old axe blade into the crack until it can stand without being held. Then drive it in farther with the sledge.

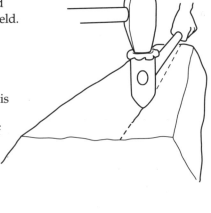

5 When the crack is wide enough, insert the end of the crowbar or wrecking bar and prise apart the slab.

To trim schist to a more precise shape:

1   Prop up the slab and wedge it in position with stones.

2   Hold the small bevel-pein hammer against the bottom of the surface to be cut away, with the head angled downward about 30°.

3   Hit the bevelled hammer with the lump hammer to chip away at the face of the slab. Remove the face bit by bit, gradually moving the bevelled hammer higher on the face as the lower part is cut back sufficiently.

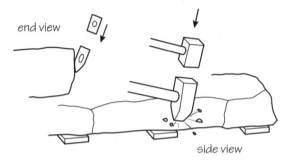

side view

4   As you near the top of the slab, remove the props. Finish squaring off the top face by removing small chips of stone. To do this, hit the bevelled hammer while holding it perpendicular to the top face as shown.

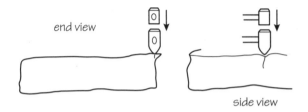

side view

6   Rebuilding a free standing wall

This chapter covers design and construction procedures basic to all free standing dry stone walls. It describes procedures from the viewpoint of rebuilding a wall, as this is more usual than building an entirely new wall. Additional points are included on the building of new walls (p58) and the repair of small gaps (p57). More detailed technical information about walling on slopes, curves and across difficult ground is given in chapter 7.

Every area has its own terminology, which tends to hide the fact that similarities in their walling methods are more important than differences. The terms and procedures used in this chapter are those of the old West Riding of Yorkshire, which includes the Pennine limestone, Millstone Grit and Coal Measures. Further details of regional styles of walling are given in chapters 1 and 11.

General features

These vary according to the wall's purpose, its age and the type of stone in which it is built. Those which enclose cattle are usually about 4' (1.2m) from the ground to the top of the coping, whereas walls to fence sheep, particularly moorland varieties, are usually at least 5'3" (1.6m). Garden walls can be any height. Old walls, predating the Parliamentary Enclosure Acts are usually more coarsely built, being wider at the base with a gradual batter and few throughs. The most highly-designed walls are invariably the major enclosure walls, or march dykes as Rainsford-Hannay (1957) calls them. Whatever the age of the wall, the more regular its stone the less batter is required. For further

discussion of batter see page125.

The diagram below illustrates the construction of a typical Pennine wall. The pattern of walls varies even within an area, depending on factors such as stone type, local tradition and the whim of the builder, but these differences are often only minor modifications. The general principles outlined below apply to most other walls.

Dry stone walls are semi-flexible structures, with the stone settling over time. The basic principles involved in building a dry stone wall are aimed at reducing the potential for movement during this settlement. Sound building technique will result in a strong structure, and it is important to note that most of the strength is internal and cannot be readily seen from the outside of the wall. Consequently, a solid wall may not look perfect. Conversely, a wall can also be built to look good on the outside at the expense of internal strength. However, an experienced waller should be able to build a wall which is both strong and looks good, with 'tight' faces, that is good stone to stone contact and a minimum of gaps.

Similarly, a good, even line and batter, with no bulges or depressions in the face of the wall, will mean that all the forces are correctly displaced within the wall.

The stones are set level in roughly graded layers with the biggest at the bottom and the smallest under the coping. Throughs are usually in two rows, at about 2' (600mm) height at 1'9" (525mm) centres, and 4' (1.2m) height at 2'4" (710mm) centres. If the wall's height under the topstones is

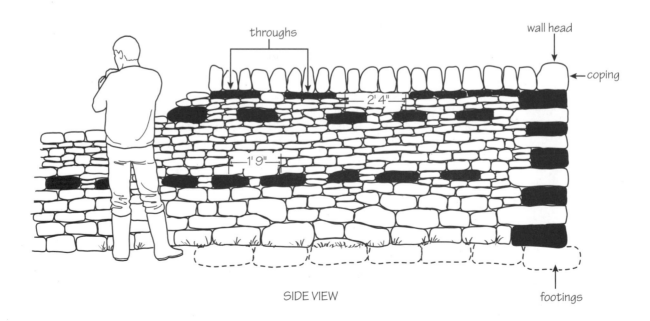

SIDE VIEW

SECTION THROUGH WALL   SECTION THROUGH WALL HEAD

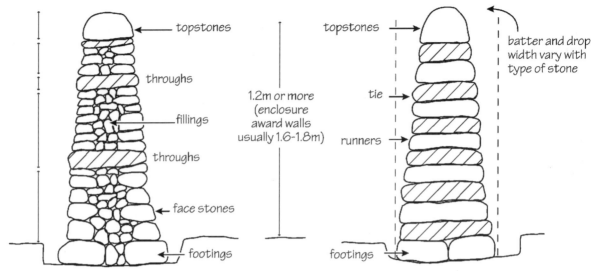

topstones

throughs

fillings

throughs

face stones

footings

bottom width 1'8"-3', depending on stone type

1.2m or more
(enclosure
award walls
usually 1.6-1.8m)

topstones

tie

runners

footings

batter and drop
width vary with
type of stone

5' (1.2m) or more, the same number of throughs should be used, but in three rows. Throughs in different rows should be staggered for greatest strength.

The coping is often upright, with even-sided topstones.

The pattern of throughstones and coping can vary considerably from place to place. For example, throughs may be flush with the wall faces, may project a few inches on one or both sides, or may form a continuous layer. Variations in coping can be even more pronounced, and might, or might not include a coverband below the topstones, as shown in the diagram. These variations are described in more detail on pages 130-139.

Walling procedure

The following is an outline of the procedure for carrying out a major repair of a length of dry stone wall. The work is described in detail in the subsequent sections. For simplicity, the diagrams below illustrate the wall part way along its length. Unless repairing a gap, one would normally start with a wall head and then proceed along the wall.

1   Dismantle the wall, setting out the stone alongside the line of the wall, while leaving enough room to work (p47).

coping   footing   leave working
                                            gap of 2-3'

2   Line out and clean the foundation trench (p48).

3   Put in the footings (foundation stones) along the entire trench. Place fillings between them as you work (p54). Backfill the outside edges.

4   Set up the batter frames or line bars. These are described in chapter 4 (p32), with their use discussed further below (p49).

guidelines

5   Raise the lines to a level about 1' (300mm) above the foundation level. This height will vary with the size of the stone, and the experience of the waller. For smaller stone, and when you are first learning, raise the lines in increments of about 6" (150mm), depending on stone size. Build the layers to this level.

6   Raise the lines to the height of the bottom of the first row of throughs, normally about 2' (600mm) above ground level. This may be lower if three rows of throughs are being placed. If there is only one row of throughs (as shown here), this is normally about half way up, at about 21" (530mm).

7   Build the courses up to the lines and level them off to take the throughs.

8 Lay the first row of throughs (p55).

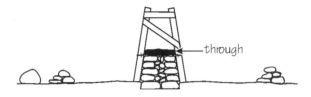

9 It can be a good idea to move stone nearer to the wall at this point, to aid stone selection. Ensure you maintain a clear working area alongside the wall.

10 Where there is only one line of throughs, raise the line in 1' (300mm) increments, or repeat points 6-9 for each row of throughs.

11 When there is less than 1' (300mm) to the level of the bottom of the topstones, or after the final row of throughs, raise the guidelines to the height of the top course, that is the top of the wall minus the topstones.

12 Build the courses up to the lines and level them off to take the topstones.

13 Normally the topstones are placed after the entire wall is built to the top course. However, on long stretches, or where the wall may have to be left unfinished for some time, it is worth placing topstones on the finished sections to protect them (p56).

14 Clean up at the end of the day's work, and shift unused stones from any completed wall to the next section to be built. Leave unfinished sections in stepped layers, unless you have finished the section at a head, so that the next section will bind into it well.

Dismantling

Dismantling, also known as ridding out, or stripping out, is an important process. Sorting the stone as you dismantle the wall enables better wall building, as it is easier to find the stone you need, and to choose the right size stone at the right height. It is also easier to check that you have enough coping and throughstones. This avoids the irritation of, for

example, uncovering a large stone buried beneath a pile of smaller ones when it is too late to use it.

With experience you will discover the best method of sorting and setting out the stone to suit your preferences. Many professional wallers sort out piles of specific shapes and sizes of stones which they know will be useful. For example, longer small faced stones resembling 'fingers' or 'bones' are useful for filling awkward gaps. Odd shaped stones need to be identified so they can be used to their best advantage. With proper sorting the right stone should come to hand at the right time.

1 Remove all the stone which is lying on the ground alongside the wall, taking care to set aside any topstones. Where the wall has suffered a major collapse, work into the pile from the edges wherever possible, and where it has collapsed to one side, pass some of the stone to the other side of the wall. Take care not to cause any more of the wall to collapse, removing unstable stones from the wall once you have access to them. Where the collapse is quite large, you might need to move the stone twice, initially separating and spreading the stone, before sorting it as outlined below.

2 Once the debris has been cleared, remove the remaining topstones from the section to be repaired. Take care to remove the stones safely, bracing yourself against the wall for larger stones, getting a firm grip on the stones, and maintaining correct posture and correct carrying (p22). Take care not to dislodge stones immediately below the coping by dragging them off the wall. Place the topstones in a line at a distance from the wall equivalent to around one and a half to twice the height of the wall, which is normally about 7-9' (2.1-2.75m). Place them in a rough imitation of the style of cope on the wall, so that you can see if there will be enough. In any case, it's best to add a couple of stones, selected during the dismantling of the wall, for every metre of wall to be rebuilt.

3 Start removing stones from along the length of the wall. Remove layers rather than concentrating on a short section, as this lessens the chance of further collapse. Keep the stone to its original side of the wall, to ensure an even distribution of stones on both sides.

4 When working on a slope, however slight, take care not to destabilise the wall uphill of the section being dismantled. Always leave any standing wall well stepped at its exposed end (p57).

5 To avoid accidents, place stones on the ground rather than throwing them. Gently tossing smaller stones is acceptable, but you need to always be aware of other workers and passers-by.

6 Grade the stone as you dismantle the wall, placing smaller building stone nearer the top stones, with larger stones nearer the wall. Ensure you maintain a clear working space of 2-3' (600-900mm) alongside the wall. This avoids tripping over stones, enables you to maintain a better posture when working, and facilitates a hasty exit in the event of any collapse of the old wall during the dismantling process.

7 The filling or hearting should be placed in piles at 3-6' (1-2m) centres, close to, but not in your working space. Hearting is used throughout the building process, and is needed close to hand. Leave ample room, as there is usually more of it than you expect, and you do not want it spilling over into your working space or onto the building stones. Ensure you have an even amount of hearting on both sides of the wall.

8 Take care when removing throughstones and get help if necessary (p23). The throughs are normally placed beyond the coping stones to ensure they are easily accessible and do not get mixed with the topstones or larger building stone. Some wallers prefer to put the throughs to the near side of the topstones, in which case you will need to start with the topstones set out further from the wall.

9 It's a good idea to place large and irregular stones with their 'faces' (the part of the stone which will be seen in the finished wall) towards the working space, to make it easier to assess their shape.

10 Finally remove the foundation stones, getting help where necessary. These should be placed on top of the building stones immediately alongside the working space. With very large stones, it's advisable to roll them into the working space and leave them there, rather than risk injury from lifting or rolling them on top of the building stone. Sometimes some of the foundation stones can be left in situ. This is dealt with under gapping (p57).

The foundation

A wall is only as strong as its weakest point, and the lower this point is in the wall the greater the potential for collapse. Poor foundations are the source of most serious collapses, and no amount of careful building higher up can correct problems at the base. With between one and two tonnes of stone in every metre length of wall, the foundation must be wide, solid and firm, with an even distribution of stone sizes to resist unequal settling.

LINING OUT

As the following information relates to rebuilding, there will be an existing foundation trench left by the removal of the old foundation stones. It's best not to disturb this too much, as it will be very well compacted by the weight of the old wall.

1 First remove any loose soil or stones from the old trench, piling them neatly to each side. Then using pegs and lines, set the lines about 1" (25mm) above ground level.

2 'Nick out' along each line. Face the line, holding the spade vertically with the back of the blade about 2" (50mm) from the field side of the line, and parallel to it. Push the blade down to the existing trench level using the foot if necessary. Do this along the entire line, and then work along from inside the line removing the nicked out section level with the base of the foundation trench, leaving a right angled rather than a rounded profile to the base.

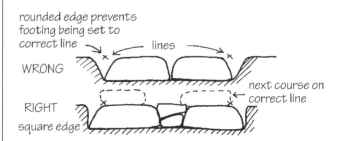

Digging and profiling the trench slightly wider than the proposed foundation ensures you have space to maintain the correct width, and makes it easier to set the stones in line.

PLACING THE FOOTINGS

1 Set the lines about 1" (25mm) higher than the proposed top height of the foundations. If the foundation stones are fairly even-sized and fit within the trench, you can use pegs and line. Where the foundation stones are more blocky or irregular, you will need to set the batter frames up at this point in order to get the line high enough.

2 Use the biggest stones in the foundation, except those which would make good throughs, or which you want to reserve for wall heads or other features. Ideally the stones should come up to but not above ground level, but any stones larger than this should be used here, rather than higher in the wall.

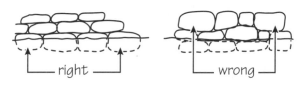

3 Be sure that each stone sits on a good bed or base. Check for steadiness by standing on them. Avoid using wedges as much as possible, since wedged stones are likely to tilt or slip as the wall settles. Minor wedging at the centre of the foundations is permitted, but major irregularities in the base of the stone should be fitted by 'sculpting' the trench.

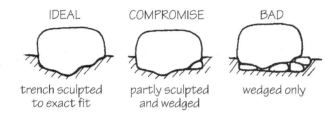

IDEAL

COMPROMISE

BAD

trench sculpted
to exact fit

partly sculpted
and wedged

wedged only

4   Lay the foundations in two parallel lines along the foundation trench with their long edges into, not along, the side of the wall. Very large stones may have to be placed along the wall, to avoid having to use stone which is far too small on the other side of the foundation.

5   Make sure that the inside edges of adjacent stones are touching for as much of their length as possible, selecting complementary shapes wherever appropriate.

6   Alternate longer stones on opposite sides of the trench, rather than grouping them on one side only.

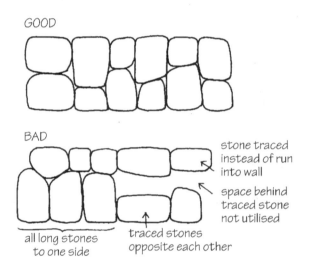

GOOD

BAD

stone traced
instead of run
into wall

space behind
traced stone
not utilised

all long stones
to one side

traced stones
opposite each other

7   Try to match adjacent stones for height to make building on them easier. Small differences can be accommodated by digging in the larger stone. Larger differences are accommodated during the subsequent building.

8   Most professional wallers leave a gap of at least 1" (25mm) between the inside edges of the foundation stones, to promote drainage within the wall. Others maintain that water will drain through anyway, and that it makes a stronger foundation to butt the stones up as close as possible, effectively making a solid foundation across the width of the wall. In practice, irregularities in the stone will create spaces, but try and make them no more than 1-2" (25-50mm).

9   Pack between the two rows of footings with angular, free-draining fillings (p54).

10 Fill any gaps between the outside faces of the foundation stones and the edge of the trench to neaten the base and prevent the chance of twisted ankles.

Use of batter frames

With new walls, the degree of batter is sometimes specified in the walling contract, if there is one, and occasionally this may happen for major rebuilds. However in many cases, and for smaller works, there will be no specification.

To get an idea of the required batter, look at the wall you are repairing or at similar walls in the area. However, you need to allow for any movement that has occurred in existing walls, as they are likely to be very slightly wider than when originally built. If you follow them accurately, you will have to use more hearting and hence will run out of stone before you have reached the required height. Consequently, it is often a good idea to narrow the wall by 1-2" (25-50mm). From the existing wall, narrow the new wall gradually over a distance of 3-6' (1-2m), and then continue with the new dimensions. This approach ensures that the repair merges with the original wall rather than having a sudden step.

PROCEDURE

Batter frames and line bars are described on page 32. Experienced wallers may dispense with them, except when walling long sections or working to precise specifications, but beginners and groups of volunteers should use them to ensure accurate results. The only time there is no need for beginners to use frames or bars is when repairing small gaps.

The batter frames and guidelines should be set up after the footings have been replaced. Normally you would then start building at the wall head, setting up a frame or pair of line bars just beyond the end of the wall, with the other frame or pair of bars a convenient distance along the footings. Some wallers prefer to set the end frame about 3' (1m) from the head (p89).

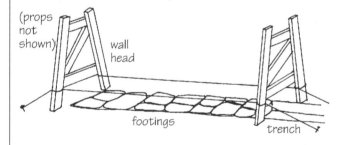

(props
not
shown)

wall
head

footings

trench

This distance may be determined by the amount to be completed that day, or by a particular feature in the wall such as a stile. The lines are then attached between the two frames or pairs of bars and the wall is completed to its full height. From this point on, you only need to use one frame. This is set up at the end of the next section, and the lines are run from it to the 'working face' of the wall.

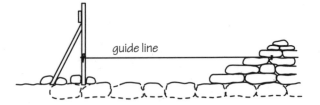

guide line

Sometimes however it's difficult to attach the lines into the wall accurately, and wallers who use line bars find it easier to lean the bars against the wall and attach the lines to them.

On shorter rebuilds it's usually possible to run lines between the solid sections of wall, or to use line bars against the wall. On longer sections, over about 16' (5m), it will be necessary to have a frame or bars mid way along the length. As the frame gets in the way of building the wall, you will need to leave a gap around the frame and build it up after the frame is removed. Bars are more convenient, as you can continue building the wall under the bars. For longer lengths divide the work into a number of sections in order to keep the line tight.

An alternative to using intermediate line bars is to build the wall up to the correct level at about the midpoint of a section. Then wrap a rag or bunch of grass around the lines to keep them from chafing and anchor them temporarily with a stone placed on top. This is helpful in group work, to limit the movement of the guidelines if they are accidentally knocked.

Batter frames

As described on page 32, batter frames can be made so that either their inside or outside measurement gives the profile of the wall. Below, and in the diagrams on pages 46-47, the batter frame is shown with inside measurement to fit the profile of the wall, so the frame is erected accordingly to straddle the foundation trench.

To set up the batter frame and guidelines:

1 Set the frame squarely across the foundations so that its feet are at ground level and its centre line is over the centre line of the trench.

2 Check the frame for plumb in both directions and prop it up with a board placed against the upper crosspiece. Anchor its feet and the end of the prop with stones.

3 Tie the ends of both guidelines to metal pins or wooden splints or pegs.

4 Fasten the lines to the legs of the frame about 1' (300mm) above ground level. To do this, bring the lines inside the legs, wrap them around the legs twice and push the pins or splints down the back to secure. An alternative method is to wrap the line around the leg once and then secure the pins in the ground along the line of the wall. This method can add stability to the frame by helping to secure it, although care has to be taken not to move the frame when tightening the line.

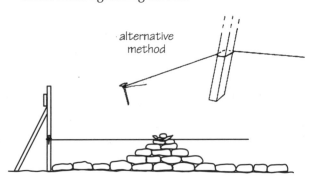

alternative method

5 Fix the other end of the line to the other frame, or into the existing wall by pushing a pin, splint or trowel into a convenient crack at the correct level, and wrapping the lines around the ends. Make sure the lines are taut.

Line bars

1 Using a lump hammer, knock a line bar about 6-12" (150-300mm) into the ground at approximately the finished batter. If the bar is unstable, knock small wedges of stone into the ground alongside it. Repeat this on the opposite side of the wall, taking care to ensure that their bases are the correct distance apart.

2 Check that the batter on both bars is correct by eyeing the angle to the existing wall or batter frame, and by checking that they are the correct distance apart at the finished height. Adjust the bars as necessary. Care has to be taken to ensure the batter is not lopsided. An adjustable angle spirit level can be used to check this. Hold the level at right angles to the wall, because if you move the level around the bar the bubble will give different readings.

3 Knock the bars in another 6" (150mm) or so.

4 Attach a securing clamp (p33) to ensure the bars do not move during the building process.

5 Carry out steps 3-5 above as for batter frames, wrapping the lines inside the legs and securing the lines into the ground.

Note that if the foundation stones are already in position, line bars can be used in the same way, knocked in immediately next to the foundation stones, and just touching them.

Building

PRINCIPLES

When building or rebuilding a wall, there are eight basic principles that you should try to apply to the placing of each stone. These points are explained in more detail later in this chapter.

1 Place the biggest stones at the bottom, except for throughs and topstones.

2 Place the stone lengthways into the wall, and avoid 'tracing' it, that is placing it with its long axis along the wall.

3 As you place each stone, make sure it is touching its neighbours below and to the side for as much of its surface as possible. As your skill develops, you should also achieve good contact within the wall itself.

4 Place stones in such a way that you can subsequently build on top and alongside them. Avoid sharply angled tops and faces, and small, sharply angled steps between stones.

5 Taper the wall, following the correct batter for the type of stone.

6 Break, or cross, the joints.

7 Place the stones so that they sit solidly on those below, with a minimum of wedging.

8 Set the stones to the true horizontal, rather than with the slope. This keeps the weight and forces within the wall perpendicular, reducing the potential for movement.

Wallers will continually disagree over the relative merits of these points. The order above is an attempt at prioritisation, but this will vary with factors such as stone type and the interaction of the principles. For example, when using small stone which has little length to place into the wall, the crossing of joints becomes more important.

At first it might seem that there's a lot to worry about, but even the best wallers rarely achieve all the principles for every stone. The key is to place each stone to meet as many of these principles as possible, without seriously failing any one of them, or compounding the failures. For example, tracing the odd stone is unlikely to seriously weaken a wall, but tracing a stone that is also out of batter will. Similarly, grouping traced stones alongside or on top of each other can create a serious weakness, as can creating a running joint (p54) with a traced stone.

Finally, there is a ninth principle, not related to individual stones, but equally important. Keep the middle full.

LAYERING

Dry stone walls are built up in more or less regular layers, not only for appearance, but to ensure symmetry and stability along their length and across the section of the wall. Layering differs from coursing, in that although all walls are built in layers, those in a coursed wall are far more regular, with the stones in any one layer of more or less the same height. In all walls, the layers are graded with the biggest stones at the bottom, and the smallest at the top.

It is usually best to place each layer along the entire section, before beginning on the layer above. If you do this, and at the same time always look for the biggest remaining stone to use next, you should have no trouble grading the courses.

Build up both faces at the same time, and keep them well filled in between. Never put stones on succeeding courses until the wall below is steady and complete.

Grading

Place the biggest stones at the bottom, except for throughs and topstones. There are three reasons for this rule.

1 Small stones on top of big stones are less likely to slip or settle badly.

2 It is much less tiring and hazardous to use the big stones near the base, than to heave them up to waist or chest height.

3 Stones should be placed with their long edges into the wall, and to do this, it is necessary to use the big stones lower down where the wall is widest.

The following points should help you grade the layers properly:

a Determine the height of each layer by the biggest stones you plan to use in it, discounting the occasional misfits, which must be accommodated in more than one layer. Try to keep to this height along the whole layer, but differences inevitably occur where the wall is not strictly coursed. In the lower layers, it is best to try and leave large steps of 3" (75mm) or more, rather than small ones, to avoid the excessive use of small stones low in the wall. Where there is suitable stone available, another alternative is to use stones with complementary slopes to allow the secure setting of a slightly larger stone on the next layer.

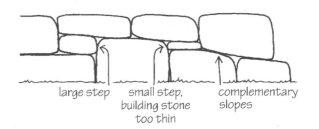

large step   small step,   complementary
               building stone   slopes
               too thin

Take extra care to level up the layers on which throughs and topstones are to be placed. You may have to use thin stone to make good any small discrepancies in the heights of stones in these layers.

b The regularity of grading which can be achieved depends on the type of stone available.

c At any given point, use stones of roughly equal size and weight for each face of the wall. If you can't always follow this rule, avoid putting all the biggest stones on one side of the wall in any given length, or it may settle unevenly across its section.

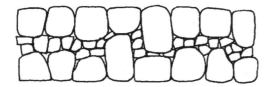

d If you have to mix big stones with small ones to complete the layer, try to space the bigger stones fairly evenly along both faces of the layer, rather than putting them altogether, which not only looks bad, but might cause the wall to settle unevenly along its length.

PLACING THE STONES

Use both hands to pick up and place stones, other than fillings or very small stones. This is safest, and gives you the best sense of shape. After positioning each stone, test how easy it is to shift it with a downward and outward pressure from your hands. It should be steady, with succeeding courses making it sit even more firmly.

Place, don't drop, the stone on the wall. This is better for the wall and for your fingers. See pages 22-25 for health and safety advice.

When working alone, build from both sides at first, stepping back and forth over the wall as necessary. When this becomes difficult, you may be able to adjust stones in the opposite face by putting one hand on a stone on the far face, and leaning over. This is better than stepping on the wall to cross it, which tends to disrupt both faces.

Once the wall is a few feet high, you can either work mainly from one side or continue to cross over or walk around it at frequent intervals. For beginners, it is best to work equally from each side, concentrating on the near face each time. Where you have to cross over the wall, as when rebuilding between existing sections, step carefully on a face stone on the far side, and check afterwards to be sure it has not been displaced. Do not put your weight on the filling.

Note the following:

a Place each face stone so that its top is either level, or slopes slightly upwards towards the centre of the wall.

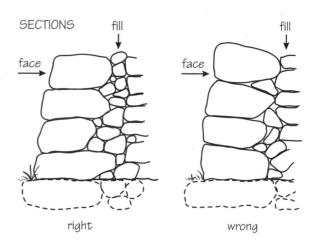

Never place the stones so they slope downwards towards the centre, since they tend to tilt more and more as the filling below them settles. This brings their weight and that of the stones above them more and more onto the filling, rather than onto the face stones and foundations below. Inward-tilting stones also feed rainwater into the vulnerable heart of the wall, increasing the likelihood of frost damage. Both processes are likely to cause the wall to eventually collapse inward.

b Try to place each face stone with a flat side downward so that it is solidly bedded. Even if this means that the upper surface is rounded, it is usually easy enough to create a good bed for the next layer by placing small flattish stones to either side. If you put the round side downward, the area in contact with the stone below is small, and it may be hard to wedge the stone so that it sits firmly.

c Don't place stones so that they act as down-thrusting wedges.

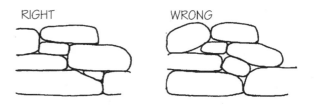

This is especially tempting when using irregular blocks of limestone, but it tends to force neighbouring stones apart and weakens the wall.

d Given the above restrictions, place each stone so that the flattest edge, or the one most nearly perpendicular to the bed is outermost, to form the face of the wall.

e Each stone's face should be in alignment with the wall's batter. When building to a guideline, the stone should be almost touching or just brushing the line, but not displacing it or a bulge will result. Where you are setting stones below the height of a guideline, look down from the guideline to the last layer to get the precise position.

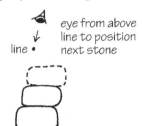

eye from above
line to position
next stone
line •

f If a stone is too long to set into the wall, and will not sit firmly when traced, then you may need to break it up into smaller pieces.

g Avoid placing stones so that they project beyond the general face of the wall, if possible. Where this has to be done with large stones which would not otherwise sit properly, make sure they are really solid, as shown left.

SECTIONS

right   wrong   right

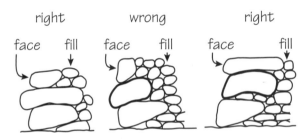

face   fill   face   fill   face   fill

The middle diagram shows a stone which should never be placed sticking out of the wall, because it will be forced down and out by the stones on top. Place this type of down curved stone further back, so that it is driven strongly against the stone below, as shown right.

h Most sedimentary and metamorphic rocks have a definite grain along the bedding planes or lines of foliation (p36). Try to place face stones so that the grain runs horizontally, even if the upper surface is tilted because of this. Stones best resist weathering this way.

SIDE VIEWS

right   wrong

i Placing the smooth outer surface of a stone in the face not only looks good, but also tends to deter climbers, while irregular inner edges bind best with the fillings.

j As your walling skills develop you should try to achieve a good fit between stones inside the wall.

PLAN
good internal contact

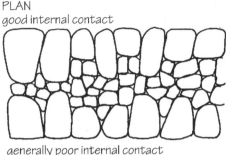

generally poor internal contact

Wedging

Ideally a stone should always sit firmly without rocking, but this is not always possible. If necessary, it can be secured with a small wedge-shaped stone tucked underneath and behind it.

Wedges are also useful to raise face stones at the back, to ensure that the top surfaces are level or slightly tipped down and out. Wedges may be any size and shape, as long as they have a sharp angle to fit snugly in position. Test the face stone after wedging to check that it doesn't rock back and forth, or loosen when weighted down. If you need to break up big stones to get suitable wedges, make sure you have plenty left for the wall face.

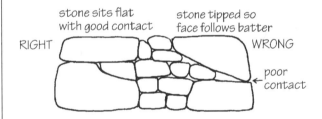

stone sits flat   stone tipped so
with good contact   face follows batter
RIGHT   WRONG

poor
contact

Keep wedging to a minimum, and always use one wedge the right size rather than several thinner wedges, which are more likely to become displaced or settle. Also be careful not to tip stones so much that their surface contact with the stone below is diminished.

FITTING STONES TOGETHER

Wallers talk about 'tight' and 'slack' walls or faces. A tight face is one where the stones are fitted together closely with few gaps between the stones. A slack face has plenty of gaps. A tight face not only looks good, but is stronger than a slack face because there is more friction between the stones, and less potential for movement. The degree of tightness is often relative to the size and shape of building stone, so a wall of small, regular stone will naturally be tighter than one built of large boulders.

a Stand back and check the wall after each layer. You should be able to see if part of the face is too slack, or if a joint (see below) is developing, and can then rectify the problem before it is too late.

b When finding a stone to fit against an awkwardly shaped neighbour, it may be easier to feel the needed shape than to estimate by eye. You may find it helpful to shuffle the stone around in your hands while looking at the spaces in the wall, to get a better idea of the required fit.

c Use the best stones for the face. Awkward or misshapen stones can go in the centre. Break them up only if they are too big to use whole for filling, or if they are too smooth to 'bite' (p35). Many wallers will tell you that 'every stone has a home', and occasionally you can get them to admit that sometimes this home might be underneath a well placed sledgehammer blow.

d Normally work in sequence, placing one stone and then its immediate neighbour, continuing along the layer ensuring each stone touches the stone below and to the side. An alternative is to work on a short section, of about 3-6' (1-2m). Pick up a likely stone and look to see where it will fit in that section. If it doesn't fit first time, instead of discarding it or carrying it up and down the wall looking for the best place, try it in different ways in the immediate area where you are working. This saves time and effort. You should be able to get a good fit with the stones below, but you need to be careful not to leave gaps which are of a size or shape which are likely to be difficult to fill. With experience this becomes easier to judge, and most stones will be placed correctly at the first try.

Joints

An important rule is to cross or break the joints, to achieve a good bond between layers. This rule is often expressed as the waller's prayer: 'One on two and two on one'. Properly crossed joints, as in a brick wall, distribute the pressure from each stone downward and outward evenly over the entire wall. Uncrossed joints channel this pressure into lines of weakness which show up as seams that widen as the wall settles. This weakness increases geometrically for each additional uncrossed joint in vertical line.

SIDE VIEWS

right   wrong

Even an expert waller must sometimes leave one uncrossed joint to make the stones sit firmly, or to bring up the course between two taller stones, but the hallmark of hasty or careless walling is a seam of two, three or even four uncrossed joints, usually referred to as a 'running joint'.

In the ideal wall, the crossing would be very regular and even, and not just 'one on two and two on one', but 'half on one and one on half'. In practice this rarely happens, but it is important to bear in mind as joints which are minimally crossed are effectively running joints.

good overlapping   poor overlapping

FILLING

Keep the middle full, or as the Scots say, 'keep your heart up'. Filling, packing or hearting is an invisible but essential component of every dry stone wall. Without it, the face stones settle inward and the wall collapses in the centre. In this respect it also plays an important role in securing wedges. If a face stone is wedged, and the wedge moves during settlement, the process of collapse is accelerated. Without good hearting, there is nothing to hold the wedges in place.

Filling should be used at every layer to help bind and steady the face stones, provide drainage, and create a base for the layers above.

a Use solid rocks, not topsoil, earth, sand or fine gravel. Fine material washes or settles out of the wall.

b The size of the filling stones depends on the type of face stones. Walls of irregular shaped stones should have larger filling, whereas walls of regular stone can have filling of coarse gravel, at least 1" (25mm) diameter.

c Filling should be angular to bind properly under pressure. Rounded, water-worn stone, particularly of small size, should not be used, as the stones tend to slide on one another, and the overall effect is like trying to build a solid wall on a bed of ball-bearings. Split water-worn and other too regular filling with a walling hammer before using them.

d Convert very big or awkwardly shaped stones into filling only if you know you have plenty of face stones. The shaping of face stones will create some filling.

e Use large filling between the foundation stones and in the lower layers, and smaller ones in the upper layers. Filling usually grades down less quickly than the face stones, so that by the top layer, the filling may be almost as big as the face stones.

f Place filling in position carefully, one stone at a time. Do not throw or shovel them in haphazardly, since this produces a poorly consolidated centre, and also tends to include soil with the fill, which eventually washes out of the wall. This aim is not to get the wall up quicker by using filling, but to provide a sturdy structure that tightens as it settles.

g Start placing the filling from the face stones towards the centre of the wall. Use smaller stones to fill any nooks and crannies between the face stones, then place larger stones in the bigger voids, trying to find one stone for one space, then fill any smaller gaps which remain.

h Make sure the filling doesn't dislodge face stones, and that each is held by its neighbours so that it cannot settle or be washed out of the wall.

i Keep the filling at the same height or a little higher than the tops of the face stones in each layer. It is best to add fillings as you work, rather than finishing a layer of face stones and returning to fill in between. Check the completed layer before starting the next one, to see if any low spots need additional filling.

Throughs

'Throughs' or 'throughstones' straddle the wall, connecting one face with the other. They help keep the wall from bulging outward as it settles by tying the two faces together into a single unit. This maintains the wall's equilibrium by distributing the weight of upper layers equally onto both faces below.

The number and spacing of throughs shown in the diagram on page 45 ensure a very strong wall. Generally it is recommended to have a maximum of 30" (750mm) between rows, and a maximum of 39" (1m) centres between the throughs in any row. However, it is worth using throughs even if they have to be 6-10' (2-3m) apart or more.

The patterns of throughstones vary considerably from area to area, and across stone types. See chapter 11 for further details.

When placing a through, keep the following points in mind:

1 Be especially careful when lifting and placing throughs. Your back and fingers are at risk (p22).

2 Use the longest and heaviest throughs for the lowest row.

3 Before placing the throughs, bring the layer below level with the guideline, ensuring that the wall is the same level on both sides. If the through is sloping across the wall, the next layer will tend to slide off.

4 Fill the layer well to make a secure bed.

5 Place each throughstone with its flattest side down. Don't wedge it, but shift it as necessary or adjust the filling if it doesn't sit securely at first. The through's weight must rest as much on the face stones on both sides, as on the filling between. Some wallers drop the throughs onto the wall from a height of about 2-3" (50-75mm), to ensure they bed well. Care has to be taken to avoid trapping fingers and to drop it level so that the weight of the stone does not bear down on one side of the wall, possibly displacing it. This method is not recommended for large, heavy throughs, as it is likely to pose a personal risk, and is also likely to damage the wall.

6 It's important to ensure that the through crosses the joints on both sides of the wall.

7 After placing the throughs at the correct spacing along the entire section, build up the wall between them with face stones and fillings. Choose stones that fit around the throughs, rather then shifting the throughs to fit the face stones. Continue to add succeeding layers in the usual way, using the tops of the throughs as beds for the stones above.

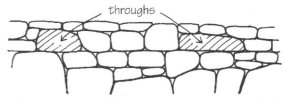

8 If a second row of throughs is to be put in, level off the layer as before, and place the throughs so that they are staggered with the ones below.

Three-quarter throughs

Where throughs are scarce, it is advisable to use a pair of three-quarter stones as a substitute for a single stone. There are two alternative methods for setting three-quarter throughs, by placing the stones either adjacently or overlapping.

In the adjacent method, you carry out points 3-5 as for standard throughs, ensuring that each stone crosses the joints on its side of the wall. It is also important that you select a pair of stones which fit together well along their inside faces.

PLAN   adjacent method

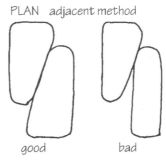

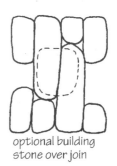

good   bad   optional building
                                               stone over join

Some wallers place a third building stone, rather than hearting, over the joint between the throughs. It is thought that this distributes weight from above across both the stones, helping them to act as a single unit. If you do this, be careful to leave enough space on either side to place face stones which are sufficiently large to maintain the integrity of the wall.

In the overlapping method, you place one three-quarter through, following points 3-6 as for standard throughs. Then:

1 Add another layer to the wall immediately opposite the first three-quarter through. This layer must be built to the same height as the three-quarter through, with the face stone touching the three-quarter through inside the wall. Build it in such a way that you avoid creating a joint when you place the next three-quarter through.

2 If there are any small gaps between the second face and the three-quarter through, fill them with hearting.

3 Place the next three-quarter through so that it crosses any joints and sits firmly on top of the first three-quarter through, with good contact along the length of its base.

SECTION overlapping method

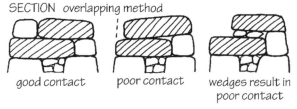

good contact   poor contact   wedges result in
                                         poor contact

Regardless of which method you employ, you must remember that three-quarter throughs are precisely that. If they are longer than three-quarters, then the stone used to build opposite will be too small. If they are shorter, then they are nothing more than a couple of good building stones, and will not bind properly.

Finally remember that three-quarter throughs are always used in pairs. Used singly, a three-quarter is merely a long building stone, and does little to bind the two sides of the wall.

Coping

The coping is the line of stones along the top of the wall which protects the structure beneath. Regional names include the cap, comb, cope or topping. The stones are called topstones, copestones or toppers.

a The coping weighs down the courses below, and bonds both faces together so that the wall settles into a solid unit.

b The coping protects the face stones and fillings from the weather, animals and people. Without them, walls tend

to flake away course by course, especially if they are made of small or fissile stones. Sheep will almost inevitably jump a wall where the topstones are missing, dislodging stones and speeding up collapse. The coping needs frequent inspection and repair, since once a few stones are dislodged a gap is likely to start.

There are many types of coping, and with most stones a choice is possible, based not only on practical requirements but on personal preferences as well. Where there is no good reason for doing otherwise, it is usually best to follow the example of the surrounding walls. Some of the variations are shown on pages 132-138.

Procedure

The following steps produce a neat result when placing topstones of a relatively even size. Much of this procedure will apply to most alternative types.

1 Determine the height of the coping. This may be set by specifications and is usually 10-12" (250-300mm). Note that it is the overall wall height which is important, not in most cases the height of individual topstones. Thus the wall should be rebuilt to a height which allows for the finished height including the topstones to match the finished height of the original wall. Where the topstones are very irregular, judge their height from their topmost parts, since this determines the profile of the top of the finished wall.

Depending on the finish required and time available, long stones can be trimmed to length before they are set in position. Trimming also provides chips of stone which may be useful for wedging the topstones, or can be used as filling in the next section of wall.

Where the wall top is irregular, use slightly larger topstones in the dips, and slightly smaller stones on the rises.

2 Run a line from the top of the coping either side of the gap. For longer sections, or where you are coping part of a repair, place a stone of the determined height at the end of the section you wish to cope. Select a stone with a good base for this, and wedge it as necessary to hold it in place. Then run the line over this stone.

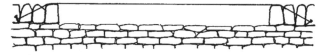

3 If you are working on a section longer than about 10' (3m), place another stone to the correct height about half

way between the end stones, and wedge as necessary. This prevents the line from sagging, which would result in a dip in the profile of the coping. It can be a good idea to place a small stone on top of the centre top stone to keep the line steady as you work.

4   Work from one end in a sequence, starting at the bottom of any slopes, however shallow. For more details about coping on slopes, see page 64.

5   Place the stone on its thickest edge, centrally on the wall. Stones which are too short to straddle the wall should still be placed centrally, and distributed along a length, rather than being grouped together.

6   Select the next stone so that it complements its neighbour, trying to maintain close contact across the wall.

7   Ensure that the stone is vertical. The stone should sit solidly of its own accord, but occasionally this is not possible and a small wedge will be needed to secure it. Make sure the wedge does not protrude beyond the inside edge of the topstone, otherwise it will make placing the next stone awkward.

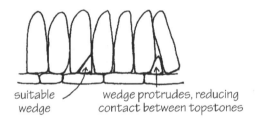

suitable wedge

wedge protrudes, reducing contact between topstones

8   Repeat steps 5-7 until the length is completed.

9   If you have plenty of wedges, it's a good idea to then pin the front and back by placing a wedge between any irregular stones. Choose wedges that are only very slightly larger than the gap, perhaps 2-3mm, otherwise they are likely to force the topstones apart and create more gaps, or disintegrate on being hammered in.

10 Wedge any gaps between the stones to 'lock' the top. Choose stones as above. For more details on coping see pages 132-138.

Gapping

The process of rebuilding a small gap is essentially the same as rebuilding a wall. However, careful consideration needs to be given to deciding how much of the wall needs to be taken down before a repair can be carried out.

1   Remove all the stone from alongside the gap, and set out as outlined on page 41.

2   Remove at least 24" (600mm) of coping either side of the gap to ensure that if any other stones topple it does not

instigate a collapse. It can be a good idea to lean a topstone against the remaining coping to hold it in place.

3   Examine the wall on either side of the collapse, and dismantle all that is unstable. This usually means leaving the original wall well raked and stepped so it is stable and easy to build into.

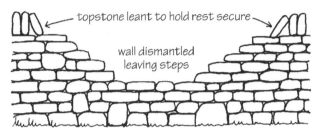

topstone leant to hold rest secure

wall dismantled leaving steps

Don't forget to always leave the safety margin of at least 600mm of coping-free wall either side of the gap. As you get more experienced you will be able to work out, by studying the face of the wall and the overlap of stones, exactly how far along you will have to dismantle. Remove all the coping up to and beyond this point.

4   Dismantle the remainder of the gap until you have found the cause of the collapse, or until you are sure that the wall is solid enough to build onto. Even if it appears stable, carefully check the wall below. Most collapses higher in a wall are caused by movement lower in the wall. If there are any signs of movement, such as a bulge or loosening of the face stones, then it is advisable to dismantle the wall to a level below these.

Assessing the foundation

Often the cause of a collapse is movement of the foundations. If you expose the foundations during dismantling you need to check they are suitable for building on.

a   The stones should be in line. It isn't a problem if they are slightly outside the line provided they are not tall stones, which would create a step in the repaired face. If they are inside the line they must be replaced or reset, because if you build on them you will not be able to maintain the correct line and batter.

b   Foundations in an old wall should be solid, especially considering the weight of stone which has been pressing down on them. Stand on each edge of the stone, and if it moves at all it should be replaced or reset.

c   Even if the stone is in line and solid it still needs to be suitable for building on. Often foundation stones have tilted so that they are lower on their outside face, and if you build on them the weight of the wall will be forcing out the lower layers. Sometimes the stone itself is just not suitable, because in old walls you may find the most awkward stones have been used up in the footings. Replace them rather than repeat the mistake.

New walls

The basic principles of building apply equally to new walls as they do to repairs. However, new walls do have a number of additional considerations:

SUPPLY OF STONE

Sources of stone and methods for calculating the amount which you will need are set out on page 38. Stone obtained from a quarry may not have sufficient throughstones or coping, and these might need to be specifically ordered. If possible order filling separately, so that you can make specific piles of filling alongside the wall rather than having to scrabble through piles of stone trying to find it, or having to break up too much stone. Washed stone of 5" down to 1" (125-25mm) diameter is best for filling.

Organising the stone supply along the wall will depend on the specifics of the site and supply arrangements. Ideally spread the stone along both sides of the wall, remembering to leave your working space clear (p48). Leave room for sorting the stone, remembering that fairly homogeneous stone will need less, and mixed stone more sorting. Provided your estimates of stone quantity are fairly accurate (p38), spreading the stone evenly, or in even piles, should result in the least amount of carrying. If supplying from a stockpile on site, spread stone along a section of about 10 yards (9m), rather than the whole length of the wall. Add to this from the stockpile as necessary, and move unused stone along to the next section of wall as required.

If you are unloading and setting out by hand, you can sort the stones roughly as you go, just as when dismantling (p47). Keep likely throughs and topstones to one side. Don't spend too long sorting stone which is already on the ground, but sort the stone for each layer as the work progresses.

Care really has to be taken to ensure you have enough topstones if these are not being supplied separately. Spend some time sorting them from the pile before work commences, and add to this as building progresses. Set them out in the same way as for a rebuild (p47), to ensure you have enough.

DIMENSIONS

New walls are usually built to a specified set of dimensions. Where these have not been given, the following points will help determine the dimension.

As a general rule of thumb, the base width of a wall should be half its height, measured from the bottom of the trench to the top of the coping. The top width, below the coping, should be half the base width.

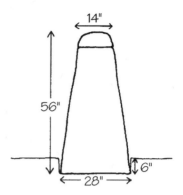

The height will be determined by the purpose of the wall, normally at least 4' (1.2m) from the ground to the top of the coping for cattle, and at least 5'3" (1.6m) for sheep, particularly moorland varieties. Essentially the height will depend on what the client wants.

Whilst the rule of thumb given above is a good general guideline, you should also check the local walls built out of similar stone to get an idea of the local practice. The size and shape of stone supplied will partly determine the dimensions and batter of the wall. Note the following:

a   For any given stone, the taller the wall, the wider the base.

b   The top width of a wall should never be less than 12" (300mm), with a general minimum of 14" (350mm) being more appropriate, regardless of stone type and height.

c   When using larger boulders for building, the rule of thumb may not apply, as the size of the foundation boulders will make a base wider than half the final height of the wall. For example, foundation boulders 1'8" (500mm) long will make a base width of at least 3'4" (1m), which is wider than the 2'10" (870mm) indicated for a wall 5'8" (1.74m) high.

d   The top width will also need to be greater when using bigger stones, as it is not normally possible to increase the batter without creating steps between the layers of stone. If a step of more than about 1" (25mm) is made, this may give a foothold to sheep. With many boulder walls, or those of blocky, square stone, the batter needs to be nearer the vertical to counteract this. In this case the top width will definitely be more than half the base width.

e   Conversely, walls of smaller stone or walls with a lot of traced stones (p51) may require more of a batter, as there is little length binding the stone into the wall.

f   Some stone types have mainly longer, thinner stones, with small 'faces'. As the wall is thus mainly built of stones with their long length into the wall, a near-vertical batter can be achieved.

All walls should essentially have an 'A' shaped profile for stability, and the face should never be built plumb vertical. It may be local practice, especially with older roadside, and especially estate walls, to have different batters on the two faces. Generally the roadside or public aspect is nearer vertical because larger face stones have been used for good appearance. See page 126.

For the first section of work two batter frames or sets of line bars will be needed. These should be set up as explained on page 49. Once a section has been completed, proceed as for a rebuild.

FOUNDATIONS

If possible dig the foundation trench before the stone is set out, as this makes soil removal easier.

1 Clear woody plants, coarse tussocky vegetation and stones from the line of the proposed wall. Don't bother trying to move solidly embedded boulders.

2 Mark out the foundation trench using guidelines set about 1" (25mm) above ground level, stretched tightly between stakes or metal pins over as long a length as is practical. The lines should be set about 2" (50mm) wider on each side than the foundation width, to allow room for manoeuvre and adjustment of the foundation stones (p48).

3 Nick out along this line (p48), and remove all the turf from between the two lines.

4 Dig the trench down to firm subsoil or bedrock. This is usually between 4" (100mm) and 12" (300mm) deep, with 6" (150mm) about average. If you haven't hit subsoil by 12" (300mm), there is little point in digging much deeper, and it's best to compact the soil with your feet or with a mechanical vibrator if available. If the soil is particularly soft you may need to dig a wider foundation, as if you were building on wet ground (p71).

5 Pile debris from the foundation neatly for removal or re-use, placing it at sufficient distance from the foundation to leave space for setting out the stone.

BUILDING

Building techniques are the same as for rebuilding, as detailed earlier in this chapter. However, as you are creating a new wall out of the stone supplied, rather than rebuilding with already-used stone, there are possibly more choices open to you about how you use the stone. It's important to take time to sort new stone properly before you start building, rather than just starting with the first stones that come to hand from the top of the pile.

Throughs

Considerations regarding throughs are closely related to those which determine batter.

a Where the face stones lack length into the wall, it's advisable to use more throughs than standard to help bind the two faces together.

b Many bouldery walls, or walls of stones which have good length into the wall, in effect already have numerous three-quarter throughs, although they may not be set in pairs. Walls of this type of stone therefore do not need full throughs.

c Some walls, such as those of slate waste, shales and mudstones, have to be built with a lot of traced stones (p51) because of the shape of the stone, which is too long to be placed into the wall. The stone shatters if you try to shape it. Walls of this type should have a smaller vertical gap between the rows of throughs, to compensate for the traced stones. Rows should be about 1'6" (500mm) apart, with throughs staggered, and centred at a maximum of 2'6" (750mm).

d Walls over 6' (1.8m) should have throughs spaced as above.

e The more vertical the batter, the greater the need for throughs.

The use and abuse of concrete and mortar

In a masonry wall, concrete or mortar is usually essential to bind the stonework together. In contrast, a dry stone wall is designed to settle into a durable structure without any cement. The fact that many miles of completely unmortared wall have stood intact for centuries, often with no maintenance or repair, proves that with proper construction and materials no binding substance is necessary. However, old and new walls may incorporate concrete or mortar, and this is not always a mistake as mortar has its uses. These include:

a To strengthen the coping on an otherwise dry wall. Buck-and-doe coping, and upright or flat coping using small, light stones are vulnerable to being dislodged by animals, vandals or traffic vibration. Coping adjacent to stiles is also likely to get knocked.

b To strengthen the entire wall against vibration from heavy traffic. Roadside walling is often mortared throughout, and given a solid concrete topping or a heavy layer of mortar below the topstones.

c To strengthen walls made of fissile or very regular

stones which would otherwise tend to slip apart on settling.

d To make a sturdy coping easier and faster to place.

e To provide a solid foundation where there is a lack of suitably large footing stones.

f To strengthen a wall head made of small stones, or a stile which uses stone stoops or wooden posts.

g To anchor fencing standards into the wall (p105).

h To create a horse jump or other special feature.

However, in most cases the disadvantages of concrete and mortar in otherwise dry walls far outweigh their advantages. Drawbacks include:

a Materials and transport costs are considerably higher.

b New walls settle by about 3" (75mm) in their first few years. As this happens, dry walls increase in strength and cohesiveness, since every stone shifts into the tightest relationship with its neighbours. Dry stone walls with mortared topstones tend to settle away from the rigid copings, and without the weight of the topstones to anchor them the stones below are easily dislodged. The result is often as shown.

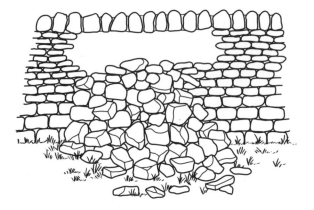

Vibration from traffic may cause more than normal settlement, so the likelihood of gaps forming beneath a mortared cope is greatest on roadside walls.

If mortar is used in the body of the wall, the coping may settle at the same time as the wall, but the wall itself may develop humps or bulges due to reduced flexibility.

c Water expands by one twelfth when it freezes. Dry walls are built so that water drains freely through and into the subsoil. Concrete or mortar can trap rainwater which may break and dislodge stones when it freezes.

d Gaps are more difficult and dangerous to repair if a mortared coping is still in place across the gap. You may need to use a sledgehammer to knock the coping down.

e Vehicles which hit partly mortared walls are likely to suffer more damage than those which run into dry walls. Damage to the wall is also likely to be more extensive, as the wall tends to be dragged out in a unit.

Cement-based mortars are rigid and brittle and especially prone to poor settlement. In some cases cement mortar is stronger than the stones themselves, so that the stones deteriorate before the mortar. Lime and sand mortar should be used rather than cement and sand, to retain some flexibility (p138). This is also preferable botanically (p14). However, where a wall head or other part of a wall is to be mortared throughout, a small proportion of cement can be added to the mix for extra durability.

7 Technical walling

This chapter looks in detail at some of the more advanced walling techniques required when building walls on slopes, around curves and in other situations where the physical conditions are difficult. The basic principles of walling described in chapter 6 still hold true, but extra time and care, together with some 'tricks of the trade' are needed to achieve a sound structure which will overcome the physical difficulties of the site.

Building a perfect structure out of a material as variable as stone is almost impossible, and compromises are inevitable throughout the process. Even expert wallers frequently do not agree on the best solution to a technical problem, and whilst alternative approaches exist, many of the arguments are rather theoretical. A further complicating factor is the maintenance of local traditions of building. However, the defence of tradition should not be used as an excuse for inaccurate workmanship or for ignoring alternative techniques, and decisions should be made after balancing all the factors involved. This chapter recommends techniques which are structurally sound and practical, with tradition a secondary factor.

Walls on slopes

This section applies mainly to walls which run up and down slopes. Walls across slopes are considered on page 66. Gravity has the advantage on slopes, and poorly built walls are prone to serious gapping and eventual collapse.

DISMANTLING

Particular care should be taken when dismantling walls on slopes to ensure that the section of wall uphill of where you are working is stable and not likely to collapse onto you during the dismantling or rebuilding process.

The process for dismantling walls on slopes differs slightly from that outlined for standard walls. Follow the principles on page 47, adapting them as follows:

a Always dismantle the wall in a downhill direction, starting at the top of the section to be dismantled.

b Remove sufficient topstones to ensure the rest are stable, and not likely to slip and cause a cascade. The technique of roping the topstones for added security is described on page 65.

c Remove the stones in layers, as for a standard wall, but note that the layers conform to the true horizontal, rather than running the length of the wall.

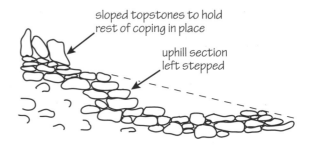

sloped topstones to hold rest of coping in place

uphill section left stepped

d Step the exposed end of the uphill section further back than you would for a standard wall, to ensure its stability.

e As you remove the stones, place them slightly uphill of the point from which they are taken. This is to counteract the tendency when working of only picking up stones which are uphill from your feet, which results in a shortage of stones at the top of the section and a surplus of stones at the bottom!

DIRECTION OF BUILDING

When building or rebuilding, start at the bottom of the slope and work upwards. This ensures that the stones are tightly butted together as you build.

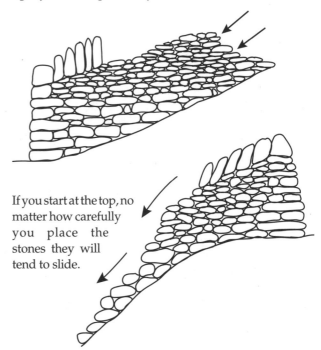

If you start at the top, no matter how carefully you place the stones they will tend to slide.

61

The easiest way to work is facing more or less uphill, choosing stones laid out to your side or just in front, which saves bending and back strain.

USE OF WALL HEADS

For added stability on slopes additional heads can be built into the wall to strengthen them, and to limit the extent of any gapping that does occur. Gaps are more of a problem on slopes than on the flat, both because the wall is subject to slippage, and because any gap which does form will tend to extend upward.

a When you build a head on a slope, it is most important that the head is structurally sound as its function is to support a considerable weight of stone. The fact that the head may be incorporated within a length of wall does not mean that any of the basic principles can be skimped, but rather the opposite. Use good runners and tie stones (p89) to bind the head to the wall on both the uphill and downhill side where possible, and carry the coping across the break

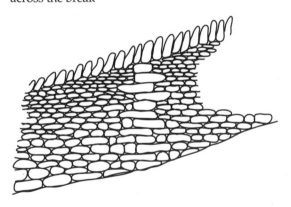

b Build a wall head at the base of a steep slope, or at a sharp upward break in slope. This head helps support the weight of the wall above it. Build the head after laying the foundations but before building the courses of the section uphill of the head.

c Where a wall runs up a steep hillside, the more heads the better. A head built every 22 yards (20m) may be appropriate.

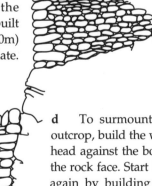

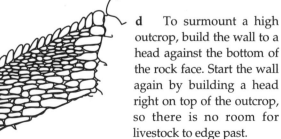

d To surmount a high outcrop, build the wall to a head against the bottom of the rock face. Start the wall again by building a head right on top of the outcrop, so there is no room for livestock to edge past.

HEIGHT AND BATTER

On shallow slopes, the true vertical dimension of the wall is kept constant. The positions of the throughs and topstones are maintained at a constant height, measured vertically from the slope.

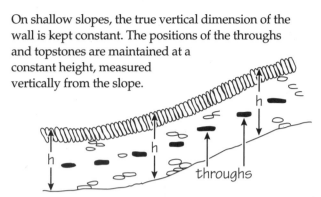

Batter frames or line bars should be used in the normal way (p49), either in pairs, or set at a convenient distance from the existing wall or wall head. The lines are set horizontally.

Place the throughs as shown, so that each row forms a staggered line. Measuring the vertical height with a tape measure or marked stick should be sufficiently accurate, although a plumb bob knotted at the height of the throughs and the topstones will give a more precise measurement.

On steeper slopes, a problem occurs if the true vertical top height is maintained. The resulting reduced height, as measured perpendicular to the slope, can allow sheep to scramble over the wall. To prevent this, the wall may have to be built higher, in effect using the vertical top height to measure the distance perpendicular to the slope.

There are various ways of measuring to maintain correct height and batter.

a If using batter frames, it should be possible in theory to prop the frame perpendicular to the slope, which will give the required increased vertical height. In practice it's difficult to prop the frame to the correct angle. Special frames can be made up for various angles of slope, but this is rather impractical.

b Line bars can be set up, either to the true vertical, or perpendicular to the slope, measured to the correct dimensions. This is probably the best method.

c A simple measured stick, held perpendicular to the slope, will give the correct heights, and the batter can be estimated by eye.

As the slope becomes steeper, the frames or line bars have to be set up closer together, in order to fit the horizontal lines. The lines can be anchored to the ground at the correct width with stones, but the frame or bars are still needed to give the batter and height.

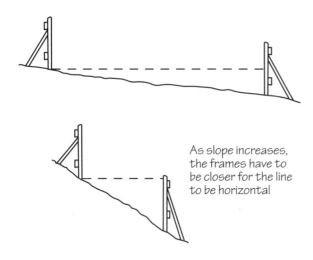

As slope increases, the frames have to be closer for the line to be horizontal

Some wallers set a line parallel to the slope (p64), as an aid to grading the stone.

FOUNDATIONS

Lay the stones on the true horizontal, whatever the slope. However large and heavy the stones, if set on a slope they are likely to slide, especially if they are slab-shaped. You can test this yourself by trying to shift a slab weighing about 1 cwt (50kg) on a flat surface. Try to shift it laterally. Then bed the same stone on a hard, sloping surface and see how easy it is to edge it downhill with a crowbar or other lever.

Follow these points to achieve level foundations:

a Dig a shallow trench along the line of the wall. Then to place each footing stone, dig out the trench a little more to make a step that is level both across and with the slope. Choose stones with flat bases. Opinion is divided as to whether the stones should be placed so they rest on each other, or independently. In practice the method chosen will depend on the degree of slope and the type of stone available. Thinner flat stone tends to be best overlapped, especially on steeper slopes. Larger and less regular stone is best placed independently, but closely butted together. Generally, the steeper the slope, the greater the need to overlap the stone.

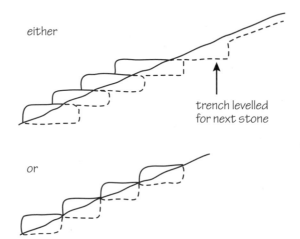

either

trench levelled for next stone

or

b Check the bedding of large, flat slabs with a spirit level and board. Take care to get the first layer level, and then the rest should follow more or less naturally. With practice you should be able to align the stones by eye, but it's always worth checking occasionally to make sure you are not being fooled by the slope, a problem which tends to occur more on shallow rather than steep slopes.

c On shallow slopes it is sometimes possible to taper the footings to form a series of ledges. The trench is still stepped to ensure that the foundation stones sit level, but each stone is slightly thinner that its predecessor, to form a ledge. Don't carry this to extremes, using stones that are too thin to make adequate foundations.

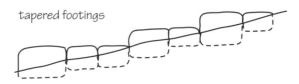

tapered footings

LAYERING AND GRADING

As with the footings, it is important that the stones are set to a true level, even though it is tempting on slight or moderate slopes to lay with the slope of the ground. Stones set with the slope are more likely to slide over each other, destabilising the wall during settlement.

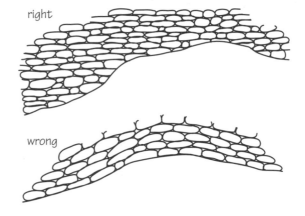

right

wrong

The layers of walls on slopes are different to those of walls on flat ground. On a slope, each layer starts with a footing stone at one end and finishes with a topstone at the other. Since the wall must be built wider at the hillside end of each layer than at the outer end, the guidelines, when viewed from above, should taper.

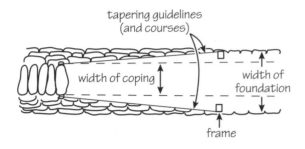

Taking a vertical line up the wall, the stones grade from bottom to top just as in a wall on the flat.

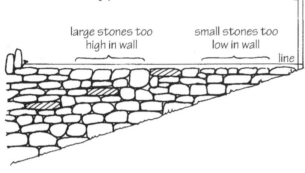

On shallower slopes you should work along a section of wall, placing stones to follow the true horizontal, rather than concentrating on building up one section. This helps ensure that you achieve an even distribution of the larger stones.

Take care to achieve the correct grading along and up the wall. Start at the footing and add the largest face stones, placing progressively smaller stones as you work outward along the layer. Keep the layer as horizontal as possible, which will mean doubling up the stones when you near the outer end.

Some wallers prefer to set their lines following the slope rather than to a true horizontal. This allows more accurate grading of the stone, by ensuring that along the wall, similar sized stones are used at similar heights relative to the ground. With this method of building you gain height and then length, rather than length and then height as in the

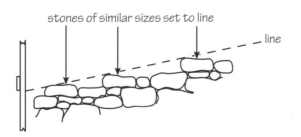

horizontal method. Building for height and then length does have the disadvantage that it is more difficult to keep the stones tight. If using this method, it can be useful to also set a horizontal line to help in setting the stones level.

Coping on slopes

Amongst wallers there is considerable debate as to whether the topstones should be placed on the true vertical, sloping uphill or sloping downhill.

Most written sources suggest that sloping uphill is best, arguing that topstones tilted uphill bind most strongly, because as the wall settles they are pulled more tightly together and held by friction. If one stone is dislodged its uphill neighbours stay firmly in place. With downhill sloping topstones, if one is displaced all the others above it are liable to fall in turn.

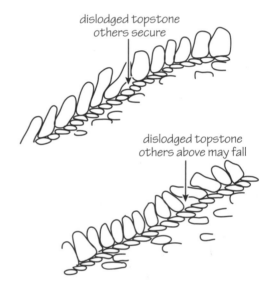

The downhill argument maintains that it is not practical to place stones leaning uphill, because if you start at the bottom of the slope you have to hold each stone whilst placing the next one. If you start from the top, the stones loosen and slip away from you.

If you start at the bottom and work up, placing the stones sloping downhill, all the stones place weight on each other, forming a very solid top. If any topstones get dislodged or a section of wall collapses, only one or two stones should fall flat which should then stop those above from toppling. This is probably the most widespread method of coping on slopes, although it's not clear whether this is because it's structurally more sound, or because it's easier to do.

Technically, vertical coping should be the most stable as the weight is perpendicular, but its use is rare on slopes. The 'uphill' protagonists tend to use vertical coping on very steep slopes, where there is not enough surface for tilted topstones to grip properly.

A useful tip when rebuilding or gapping a section of wall on a slope with downhill sloping topstones is to rope the topstones on the section uphill of the repair. Rope a fairly long section, of about 16' (5m) or more, and ensure the rope is tight. Remove the rope when the repair is complete, allowing the bottom stone of the roped section to shift slightly to close the gap left by the rope.

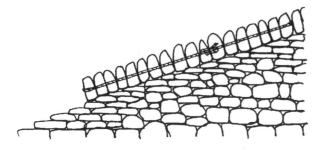

One rare, but nevertheless interesting method of helping to stabilise the coping on walls is to include long stones in the wall which project and hold the coping in place.

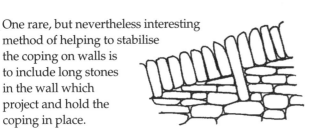

SLAB COPES AND COVERBANDS

Occasionally you will find a slab cope (p135) used on a slope. The slabs are always set to a true level, with various methods used to achieve this. One method is as follows:

a Set a line to give the final height of the wall, including the slabs.

b Place each stone so that the top corner at the downhill end touches the line.

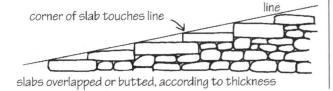

corner of slab touches line → line

slabs overlapped or butted, according to thickness

c Butt the next stone up against it. On steeper slopes, or with very thin slabs, you may have to build a layer or two on top of one slab in order to gain sufficient height for the next slab to reach the line. On steeper slopes the step between slabs might be quite large, so that an additional stone or rubble might be needed to even out the finished line of the top, either to improve its appearance or to make it stockproof.

line

The use of coverstones on slopes follows the points above, with the subsequent topstones graded in height to create a relatively uniform top.

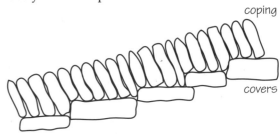

coping

covers

On steeper slopes this becomes more difficult, as the step becomes too big to easily even out with graded topstones.

Garden walls or those which do not have to be stockproof can be built with a stepped top, by constructing a series of partial heads. This works best with fairly regular, slab-shaped stone, and looks more appropriate in urban rather than rural settings.

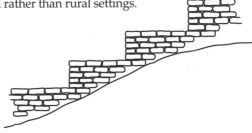

Walls on undulating ground

Generally the height of a wall follows the profile of the ground. However, walls on undulating ground, especially significant walls such as estate boundaries, may be 'evened up' for better appearance.

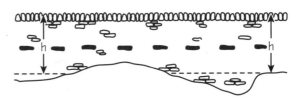

To keep the wall stockproof all along its length, the wall height is increased in the hollows. This requires extra stone, so adding to the expense and time involved in wall building and repair. Some levelling of hummocks and filling of hollows may be worthwhile, depending on the situation, the availability of stone and other factors. For a new wall on undulating ground, a day's work with a JCB may be a good investment to make the wall-building easier and cheaper. Preferably do any ground preparation some months before building the wall to allow time for the ground to settle.

When building an even-topped wall on undulating ground, great care must be taken to keep the wall width and batter constant. There are two ways of approaching this.

a The usual method is to keep a uniform batter from the wall top to ground level. This means that as the wall becomes higher, the width at the base increases. Careful measurement with line bars or use of a range of batter frames is necessary to make sure that the foundations are built to the correct base width for the corresponding height.

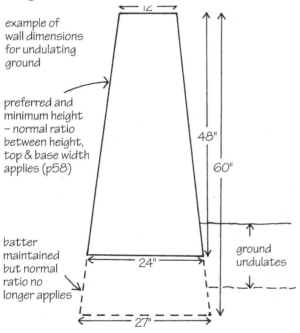

example of wall dimensions for undulating ground

preferred and minimum height – normal ratio between height, top & base width applies (p58)

batter maintained but normal ratio no longer applies

ground undulates

b An alternative approach, used in the Highlands of Scotland and elsewhere, is to build a platform called a scarcement, to create a level base from which the wall itself is measured and built. The scarcement is built with large foundation stones, ignoring strict grading in order to create a level top. The sides are vertical, with the width just slightly larger than the base width of the wall. Usually the wall is stepped in about 1" (25mm) on both sides.

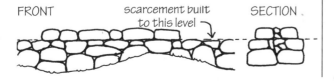

FRONT   scarcement built
               to this level   SECTION

Walls built in this way are usually very sound, as the level scarcement allows good subsequent layering of the wall, and makes it easier to build a uniform and strong wall as the same dimensions are used throughout.

Walls across slopes

Walls across slopes were traditionally built with a steeper batter on the uphill side than on the downhill.

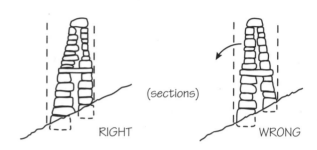

(sections)

RIGHT   WRONG

a An asymmetrical batter was thought to be structurally stronger than a symmetrical batter on a slope, because it would allow for some settlement. With a symmetrical batter, any settlement on the lower side might cause the wall to topple.

b Larger foundation stones were used on the lower side, so that they would be large and heavy enough to withstand some loss of soil on the lower side, without becoming undermined. They would also have to support a greater height and thus weight of stones than the foundations on the upper side. Here smaller stones could be used, as they would tend to get buried with downhill soil movement.

c There is also the argument that the steeper batter would look more intimidating to stock, and be more difficult to scramble up, so compensating for the lower height when viewed from the uphill side.

SECTION ALONG WALL

force

The logic of these arguments can be questioned. The asymmetrical cross-section may in fact create a shearing force which is more likely to cause the wall to tilt back, in effect pushing the footings down the hill. A symmetrical wall with level foundations should transfer the weight directly downwards, so keeping the wall upright.

force

The difference between the size of the foundation stones on the upper and lower side of the wall may also create stresses which cause the wall to tilt back and eventually collapse.

The stockproofing argument may have some validity, although in practice the general continuity of a barrier and the soundness of its construction is probably more important in keeping it stockproof, rather than the degree of batter. Stock tend to break out at a weak point where a wall has been damaged or has partially collapsed.

In summary, it seems likely that a wall built with symmetrical batter on solid, even foundations should be just as strong and more durable than a wall with asymmetrical batter.

FOUNDATIONS

Especially on steeper slopes, it's a good idea to excavate a foundation platform rather than a trench, as the lip of the trench will anyway get displaced during the building process. Dig the platform to leave a ledge of about 12-18" (300-450mm) between the slope and the edge of the wall. This gives an even surface to stand on during rebuilding, and reduces the chance of soil eroding from immediately below the wall. Put the soil from the excavation just downslope, and then replace it up against the downside of the wall at the end of the rebuilding process, to give extra protection to the base of the wall. Bank it up to remove any ledge which might encourage sheep to walk along or shelter immediately below the wall.

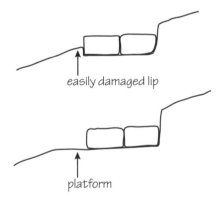

easily damaged lip

platform

This amount of excavation does involve additional labour, as well as possibly additional stone in order to bring the wall up to the required height. However, this investment is likely to be worthwhile in producing a wall which will stand for a long time without the need for repair.

Curves

It may be necessary to curve a wall in order to follow a boundary line, avoid a tree, pool, hollow or other difficult spot, or to incorporate an immovable boulder into the wall. Gradual curves are preferable to corners where either are

possible, since they generally require less specialised stone, and if built correctly, are likely to prove more durable. However, most wallers tend to agree that a curve is possibly the hardest 'standard feature' to build. Tight curves can be especially tricky, due to problems judging the batter, and in this case a corner may be more satisfactory.

There are a number of common faults to watch out for when building a curve.

a There is a tendency for the outside of a curve to be built too close to the vertical, and the inside to be too sloping.

b Bulges and flat spots can result if the wall is not a true curve.

c Stones are often not sufficiently tight to their neighbours.

Faults a and b are caused by building the curve by eye, and fault c is a result of unsuitable or incorrectly used stone. These may seem minor faults, but when compounded, can result in an insecure structure. The interior of a curved wall is particularly difficult to build, and extra care needs to be taken to construct it as strongly as possible.

MARKING THE LINE

Curves can be marked out on the ground with a length of rope or hosepipe. Mark the inner edge of the curve, 'nick out' along it, and then measure the width of the wall outwards, to give the outer edge of the curve. Semi or quarter circles can be made by sticking a crowbar in the ground with a rope loosely tied around it and marked at the required radius. In practice few curves are this regular, but need to be fitted to join two sections of walls or to go around certain features.

PLACING STONE

Although the basic principles of placing stone apply (p51), there are two main complications to building on a curve, both of which increase in severity as the curve becomes sharper.

a Butting the stones tightly together within the wall is difficult. The outside of the curve may look 'tight', with good stone contact, but this may mask poor stone contact within the wall.

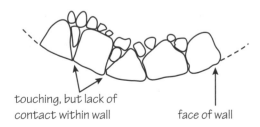

touching, but lack of
contact within wall

face of wall

Poor stone contact between the stones on the inside of the curve tends to show as a 'slack' inner face.

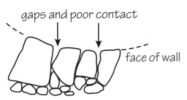

gaps and poor contact

face of wall

If the inside of the curve looks 'tight', it probably means that the stones have been well fitted together, with good stone contact.

For good stone contact, try and select stones with complementary internal edges. Often it will be necessary to dress the stones to fit.

b Setting the stones to the correct curve.

On the outside of the curve it is the corners of the stone which should be set to the curve. On the inside of the curve it is the centre of the face of the stone which should be set to the curve.

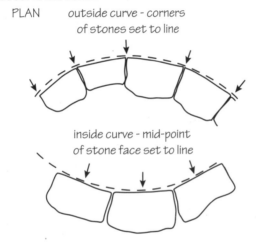

PLAN   outside curve - corners
of stones set to line

inside curve - mid-point
of stone face set to line

To achieve this save stones which have slight curves to their faces for the appropriate side of the wall. Avoid using longer stones on the inside of the curve, and on the outside a small amount of dressing of corners will help get more of the stone in line.

Mistakes in the alignment of stones result in inaccurate batter, flat spots and dips. One misplaced stone almost inevitably results in the stones on the subsequent layer compounding the mistake. Given the difficulty of assessing batter on curves by eye, this is often not obvious until the wall is completed.

COVERS AND COPING

Careful selection of stone and a fair amount of dressing are required to produce a good result. Ideally the covers should fit the curve, but in practice this is difficult, and often they will need to poke a little out of line to allow a good match with their neighbours.

To fit the coping, some of the stones need to be wedge shaped, and of sufficient size to span the wall top.

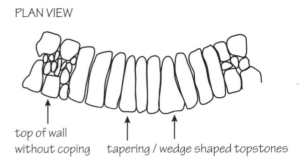

PLAN VIEW

top of wall
without coping   tapering / wedge shaped topstones

Less satisfactory are small wedges, fitted to 'fanned' cope stones, as the wedges tend to pop out with settlement. If fanning is unavoidable, select wedges which fit as closely as possible to the size and shape of the gaps, to give maximum stone contact so they are less likely to loosen.

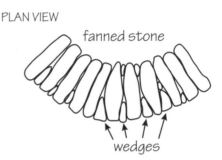

PLAN VIEW

fanned stone

wedges

Obstacles

BEDROCK

Bedrock in the line of the wall should be treated as foundations, which is not a problem if the bedrock is relatively flat and regular. However where it is sloped, stepped, or has awkward lumps it is more difficult to build on.

A wall normally has to be continued even over awkward bedrock, as fencing to stockproof the gap is also difficult. Route the wall over the flattest part of the bedrock.

One advantage to building on bedrock is that the wall is less likely to settle, and provided the wall itself is well built, can last a very long time. Often walls on bedrock form the only more or less intact sections of older upland walls. Walls on bedrock tend either to collapse overnight if there is a problem, or last indefinitely if well built, rather than degrading over a period of time.

Slopes

The only feasible way of building on bedrock which slopes up or down from the face of the wall is to use stones with a triangular profile.

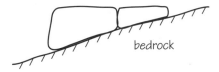

bedrock

This is far from ideal as the angle of the slope will tend to force the stone out of the wall, a problem which becomes more severe as the slope becomes steeper.

To minimise problems select stones which meet the two following criteria:

a The angle of the base of the stone should match the angle of slope of the bedrock, giving good stone to stone contact without the need for any wedging.

b When in position, the top of the stone should be as close as possible to horizontal to facilitate sound subsequent building.

These criteria are more important than choosing a stone which matches exactly the correct line or batter of the wall.

The next step is to ensure that these stones are well tied back into the wall so that they are held as securely as possible.

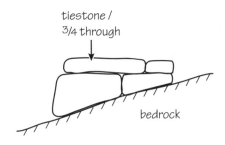

tiestone / 3/4 through

bedrock

a Select a suitable stone, even if it has to be fairly thin, to level up with the top of the triangular stone.

b Place a tie stone on top of these two stones.

c Level off with a smaller stone, and then place another tiestone as shown.

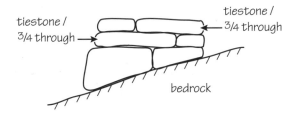

tiestone / 3/4 through

tiestone / 3/4 through

bedrock

When building a length of wall in this way with triangular foundation stones, use as many tiestones as possible. Choose the longest stones for the first layer of tiestones, which should be at least three-quarter length and preferably full through stones. Subsequent layers of tiestones which lap

onto these should at least reach the centre of the wall. The tiestones not only help secure the foundation stones, but distribute the weight of the wall evenly across the foundation, so that none of the triangular stones is taking more weight that it needs to.

Lips

Building over lips has similarities to building on slopes.

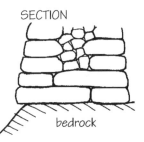

SECTION

bedrock

Start the wall with a three-quarter or full through, continuing as shown in the diagram. Always build up first the side of the wall away from the lip, to prevent the wall overbalancing. The weight of the wall on the back of the upper tie helps hold everything in place, and the result can be surprisingly secure. Whilst it is best to use full through stones, in practice it is sufficient if at least half the length of the first tie is sitting on bedrock, and is held by a tie running more than half way into the wall.

Where there is a shelf below the lip which would take a layer of stones, this can be utilised, but these stones are merely to improve the appearance of the wall, and should not be considered as load-bearing.

Mini-smoots

Small smoots can be constructed (p93) to bridge lumps, lips and some slopes. Normally these only need to be one sided, with the 'back' of the wall built as normal.

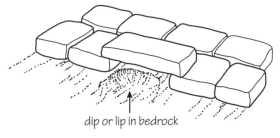

dip or lip in bedrock

One interesting use of this technique can be found in Llanberis, North Wales, where a series of one sided smoots form the footings of a wall on bedrock. It's not certain why

bedrock

this technique has been used in this particular situation, but it could be a useful approach when you do not have sufficient triangular stones for the footing. In this case use what you have got and bridge between them, rather than relying on poorer stones to support the wall.

It is possible that this will place more weight on the triangular footings that are used, and the footings cannot be tied back until after lintels have been placed. Its viability as a technique will depend on the specific situation and the stone available.

BOULDERS

If there are boulders within the line of the wall which need to be incorporated into it, plan the exact line in advance to make best use of the boulder, and to avoid any sudden kinks. Avoid a line which will leave the boulder sticking out on both sides of the wall, as this may give access to stock from both sides. Take the line that leaves the boulder protruding on one side only, to minimise the amount of extra stockproofing needed.

It is not essential to build wall heads at the boulder, although it is advisable to take extra care in ensuring that the stones alongside the boulder have their lengths running into the wall, and include at least as many throughs butting up against the boulder as there are courses of throughs in the wall.

Ensure the wall fits tightly against the boulder by shortening or lengthening each layer to conform to the boulder's contours. As a last resort use pinnings (p130) to ensure a tight, close fit.

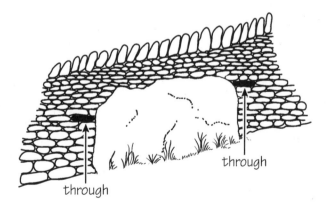

If the boulder is lower than the top course, continue the courses straight over it as if you were building on bedrock.

Stockproofing

If the boulder is higher than the top course it can be used as a base for the coping, which is continued over it uninterrupted. The coping acts as a visual deterrent to stock, by increasing the height of the boulder.

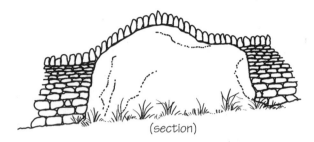

(section)

Alternatively, where the boulder is sufficiently steep-sided to be stockproof as it is, the coping can be stopped where the wall abuts the boulder, finishing with a blocky stone.

Boulders which are lower than the finished height of the wall may still need to be stockproofed, as a lip or bulge as small as 1" (25mm) can give a foothold to agile hill sheep. Stockproofing will either require adapting the coping, or building the wall higher.

Where the projection is only a few inches it's normally sufficient to project the coping or the coverstone by about 4-6" (100-150mm).

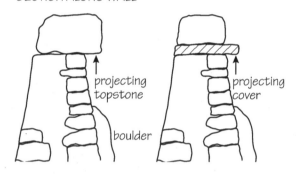

SECTION ALONG WALL

projecting topstone

projecting cover

boulder

Smaller coverstones can also be used, as long as at least half their length is on the wall and anchored by the cope. The arrangement of the coverstone and coping can be adapted as shown, to provide an overhang where the boulder projects on both sides of the wall.

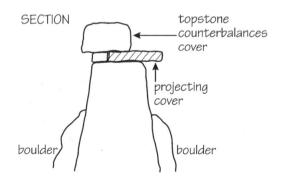

SECTION

topstone counterbalances cover

projecting cover

boulder

boulder

Another option is to create a double cope, projecting from both sides. This tends to be the least stable of the methods as the weight of stone on the wall may barely counterbalance the projection unless the shape of the copestones are suitable for overlapping.

PLAN VIEW
Double coping

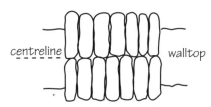

Double overlapping coping

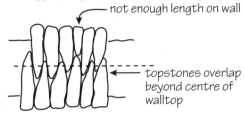

Where the boulder projects too far to be stockproof with an overhanging cope or cover, then the height of the wall must be increased.

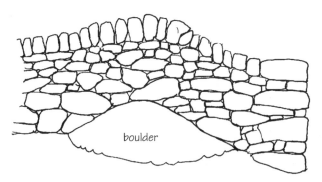

In this example at Blaen y Nant, Nant Ffrancon, North Wales, the height of the wall has been raised over the boulder and then gently curved back to normal. By using larger coping stones at the apex, grading down as wall height diminishes, a smooth curve has been made.

WET GROUND

Where there are patches of ground which are sufficiently wet at all times of year to be a barrier to stock, the wall can be brought to a head at either side and the wet ground left unwalled. More often though the wet ground will have to be walled or fenced off in some way.

In wet ground it may not be possible to reach ground firm enough to make foundations, even by digging quite deep. In order to support the wall and to try and prevent uneven settlement, use large slab-shaped foundation stones which will help spread the weight of the wall.

These should be laid to form a scarcement (p66) at ground level, the wall itself then being stepped in and built to its normal dimensions. Where the supply of stone is limited,

WET GROUND

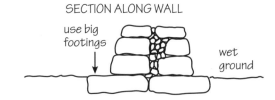

you may need to sacrifice height in order to build stronger foundations. A lower, but more stable wall is usually preferable to a normal height wall which is likely to collapse.

The recommended gap of 1-2" (25-50mm) between the two rows of foundation stones (p49) should be increased to 4-6" (100-150mm), and water smoots (p96) constructed in hollows or wherever water may try to drain across the line of the wall, remembering that the wall itself becomes a channel for water. Digging short lengths of drainage ditch from the smoots can help them drain the wall more effectively. Eventually any drainage measures within the wall are likely to become blocked, but in the short term they should lessen any uneven settling, so helping to ensure the wall's long term stability.

In some situations there may be no alternative but to fence across the wet ground. Use high tensile wire which minimises the number of fence posts needed, as these are difficult to anchor securely in wet ground. See *Fencing* (BTCV, 1985) for details.

TREES

Trees and walls make poor neighbours. A tree immediately next to a wall can push it over as the trunk thickens, and surface roots displace the footings. Even at a distance, 'root-heave' can destabilise walls as the root plates of large trees shift in the wind. The most common problem is of root growth which gradually works into any point of weakness, such as a running joint, initially displacing one or two stones which then causes collapse of the stones above.

If the line of the wall can be moved, choose a line which is at least 6' (2m) clear of any trees. Where the line cannot be moved, some felling and removal of tree stumps may be required. If it is necessary to preserve both the trees and the wall line, the following tactics should lessen the inevitable damage and uneven settling.

Bridging roots

Bridge robust roots with small smoots (p95).

Ideally, at least 12" (300mm) should be left on either side of the root, and about 6" (150mm) above the root, to give room for growth, and to give sufficient clearance from the effect of root heave. In practice the gap will be dictated by the length of the lintel available. Use the longest stone available, even if it is quite thin. Techniques for strengthening thin lintels are described on page 96. Clearance from the root is probably more important in the long term life of the wall than the strength of the lintel. Smoots are usually constructed as shown above, but some examples occur where the root or tree buttress is bridged with a low arch of mortared stone.

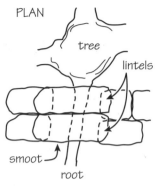

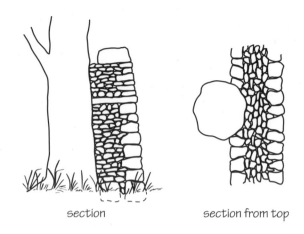

section   section from top

If there are problems with smoots being large enough to allow lambs through, gaps can be blocked temporarily with stones or similar during the lambing season. Alternatively, a short wooden or metal stake can be driven in at the smoot, sufficient to block the passage of lambs in the short term, but which will become redundant in the long term as root growth fills the gap.

Build the wall to a head at either side, and erect the section of post and rail fence in front of the tree.

If leaving a gap is not acceptable, then the wall should be built with only once face where it abuts the tree. As the trunk thickens the fillings should compact up to a point, without pushing out the face. In the longer term rebuilding may be necessary.

Trees in the line of the wall

Given that walls and trees do not mix, the best solution is to leave a gap for the tree. This gap should be as wide as is acceptable to the parties involved. Normally allow at least 3' (1m) either side of the tree, or at least 12" (300mm) clearance from any exposed roots. Given that standard treated softwood rails ('motorway rails') are 12' (3.65m) long, this may be a convenient size for the gap.

A rare alternative to this method can occasionally be found where wall heads are built 12-24" (300-600mm) from the tree, and the runners extended to help stockproof the gap between the head and the tree. This method is likely to last longer than building against the tree, but is dependent on having suitable runners.

8   Retaining walls and stone hedges

Retaining walls are built to stabilise and retain terraces, banks above and below paths and tracks, and other steep slopes where soil slump or rock slides may cause problems.

Stone hedges are free-standing stone-faced earth banks used as farm boundaries and stock fences. They are characteristic of South West England, Pembrokeshire, the coastal area of North West Wales, Anglesey and the Cumbrian coast. The techniques used in retaining walls and stone hedges are similar, but stone hedges have particular design features and variations. There are also intermediate types. In areas where stone hedges are traditional, retaining walls tend to be built to the same pattern of stonework as stone hedges, rather than to standard dry stone wall patterns.

Many retaining walls, stone hedges and some standard dry stone walls are finished with turf, instead of, or in addition to, coping stones. Turf tops are described towards the end of this chapter.

Retaining walls

Most retaining walls are built to a similar design to free-standing walls. They are made up of horizontal layers of face stones, wedged and packed with smaller stone fillings, and have a batter which tapers from wide at the base to narrow at the top.

The diagram shows the two main variations within this 'standard' form. Yorkshire wallers usually build a normal two-faced wall, although the hidden inner face is left rougher and with a steeper batter than the outer face, and large face stones are placed so that they project into the cavity between the wall and the bank. Scottish dykers build a one-sided wall, using various sizes of fillings which bind not only with the outer face stones but with the earth bank behind. A third variation is found in North Wales and other areas where slates, schists or mudstones are common. Here the face stones are generally set with a good length into the wall, and the fill may include soil.

Each of these styles ensures that the wall sits solidly on its own footings. The Yorkshire style may be best where there are plenty of face stones and small fillings, or where the wall projects above the bank so that its top is free standing. The Scottish type is most suitable where many of the fillings are large and irregular and so bind well with the earth bank. The Welsh style is suitable only where there is an abundance of long building stones.

Retaining walls are generally built to protect a vertical or near vertical bank from erosion. Most banks are quite stable, except at the exposed surface, and place little pressure on the wall. Hence the batter of the outside face of a retaining wall is usually the same as for a free-standing wall of the same type of stone. However, where the wall is load bearing and supporting a bank rather than just protecting it from erosion, the batter may need to be more sloped.

The base width depends on the batter and wall height. In general it can be a bit thinner than for an equivalent free-standing wall, because to some extent it is supported by the bank behind it. However, where it is bearing the load of an unstable bank, the base should be wider than for a free-standing wall. The extent to which it should be widened will be entirely dependent on the nature of the load, and will vary from place to place.

For a 3' (900mm) high wall, a base width of 1'6" (450mm) is generally adequate. However, where a high wall is subject to vibration from traffic or the bank is unstable scree or wet clay, the wall should be built wider than normal, at 2' (600mm) for a 3' (900mm) high wall, or 3-4' (0.9-1.2m) for a 5-6' (1.5-1.8m) high wall.

PROCEDURAL POINTS

The procedure for building a dry stone retaining wall is essentially the same as for a free-standing wall (p46). The following points show how to adapt normal walling techniques to retaining walls.

SECTIONS or tops can be turfed or built-up as a parapet

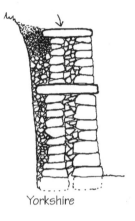

Yorkshire

Welsh

Scottish

a The wall should be dismantled as for a free-standing wall (p47), grading the stone as you go, and separating throughs, ties, hearting, building stone and any coping. As all the stone will be on one side, more space is required than for a free-standing wall. Set out the coping stones at a distance from the wall equivalent to at least two and a half times its height. Any turf should be piled neatly beyond the coping stone, with roots placed downward to protect them from drying out. Ensure that you leave plenty of space for soil. This should be piled at convenient intervals, as for hearting (p48).

Often it will be necessary to run the piles of soil continuously through the stripping-out area as shown. Care has to be taken that the soil does not spread out and engulf the building stone. Often it's possible to pile some of the soil uphill, above the intended top of the wall, ready to shovel down behind the wall.

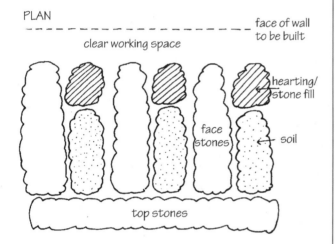

PLAN

face of wall to be built

clear working space

hearting/ stone fill

face stones

soil

top stones

b Prepare the bank by cutting it back and digging it out to a vertical face the height of the proposed wall. Whilst it is best to disturb the bank as little as possible, you will need to cut it back about 6" (150mm) deeper than the proposed base of the wall, to give room to place the stones.

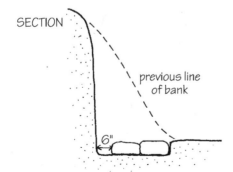

SECTION

previous line of bank

6"

c Batter frames are usually impractical to set up, but line bars (p33) can be used. It is only necessary to set up bars for the outer face, and the inside can be built 'by eye'. To help secure the line bar, additional bars or wooden battens can be driven into the bank and tied to the line bar.

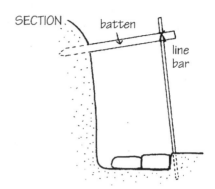

SECTION

batten

line bar

d Dig a foundation trench for the footings, down to firm subsoil or bedrock. About 6" (150mm) is usually deep enough.

e Lay the footings as for a free standing wall (p48), concentrating on running the stones lengthwise into the bank.

f If the wall has definite ends or 'heads', build these first. Choose large stones, preferably with a flat bed and two good faces.

g If the wall merges with the bank at either end, you can build it up along the whole section as convenient. Be sure to key the ends into the bank at their sides as well as at the back.

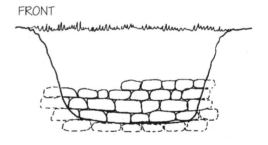

FRONT

h Build up in horizontal layers, with the biggest stones at the bottom. Keep to the principles outlined on page 51, paying particular attention to running each stone lengthwise into the wall.

In the Yorkshire style, build up both the inner and outer faces together, with fillings between, as in a free-standing wall. Don't worry if the inner face is irregular but be sure that the stones sit securely. Pack more fillings between the inner face and the bank. These tie the wall to the bank and ensure good drainage. Keep the level of the fillings as high as the face stones.

In the Scottish style, place and wedge as necessary each face stone, and pack behind it with fillings to give a solid, single-faced structure.

i   A certain amount of earth always slips down from the bank as you work. In some Scottish and North Welsh walls, soil may anyway form part of the integral structure. Any earth must be packed down well as you proceed. Place the hearting as normal, with shallow layers of soil, about 2-3" (50-75mm) before compaction, filling all voids. Ensure that the soil is very well compacted by walking on the lower layers, and compacting the upper layers with a tamper or lump hammer (p80). The soil and stone must be evenly distributed in any layer, so that pockets of soil do not develop. Where there is a lot of soil for filling, it is best to use up the hearting lower down, using a soil only fill higher up the bank.

j   Place throughs at the same level and spacing as for a free-standing wall of equal height, with their length projecting into the 'cavity' between the wall and the bank. Their outer face can be flush with the wall, or protruding, depending on the local style (p130). Wallers disagree as to whether the backs should project into the bank. Some maintain that digging throughs into the bank helps tie the wall to the bank. Others say that any digging destabilises the bank, and that the backs or 'tails' of the throughs are then held by the bank and cannot settle with the wall. As the wall settles, the throughs begin to slope, acting to shed the stones sitting on top of them.

k   If you have plenty of big stones, use some of the most awkwardly-shaped ones as fillings, rather than breaking them up. In the Scottish style, a proportion of big fillings is important to strengthen the wall, while small fillings are necessary to wedge up face stones. If you try a face stone and it doesn't fit, use it to pack the wall cavity.

l   As with free-standing walls, the type of coping used on retaining walls varies from area to area, and often from wall to wall. Try to determine the original form of coping on repairs and rebuilds, and check the local coping style when building a new wall. Flat, slab coping is far more common for retaining walls than for free-standing walls. Construct as described on page 135.

Many retaining walls do not have a formal cope, but are finished with soil and turf instead. In this case it is important to ensure that the final layer of stones is very solid, as until the turf becomes established the stones are fairly easily displaced. Make sure all the stones are set with their lengths into the wall, and avoid using very thin, light stones. It doesn't matter if the top layer is slightly thicker than the preceding layer, nor if it has an irregular top, as unlike a stone coping, the turves will sit on any irregularities. If there is a limited supply of turves, complete the outer edge of the revetment top first, before starting on the next row in. You may be able to cut additional turves from a nearby field. See page 84 for details of turf tops.

m   If the top of the wall projects above the bank top, build the projecting part as a two-faced, free-standing wall. If this 'parapet' is no more than 2' (600mm) high, there should be few problems. Taller 'parapets' should only be built on top of retaining walls built to the Yorkshire pattern, like a free-standing wall, or otherwise the weight of the parapet may cause uneven settlement and eventual collapse of the retaining wall.

SECTION
←parapet

n   Any loose stones or earth on the bank should be shovelled down behind the top of the wall, to help bind the wall and bank together.

PROBLEM SITUATIONS

a   Where the wall runs up a slope, start the wall at the downhill end, as with a free-standing wall. Make sure this end is provided with a really solid head. On a steep slope, the bottom end stone must be massive and absolutely stable to support the weight of material above. When in doubt, concrete the end to keep it from shifting.

b   Where the wall is built to retain scree or other loose material on a steep slope, several adaptations are necessary. The diagram illustrates a method which has been used successfully by BTCV at Cwm Idwal in Snowdonia, and at other sites where there may not be a level base from which to start, and where the aim is to blend the stonework with the existing hillside as much as possible.

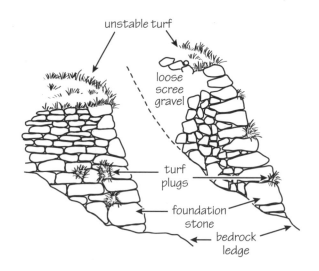

unstable turf
loose scree gravel
turf plugs
foundation stone
bedrock ledge

It is important to base the wall on bedrock. This may mean starting it considerably farther down the slope than planned, at least in places, and building up a level platform until the real footings can be placed. In order to try and promote a quicker growth of vegetation over the wall to help stabilise it, any small gaps which cannot be filled with stone can be plugged with turf. However, turf must not be used where a stone could be used instead, as this will create a weak point in the wall.

This technique and the following two points outline some of the work necessary to repair badly eroded slopes. Successful restoration may require retaining walls of the type described above, as well as stone pitched paths, stone-lined drains and revegetation by turfing and seeding. These techniques are described in *Footpaths* (BTCV, 2nd edition,1996).

c   When winning stones from a hillside for use in a wall, take them from uphill to make it easier to shift them, and to prevent destabilising the slope below the wall. To avoid initiating erosion, fill holes left by the removal of large stones with any nearby loose material such as stones, gravel or earth. Choose material which is itself liable to be eroded downslope or which has slipped down onto paths, drains or areas of turf.

d   Where runoff is likely to affect the wall, a cut-off drain can be dug above the wall to intercept the flow of water and drain it away from the wall. Preferably line the base and sides of the drain with flat stones to prevent it slumping, or fill it with stones.

SECTION

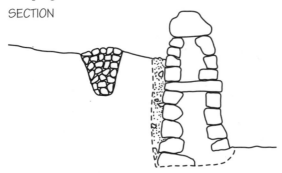

e   Where the base of the wall is a path, or is in soft soil or peat, dig down to a firm base to provide good foundations.

f   Where the bank is of inherently unstable material such as sand or wet clay, ordinary retaining walls may not be sufficiently strong. An alternative technique is to use gabions, which are large rectangular wire baskets that are filled with stones and built up in rows like giant blocks. They are frequently used in civil engineering for roadside, riverside and coastal embankments, and may be suitable for some conservation projects where the gabions can be hidden with vegetation or with properly constructed dry stone walling. They are not generally suitable for use on mountain sides or for areas where dry stone walling is traditional, as the random nature of the stone structure is obtrusive in such settings. For riverside revetments, 'soft' materials

such as vegetation or geotextiles are increasingly being used.

g   Where the wall supports a path or track, a substantial wall should be built, finished with large flat top-stones that cannot easily be dislodged. With any revetment or other structure adjoining a public right of way, including footpaths, bridleways and roads, the safety of the user must be considered. The Highway Authority should be consulted over any such work.

Stone hedges

The term 'stone hedges' is used here as a term for all free standing stone faced earth banks. They can be found in most walling areas, but most notably Devon, Cornwall and the coastal districts of Wales, and to a lesser extent in the North West of England. Remnants of various patterns can also be found through much of the Highlands and Islands of Scotland, but examples in good condition are few and far between. Generally, stone hedges are found in lower lying areas where stone is in short supply.

In Cornwall, the term 'hedge' is used for all walls, including dry stone walls. R Menneer (1994) quotes earlier texts that "all mounds, not regular masonry, are in Cornwall termed hedges". The terminology probably originated in the Anglo-Saxon word *hecg* referring to a territorial boundary, not to be confused with *haeg*, a hurdle, or *hega*, a living boundary.

In North Wales, stone hedges are known as clawdd (singular) or cloddiau (plural). Clawdd is pronounced 'clow-th' as in 'clown' and 'them'. Cloddiau is pronounced 'clo-the-eye', as in 'clod', 'the' and 'eye'. Literally translated clawdd means hedge, dyke or embankment, with Offa's Dyke known by the Welsh as 'Clawdd Offa'.

In this chapter, cloddiau is used to refer to stone hedges which have the stonework set vertically on edge, and built in more or less even layers. It is the most widespread form of stone hedge and probably accounts for the greatest overall length of any form used. It mostly occurs in Wales, but the type is also common in South Cornwall, notably on the Lizard Peninsula, and in parts of Cumbria where such features are called Cumberland Banks, Kes's or Kessies.

The term Cornish hedge is used in this chapter to refer to walls built similarly to dry stone walls, but with an earth core and concave batter. Cornish hedges are generally at least 4' (1.2m), whereas Welsh cloddiau are rarely much more than about 3' (1m). Some taller cloddiau have concave batters, but a straight batter is normal. Very often Cornish hedges have, or used to have, a shrub hedge growing on the top. Such growth is rarer on cloddiau, although Cumberland Banks are usually topped with shrub hedges. To aid the stockproofing of cloddiau without a shrub hedge, you will occasionally find a ditch on one side. This is probably where the earth core was dug, and helps to gain height on one side. It is more common on lower walls rather than taller ones. Additional material such as dead wood or gorse may have been piled on the top of the cloddiau, for extra stockproofing.

It is a common misconception that stone hedges are built with turves in their faces. This misconception is probably due to the proliferation of growth on roadside stone hedges, and on those which enclose fields not used for grazing. Any vegetative growth is due to natural colonisation and low grazing pressure. When hedges are constructed with a lot of turves in the face, there is a serious risk of collapse as the turves dry out and shrink.

One of the most important aspects of stone hedges is their wildlife role, as their earth core can be a haven for small mammals, and their faces an important habitat for plants and invertebrates. Stone hedges are more valuable than dry stone walls as habitats, as the earth core helps sustain a wider range of plants and animals.

Ignoring local or individual preferences, the main factors which determine the style of stone hedge are:

a   Type of available stone. Granite, sandstone, elvan (whinstone) and irregular clearance or river-washed stones are most suited to building in roughly level layers, with smaller stone best used in vertical courses (p82). Slate is best used upright or, if fragmented, in the herringbone pattern (p83).

b   Cost. The cheapest is stone cleared from fields, but for larger jobs, quarried stone is necessary. In Cornwall quarried slate, which is much cheaper than granite, is used increasingly even in granite areas, despite the dislike of local craftsmen. One way to save stone used on cloddiau and granite hedges is to stop at the 3-4' (0.9-1.2m) level, and finish off the top of the hedge with turf. In Cornwall, this method is sometimes used on south and west facing slopes, where exposed to sun and rain, the turves quickly grow and bind together. In the dry shade on north facing slopes or under trees, where turves don't thrive, stones are used instead. Methods of constructing these turf-faced banks are described in *Hedging* (BTCV, 1998).

Cloddiau

Cloddiau is used here to refer to stone hedges which have the stonework set vertically on edge, and built in more or less even layers. As a method of construction it is particularly strong, as the stones wedge firmly together, as with the coping on a dry stone wall. However, cloddiau are quite different in structure from dry stone walls, as the stonework serves more as a protective skin to a relatively independent earth bank, rather than the face and hearting functioning as one structure, as in a dry stone wall. Cloddiau are much wider than standard dry stone walls.

PROCEDURE

Dismantling

The basic process is similar to dismantling a dry stone wall (p47). However, it is best to disturb the earth bank as little as possible, only cutting the face back 100-150mm (4-6") more than the length of the building stones, to allow space for compacting the soil behind them. If both sides need repairing, it is best to dismantle and rebuild one face before dismantling the other. Much of the clawdd's strength is reliant on the solidity of the earth core, and it is likely that no amount of manual compaction can make up for hundreds of years of natural settlement.

The stone is set out either in lines or piles of similarly sized stone, accurately graded to facilitate building. The width of cloddiau means that throughstones are very rare. However 'bonders', stones more than three times as long as they are high, are sometimes used, and if found, these should be set aside.

Batter

As with retaining walls, frames are not usually practical when rebuilding a clawdd, and line bars are used as described above (p74). If a new clawdd is being built, a frame can be used, and should be set up as explained for free standing walls (p49).

To increase their stability, cloddiau are not as steep-sided as dry stone walls. Put another way, cloddiau have a greater batter than dry stone walls, and the batter increases

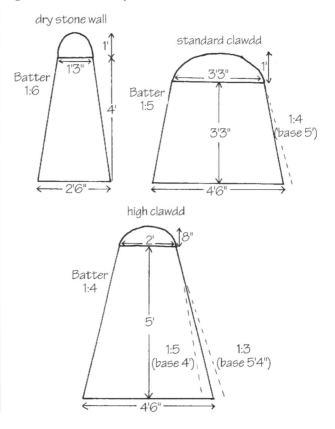

d The stone must sit on a firm base, and make a good surface to build on.

Awkwardly shaped stones, particularly those with a triangular shape, will need trimming to provide good faces and surfaces.

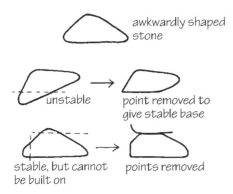

awkwardly shaped stone

unstable → point removed to give stable base

stable, but cannot be built on → points removed

When placing a stone, make a small ramp of soil inside the wall, just beyond the point the building stones will reach. Set a stone vertically on the foundation so that its top meets, or nearly meets, the string line.

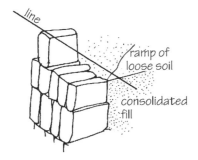

line

ramp of loose soil

consolidated fill

You may need to use a small amount of soil from your ramp alongside stones with rounder bases to ensure they don't fall over.

Avoid getting too much soil on the previous course, as good stone to stone contact must be maintained, with the stone holding the earth, and not vice versa.

When learning, it is best to work sequentially along the course, placing one stone and then the next. Use stones of complementary shapes where possible, and keep the stones tight and

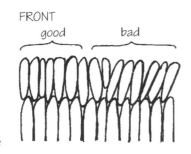

FRONT
good   bad

vertical. It is tempting to slope a stone to get it to the right height, but this will create a weak point, and put out the pattern of coursing above.

With courses of vertically placed stones, some hedgers recommend putting a turf layer about 1" (25mm) thick on each course, tamping it down well between the stones. The

argument is that this makes a bed for the next course and ensures a quick growth of grass over the face to bind it. However, this technique is not generally recommended, as the outer edge of the turf layer can become eroded before any vegetation establishes, destabilising the face. Stone and turf faces are also more likely to settle unevenly, or more quickly, increasing the potential for collapse.

Keystones

Keystones are used about every 2' (600mm) to ensure a tight finish. These stones are slightly narrower at the base than at the top, and are forced down into the course to tighten the stones in the section to either side. The distance between keystones depends on the stone size and type, but they should be placed so every stone is 'squeezed' by its nearest keystone. If the keystone is too narrow, or the gap between keystones too wide, some stones will not be 'squeezed' as the keystone is forced in.

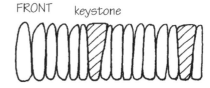

FRONT   keystone

When learning, use the following sequence to place keystones:

1   Select a suitable keystone for the height of the course.

2   Place as normal in the sequence, but alongside a stone with a good flat side.

3   Choose another flat sided stone to place beyond the keystone, with the flat side to the keystone.

4   Remove the keystone, and move the single stone slightly into the gap left by the keystone.

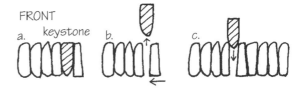

FRONT
a. keystone   b.   c.

5   Continue the course to the next keystone.

6   Force the first keystone down into the gap left for it, squeezing the building stones.

The keystone will be of little use if its immediate neighbours are not flat sided. In effect the keystone is one in a set of three, differing only from the other two in being slightly wedge shaped.

Initially this process will be a matter of trial and error, but with experience you will be able to choose the right stones to give a tight fit.

Whatever the method used for the last course of stone, turf will normally be added to completely cap the wall and give it a level finish. Consequently the last stone course does not need to have a regular top, as any irregularities will be disguised by the turf.

The process of turfing the top of a clawdd is similar to making a turf dome (p84), except generally only one layer of turf is used on top of a dome of soil. With new cloddiau an earth dome 12-18" (300-450mm) high is added on top of the last course to increase the height of the wall, and to allow for settlement of the earth core. When repairing cloddiau with a relatively stable core, settlement should not be a problem, but additional soil can be added to create a domed top if extra height is needed.

Place a line of turf on top of the last course, positioning each turf carefully so that the roots are not exposed at the edge, and tamping each one into place, butted closely up against its neighbour. If new turves are cut they should be cut to a diamond or trapezoid profile (p84) to ensure that they bind well together. Once the tops of both faces are turfed, continue by turfing the middle section of the domed top.

If you run out of turves and it's not possible to dig any more, it's acceptable to leave the rest of the top bare, as it will vegetate in time. However, you must ensure that the fragile edge of the dome is covered, to protect it from erosion.

Rule (1974) identifies a 'thatch' of three rows of turf used in certain exposed parts of the Lizard Peninsula. One row on each side is placed earth down, then a row on the back of it is placed earth upwards. More earth is packed on and a final double row is placed which overlaps the other rows by about two thirds their width. Finally an earth cover is put on to finish. This method promotes quick binding of the turf.

SECTION

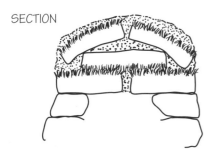

Cornish hedges

Although Cornish hedges, like cloddiau, have an earth core, in dimension and structure they are more like dry stone walls. Rather than being an earth bank with a stone skin, the stonework and earth core of a Cornish hedge make an integral structure.

The standard stone hedge design specified for roadside work by the County of Cornwall is shown below. Farm

hedges are frequently higher than this, being 6' (1.8m) or more where they border a track worn below field level. Whatever the size, the general principle is that the width of the hedge at its base should equal its height.

SECTION

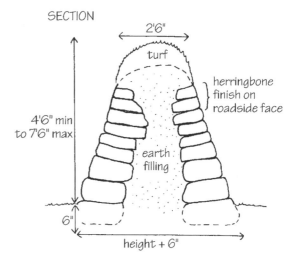

2'6"

turf

herringbone finish on roadside face

4'6" min to 7'6" max

earth filling

6"

height + 6"

PROCEDURE

Construction of a Cornish hedge is essentially the same as building a retaining wall, with a few minor differences relating to the concave batter, placement of stones and earth fill. When repairing or rebuilding a Cornish hedge you normally have to take down the earth core at least to the half way height, because the earth core is narrow and unstable without the supporting stones. The lower part of the earth core is best left undisturbed if possible.

Batter

Erect a batter frame or 'pattern' just beyond the end of the section as described on page 49. Alternatively use a frame which you can hold up against the side of the hedge from time to time (p33).

Not all Cornish hedges have a concave batter, although it is by far the most common shape for walls in the area, dry stone walls and cloddiau type structures included. With a

SECTIONS

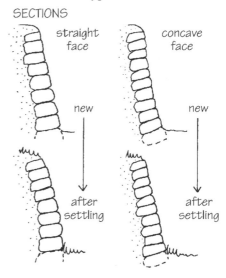

straight face

concave face

new

new

after settling

after settling

concave batter the hedge, as it settles, remains slightly concave or straightens out. With a straight batter the hedge may belly out and become weak as it settles. Another supposed theory for the concave batter is that it creates less wind turbulence, and thereby improves the shelter value.

Lines are raised at intervals of around 12" (300mm) as for dry stone walling, although when you are first learning it is best to raise them in smaller increments, about corresponding to each layer, otherwise you are likely to lose the correct curve for the batter.

Placing stones

The basic principles for dry stone walling outlined on page 51 apply also to Cornish hedges. It is particularly important for the strength of the hedge to lay stones with their long edges into the wall. However, a major difference is that stones are placed to that they tilt slightly down and into the wall, opposite to the normal method for dry stone walling. One possible theory is that this directs rain water into the bank and promotes a better growth of plants. It is more likely that the stones are tilted to help achieve the correct batter.

The first three courses are tilted strongly down into the hedge, while succeeding courses are brought gradually up so that the top layers have their faces nearly perpendicular, as shown in the diagram. A rule of thumb is to have about 3" (75mm) of batter in the first 1' (300mm) of hedge height, and to decrease this progressively to perpendicular at the top. Follow the batter frame closely.

Fill

Menneer (1994) suggests that the only correct material for the fill is 'rab', which is a soft clayey or gritty shale, or sometimes decomposed granite, used as precursor to tarmacadam in road surfacing. In practice, as with cloddiau, any soil that combines well when compacted will suffice.

As with cloddiau (p79), the earth packing is brought slightly above the level of each course so that the next course is adequately supported. Generally the rule that 'stones hold the earth and not vice versa' is followed, but some Cornish hedgers pack a layer of soil on top of the stones to help bed in the next course.

Finishing and capping

There are various ways to finish off the hedge. In the County of Cornwall specifications, the stonework is brought to within 1'6" (450mm) of the proposed hedge top, above which are placed two rows of small stones. If granite they may either be finished (trimmed) or random (rough). If the top two rows are slate they are built in herringbone, to use up the small pieces split from the 'raisers' or face stones during construction. Herringbone also provides a good rooting medium for plants.

Once the stonework has been built to the full height, the earth core is finished to a well packed rounded profile, and then the turf is laid. Alternatively, a single or double staggered row of young hawthorn, beech or other hedge shrubs can be planted on top, and then the turf laid upside down around the plants. The turf will help protect the earth bank from eroding, whilst not encouraging grassy growth which would severely compete with the young shrubs for water and nutrients. Keep the shrubs weeded and watered until they have established. Details are given in *Hedging* (BTCV, 1998).

OTHER PATTERNS

Chip and block

In Cornwall, the emphasis is on building horizontal courses in a neat masonry-block appearance, especially when using trimmed stone. However, the more regular the stone, the more poorly it binds, and trimmed granite hedges have a tendency to collapse outward or inward as the bank settles.

A method that is preferred in Devon is to build in the 'chip and block' style, where large 'blocks' and small 'chips' are used together. Although the stones are roughly graded from biggest at the bottom to smallest at the top, there is a mixture of chips and blocks within each course. The chips are used to wedge the blocks from behind so that they sit well and bond with the earth packing. The blocks are trimmed of any awkward projecting noses or inside corners which would otherwise keep them from tightening as they settle.

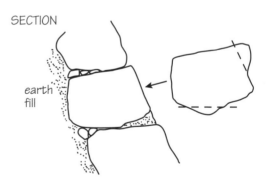

Some hedgers frown on this style, believing that the hedge can become unstable if the wedges shift as the hedge settles. The contrary argument is that the use of stone wedges rather than soil minimises settlement, and there is no problem as long as the wall is well built in the first place. The use of wedges on the face of the hedge is avoided by all hedgers.

Vertical random

Vertical random is usually associated with larger slates and some other fissile stone.

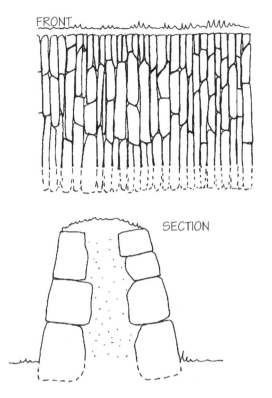

FRONT

SECTION

When building this style with non-fissile stone it is usually necessary to trim off any rounded ends to that the stones above will sit securely. With very fissile material you can usually tap the stones down securely without any shaping. Vertical joints are unavoidable, so instead you must break the horizontal joints as shown.

Other styles

Some cloddiau are built like a dry stone wall at the base, using stone not suited to horizontal coursing. Build random stonework to a reasonably consistent height along the length of the clawdd, levelling it out with the first course of vertically placed stonework.

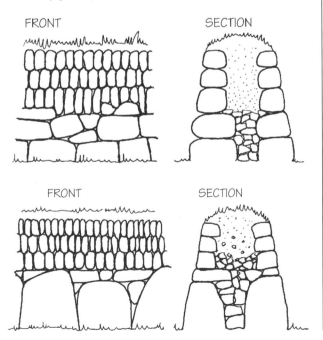

FRONT   SECTION

FRONT   SECTION

A variation used in areas with large boulders is to build the clawdd with random walling between the boulders until a relatively even height is achieved, and then finish off with courses of smaller vertically placed stone.

Herringbone pattern is used in some parts of North Cornwall, the Devon coast and parts of Exmoor, where slate, level bedded sandstone or other fissile rock is common.

This method is particularly strong as the slates bind together well, and it is impossible to build a running vertical joint.

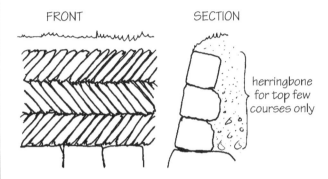

FRONT   SECTION

herringbone for top few courses only

Occasionally a course of stones is set flat between each pair of alternating courses.

Rarely, you may find a wall with all the courses sloping the same way.

'Shiners', or large stones set vertically on edge and traced can be found in many areas, and are particularly striking in some of Dartmoor's hedges. Although these break the normal rules of walling, they are stable because they have a good batter and are well tied in by other stones along their tops. This practice is explained in more detail on page 128.

At Culloden battlefield near Inverness, the National Trust for Scotland have reconstructed a turf dyke thought to be similar to the boundaries which would have existed in 1746. The Leanach turf dyke, named after the area, has 12-14" (300-360mm) of stonework, with a stone only fill, topped by turf. The overall height and top width are each 39" (1m), with a base width of 4' (1.2m).

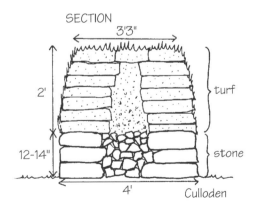

SECTION

3'3"

2'

12-14"

4'

turf

stone

Culloden

The Highland Vernacular Building Trust in Newtonmore have done a similar reconstruction, creating a bank 36"

(900mm) wide at the base, and 28" (700mm) wide at the top, 44" (1.1m) high, including a 8" (200mm) dome. The bank has three layers of stone sandwiched with turf, topped with turf alone.

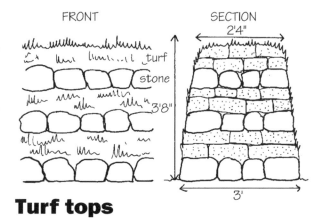

Turf tops

Another variation on the use of earth and turf in walling is to built a turf top on an otherwise standard dry stone wall with a stone filling.

Dry stone walls with a turf or 'divot' top are common to parts of Scotland such as the Highlands, Glens and parts of the Borders, although they appear to be rare elsewhere. Their presence is likely to be due mainly to a lack of suitable coping stone. Mica schists, for example, may be unsuitable because the effects of freezing can shatter the stone.

Some Scottish single walls (p139) also have, or once had, turf tops. Rainsford-Hannay (1972) quotes the Roxburgh Agricultural Survey of 1798 as recommending a layer of turves on top of the wall, placed on edge and 'condensed together' with a spade. Although this specific method seems to have fallen into disuse, there are two similar methods still used today.

Both methods are referred to as 'one up, one down'. The 'double turf' is the more usual method, whilst the second method uses 'one up, one down' to create a dome.

DOUBLE TURF

A layer of turves is placed 'grass down' on top of the wall, with a layer placed 'grass up' on top of this. The inverted lower turf rots down and provides a base for the top layer to root into. In the initial stages, the lower turf also stops soil from falling down into the wall. If wet soil freezes inside the wall it will expand and may hasten collapse of the wall. Once the turf top is established, the mat of roots should prevent any soil falling through.

Cutting the turves

a The turf should have a good root stock. If it is cut from a field which has been reseeded within about five years, the turf tends to crumble.

b The turf should be cut about 1-2" (25-50mm) wider than the top width of the wall, to ensure that the wall is covered. The extra allows for any shrinkage of the turf, or initial dying off of the edges due to drying out.

c The length of the turf is largely immaterial, although around 8-9" (200-230mm) is a reasonably effective and efficient size to use.

d The turf should be thick enough to have good roots, but not so thick that it is heavy to handle, with about 3-4" (75-100mm) usually suitable. If the soil is very thin and stony you may have to settle for a thinner turf.

e The turves should be cut to a diamond or parallelogram shape. This ensures a good overlapping of turves when they are placed on the wall, so they bind together well.

Laying the turves

Place the turves tightly up to their neighbours to reduce the chance of drying out. Press the second layer tightly down on top. Some wallers walk on the turf top, or hit the turves with a spade, to ensure good bedding.

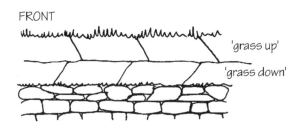

Work on short sections of 5-10m as the wall is completed, rather than leaving long lengths of wall to be done in one go. This breaks up the hard and monotonous task of digging the turf.

DOMED TURF

This method uses less turf and avoids leaving exposed edges.

1 Cut some turves as described above, but narrower, so they are about half the width of the top of the wall.

2 Place these turves grass down along the centre of the top of the wall, covering the hearting.

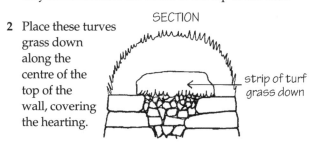

3 Cut the next layer of turves 4-6" (100-150mm) wider than the top width of the wall.

4 Place these grass up across the wall, creating a dome over the first layer. Firmly compact the turves, especially at the edges.

When the walls were originally built, the cutting of the foundation trench would probably have supplied sufficient turf for a domed top, without having to dig any extra.

HEATHER

Heather is occasionally used as a substitute for turf. The process is essentially the same, bearing in mind the following:

a Heather cutting is more difficult because of the thicker, woody roots. The bases of the turves or 'divots' are consequently less regular and usually need to be trimmed square before they can be used.

b The divots need to be about 6" (150mm) thick, as they compact more than grass turves.

c Heather divots dry out quickly, so each one needs to be squeezed sideways into place to reduce the amount of shrinkage.

FURTHER CONSIDERATIONS

a Turf tops go acid very quickly, primarily due to the very free drainage, and mosses and lichens quickly replace the grass. Whilst this non-grass turf still functions as a wall top, it will not be as strong as it lacks the binding roots of grass. Fertiliser, chalk or lime can be added to reduce acidity. In coastal locations seaweed can be sandwiched between the layers during construction of the top, to promote longer term fertility.

b Turf is normally stripped from a single area of a field. In normal circumstances this will take four or five years to recover, provided there is reasonable depth of soil remaining. The recovery process can be speeded up if the area is filled or covered with organic material, such as compost or silage which has gone off.

c On wall heads a large stone is placed on top, as in normal coping (p90). This helps prevent the end turf becoming displaced, falling off or drying out.

d Some wallers place a line of rubble on top of the turf to help hold it in place against cattle and high winds. Sometimes you will find a flat stone every five metres or so between turves. Frequently these would have had iron bars in them for stock proofing and to prevent grazing. If sheep can get at the turf it suffers badly and tends not to last long.

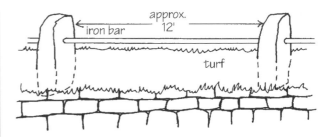

e Sometimes there is a coverband below the turf, as with some forms of stone coping. The reasons for it may include moisture retention in the turf, keeping soil out of the wall, or as a precaution in case the turves degrade.

f There are examples where a turf top has been used in place of the cover band, below a stone coping.

Galloway hedges

The 'Galloway hedge' or 'sunk fence', is a combination dry stone wall and thorn hedge, rather similar to the Irish ditch with quicks (p7) and found primarily in South West Scotland.

Galloway Hedge

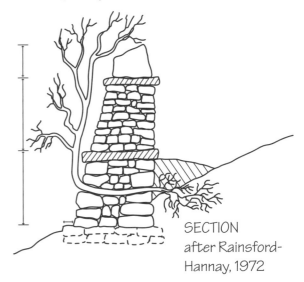

SECTION after Rainsford-Hannay, 1972

This design is especially suited to fencing along the contours of hill and valley sides, in situations where the climate is acceptable for hedgerow shrubs, but where walling stone is available as well. A wall alone would have to be very high to keep sheep from gaining access from the uphill side, and a hedge alone would likely become gappy unless frequently laid.

According to Rainsford-Hannay (1972), the Galloway hedge was invented by Hamilton of Baldoon in 1730, and copied extensively by Lord Selkirk of St. Mary's Isle. He describes its construction. First, make a horizontal cut along the slope to form a level platform, and throw the spoil uphill. Then place the foundation stones and erect a double dyke with the uphill side vertical and the other side given a good batter. There should be a scarcement (p66) of at least 4" (100mm) on the downhill side, but little or none on the other. When the dyke is raised to the top of the undisturbed soil, lay long thorn plants horizontally across the dyke with their roots in the soil. Finish building the dyke around the plants to a height of 4'6" (1.3m) including the locked top (p133).

For the first couple of years, stock should be kept off the fields to both sides of the new Galloway hedge, to allow the thorns to grow. After three years the plants should be big enough to defeat sheep and cattle. Although the combination of stone and thorn makes a good barrier, it does require trimming and general maintenance each year, which may be why few are now being built.

The above type appears to be rare in Galloway nowadays, although there are numerous roadside hedges growing out of low retaining walls, where the field height is perhaps 2-3' (600-900mm) above road or track height.

Whilst the general argument is that shrubs and trees destabilise walls, the case is not that clear when looked at in relation to the Galloway hedge. As long as the wall has been well built the growing hedge seems to tighten the stone work. Semi-derelict Galloway hedges seem particularly tight around the shrubs where the stones have been forced together. It is the parts of the walls between the shrubs which have frequently collapsed, although this may be due to the squeezing effect of the shrubs. During construction, space was probably left around the stem to allow for growth.

Stone hedge furniture

Corners

The absence of long stones in many cloddiau often necessitates the use of a sharp curve or simplified 'T' junction, rather than corners. Most changes of direction in stone hedges are accommodated by curved sections, which are built following the same procedure as straight ones, bearing in mind the problems and procedures outlined for curves in dry stone walls (p67). If a corner is necessary, this should be built following the principles described on page 92.

Heads and gateways

Stone hedges require a carefully designed gate end to allow for the extra width and batter of the earth bank. Cornish hedges often end with a head following either the 'L' shaped or overlapping methods described on page 91. This can work for lower, and therefore narrower, hedges although the downward tilt of the stone can cause problems. For taller Cornish hedges and cloddiau the face of the head can be built as if it were another section of hedge, but this

requires a good supply of rectangular stones with two or three good faces to form the corners, as well as wasting material. Usually the hedge is tapered to the gate post, as shown for a Cornish hedge.

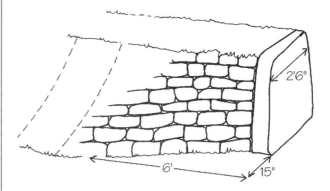

The gate post is set 15" (375mm) inside the base line of the hedge, and backed by a 3' (900mm) high head of flat stones so that it is not forced out of line as the earth in the hedge settles. The hedge's batter is progressively reduced from a point 6' (1.8m) from the post, and the base made correspondingly narrower, until at the post itself the hedge is nearly vertical. The same concave frame or pattern which is used to judge the normal batter is used to guide the reduction in base width from 5' (1.5m) or so to 2'6" (760mm) at the base.

Stiles

Stone hedges have a wide variety of stiles, mostly variants on those described for dry stone walls (p97). Stiles are rarer in cloddiau than other stone hedges, as the stone is less suited to their construction. However where stone has been imported or gleaned during the building process they can be found, the most common type being step stiles (p98). This example from the Lizard Peninsula uses serpentine slabs.

Given the width of stone hedges the steps rarely project through the whole wall. The top of the cloddiau makes a secure step.

Through stiles (p99) are rare. Step through stiles (p100) are a little more common and occasionally you will find variants of Cotswold slab stiles (p100), with an additional 'rail' over the top of the smaller slab.

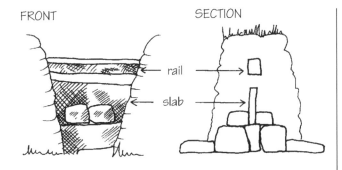

FRONT   SECTION

← rail

← slab

South western rung stiles

Rung stiles and stone cattle grids (see below) are distinct forms of stile which are common in parts of the south west but very rare elsewhere. Cornish rung stiles are usually built out of hewn granite, although serpentine ones can be found on the Lizard peninsula. Three rungs are usual, but five or seven rung stiles are occasionally found.

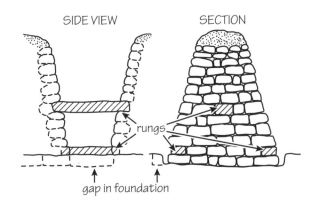

SIDE VIEW   SECTION

rungs

gap in foundation

To build a South Western rung stile:

1   Cut the foundation trench across the line of the stile in the same way as along the rest of the hedge.

2   Build one side of the foundation up to but not across the line of the stile. Bring it close enough to the gap on both sides so that the first step can be placed with its end resting solidly on the foundation's facing stones.

3   Place the first step.

4   Cross to the other side of the hedge and repeat steps 2 and 3, placing the second step on the same level as the first.

5   Lay stones between the ends of the steps to protect the earth fill.

6   Build two or three rows of hedge on top of the foundation to secure the ends of the first two steps. Face the sides of the gap as well as the outside of the hedge with stone.

7   Place the third step 12-15" (300-380mm) above the first two, and along the centre line of the hedge.

8   Finish building the hedge above the steps, giving the sides of the gap at least as much batter as the outside of the hedge. Finish the top in one of the usual ways (p84).

Stone cattle grids

These are rarer than rung stiles, although the norm in parts of West Cornwall including Zennor and Penwith. They consist of a series of parallel lengths of hewn granite, set with gaps between, and sometimes over a pit.

The usual arrangement is four or five rungs, each about 6-12" (150-300mm) wide and thick, and set at ground level. The stile opening is made to any convenient width, determined by the length of rungs available, allowing for a few inches to be embedded in the wall. They are usually wide enough for two walkers to pass with ease.

The spacing of the rungs is dependent on the width of the wall and the dimensions of the rungs. They are set so that the gaps are fairly uniform, normally around 11-12" (270-300mm), to a maximum of about 14" (360mm).

One disadvantage of this type of stile is that it has to be cleaned out from time to time, to keep the gaps between the rungs from filling with debris and vegetation. Examples exist with pits below, like a metal cattle grid, and it's possible that many were constructed this way and have subsequently become filled with soil. To completely clean out the pit would involve dismantling the stone hedge to remove the rungs, unless they are installed independently of the stone hedge. Broken rungs, which have been shored up with a pile of stone beneath the break, are sometimes found.

Similar stiles are found on the Isles of Scilly. In many instances these have the middle 'rung' of a set of five projecting up to 6" (150mm) above the level of the other 'rungs' to act as a sill.

Protection, maintenance and repair

South Western hedges of both turf and stone used to be left half built to settle, and even now are considered 'tender' until new vegetation starts to grow on them. During this period cattle can easily paw the stones loose or tear them down by climbing the banks, so cattle should be kept off the fields for several months. Alternatively a temporary fence should be erected about a yard from the base of the bank. Cattle should be kept off other retaining walls in the same way.

Once the bank is firmly bound by growing vegetation, livestock present few problems unless a stone or two is loosened in some other way. Rabbits and rats cause the most trouble since sections of stone facing may slump inward after they have burrowed extensively. If trees are planted along the top they may become lopsided over the years, and tend to break down one side of the bank, usually the one away from the prevailing wind. Trees, and to a lesser extent brambles and briars which root in the steep sides of a tall bank tend to loosen and dislodge stones. Whenever a break occurs, sheep and cattle are sure to investigate and accelerate the erosion.

Despite these problems, dry stone retaining walls and stone hedges need to be checked only occasionally once they have settled. As with free-standing walls, the quicker any break is made good the less likely it is to spread, whether or not livestock are present to increase the damage.

Once a year make a close check for dislodged stones. At this time also, unwanted trees or shrubs growing from the sides should be cut back or dug out. If the bank has a live hedge on top of it, you can renew the soil and keep the plants vigorous by shovelling up earth which has slumped to the base of the bank, and spreading it among the hedge plants.

9 Standard wall furniture

This chapter covers the design and construction of wall furniture such as smoots, stiles and gates, and combinations of walls and fences. Whatever the item of wall furniture, it is much easier to build the feature as the wall is being built, than to try and add it later. When rebuilding a long stretch of old wall, note whatever furniture it contains and replace it as before. This may be appropriate even where the feature is now redundant, in order to preserve local tradition.

Wall heads

The wall head is a specially constructed pillar which acts like a huge bookend to strengthen the wall faces and protect the centre, which would otherwise weather away and collapse. Heads should be built at the start and finish of every distinct section of wall, including:

a Where gates and other openings are taken through the wall.

b Where a new wall butts up against an existing one. While it is stronger to lock the two, this requires taking down a section of old wall, and so should only be done where the old wall is to be rebuilt anyway.

c On steep slopes, to provide stability and limit the formation of gaps (p62).

d In certain cases, to indicate changes in ownership of different wall sections (p17). The two heads are built against each other, and the coping is built across the seam to reduce its weakness.

STANDARD WALL HEADS

The ends of a dry stone wall are the parts which are most exposed to damage, and the stones are only supported on two sides rather than three. For these reasons the heads should be built of the biggest, most regular stones available, which should be selected and put to one side during sorting (p58) . Stones may need to brought in if the local stone is inadequate. Large granite or sandstone blocks are best, preferably with smooth square faces on the two or three sides where they are exposed. Take care when handling heavy stones (p22).

Procedure

When starting a new wall, build one head first. When you near the far end, build the other head and then complete the wall to close the gap.

When rebuilding heads it is best to dismantle the wall at least 6' (2m) along from the head, placing the building stones to either side of the wall as normal. Leave plenty of space for working. Separate the ties, which are long stones that run across the wall, from the runners, which run along the wall. Pair the runners for height as you go, placing the largest on the ground nearest the wall. You may need to select suitable additional stones, such as throughs, from the rest of the dismantled wall to give you a better choice.

Having excavated the foundation, the procedure is as follows:

1 Set up the batter frame or line bars as described on page 49. The frame can be set up immediately adjacent to the head where it will give the profile and the vertical line, but as it tends to get in the way when placing large stones many wallers prefer to set up the frame about 3' (1m) beyond the end of the foundation.

2 Select a pair of even-height stones and set them with their long axis along the wall. Preferably choose a pair which will meet in the middle, but failing this select a stone of the same height to fit tightly in the gap between them.

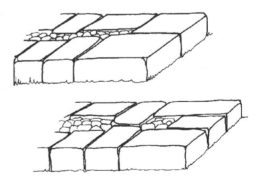

Don't place foundation stones like a tie, with their long axis across the trench, as the lack of length along the wall means they are more likely to get undermined by erosion, particularly in gateways. Occasionally you may have a slab so large that it can run across the trench, whilst also having sufficient length along the wall.

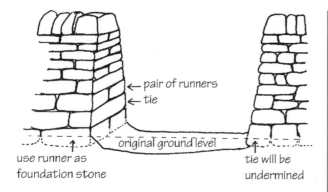

use runner as foundation stone

← pair of runners
← tie

original ground level

tie will be undermined

3 Continue laying foundations away from the wall head for at least 10' (3m).

4 Place a tie stone across the wall, taking care to choose one which is long enough to completely traverse the wall. If it is a little short you are likely to lose the correct batter or not be able to build on it satisfactorily. The correct place for this stone will be a little higher up the head.

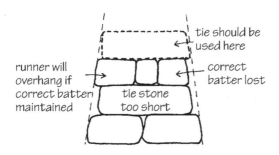

tie should be used here

runner will overhang if correct batter maintained

correct batter lost

tie stone too short

If you have a stone that is just too long use it now, as it will certainly be no use higher up. It's generally not worth shortening a tie unless a trimmed finish is required, as it's easy to take too much off. It's best to place long ties so that they project equally on both sides of the wall, but local practice varies. Ties that protrude tend to get dislodged by cattle.

5 Build up a short section of wall to the height of the stones just placed, using ordinary face stones and fillings.

6 Continue to build up layers in this way, alternating ties and runners. Build up a short section of wall along from the head at the same time, leaving it well stepped for joining into later (p57). Any gaps between runners should be tightly packed with smaller stones, and firmly gripped by the next tie.

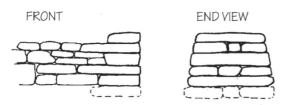

FRONT   END VIEW

7 As you build, keep checking with a spirit level or plumb bob that the head end is vertical. Some wallers set a

single bar vertically in the ground against the head as a guide, after placing the first tie.

8 Try and arrange to finish the head with two runners rather than with a tie, as this gives the strongest bed for the topstone.

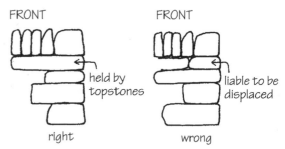

FRONT   FRONT

held by topstones

liable to be displaced

right   wrong

9 Finish the head with a large square topstone, as shown on page 45. This must be heavy enough to resist the push of the rest of the coping against it, and should sit firmly without wedging. Too small a stone here and the coping will be insecure.

Further considerations

a A common fault in heads is an absence of good runners, which results in running joints or insufficiently overlapped stones close to the head. As the head is vertical, it must be well bound into the wall to be stable.

If necessary, use one or two throughs from the dismantled wall as runners. Heads are inherently unstable, and overall the wall will be stronger if it has a good head and one or two missing throughs. Ensure that all joints are well crossed, trying to achieve 'half on one and one on half' (p54). Don't place wide ties on short runners.

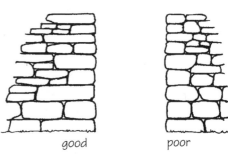

good   poor

b It's sometimes a good idea to try and use longer runners halfway up and even higher, even if this means departing from grading and placing thicker stones on thinner ones. As it is the upper part of the head which is most likely to collapse during settlement, it makes sense to ensure it's really well tied into the wall. The only limiting factor is that longer runners tend also to be wider, and may be too wide to place in pairs as the wall gets narrower.

c Heads tend to be vertical because they often form the side of a gateway. Where this is not the case, the head can be built with a batter.

d Heads should not be 'pinned'; that is, they should not contain small thin stones, which can easily work loose during settlement. Where you have to make do with less regular stone, pinning may be unavoidable, in which case it should be carefully tapped into place to tighten the ties and runners after the head is built.

Mixed stone types

Generally wallers do not like to mix types of stone in a wall, as the different surface properties and shapes of different types of stone may not bind well together. However, the importance of using good runners and ties in a head may take precedence over using the same type of stone. In the fringes of limestone areas bordering on sandstone, heads of limestone walls often contain sandstone, which is better than most limestone for making heads, unless the limestone is level bedded. In the Lake District, slate is often mixed in with the more predominant stone type, as shown in this example from near Troutal in the Duddon Valley.

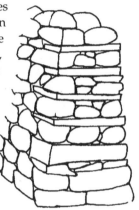

Many wallers in the slate areas of North Wales avoid using slate because they believe it fractures too easily, but there are plenty of examples in the Lakes which suggest otherwise.

This example at Mynydd Llandegai, North Wales, shows the successful use of thin stones and mixed stone types, with the head built out of reclaimed fencing slates about 5' (1.5m) long, and the rest of the wall built of small, rounded field clearance stones, which are completely unsuitable for a head.

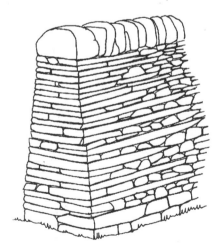

NON STANDARD WALL HEADS

Sometimes suitably long stone is not available, and other patterns of wall head emerge.

L shaped

This method, also known as 'broken ties', essentially follows the procedure described above. However, rather than alternating runners and ties, the head is built in a series of overlapping L shapes.

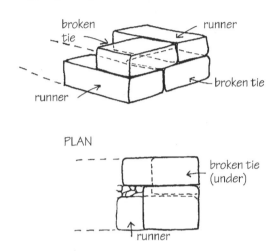

PLAN

1 Place the 'broken tie' across the end first, ensuring there is enough space for a good runner.

2 Place the runner, ensuring a good fit. Try and combine the stones in such a way that the runners and ties always touch in the middle of the wall, avoiding the use of smaller building stones to fill any gaps.

3 Build up a short section of wall to the height of the stones just placed, using ordinary face stones and fillings.

4 Repeat these steps, placing the broken tie on top of the previous runner, ensuring there is a good overlap onto the previous broken tie.

Occasionally some of the stones used might make suitable ties higher in the wall. However it is usually easier to continue with the L shape, rather than to try to revert to the standard pattern or combine the two patterns. The problems encountered with the latter are detailed below.

Overlapping

This type of head is rarer than 'L shaped' heads, and normally only occurs in walls where there are a lot of large slabs of stone such as slate, mudstone or schist. A number of good examples can be found on the National Trust's Ysbyty Ifan Estate in North Wales.

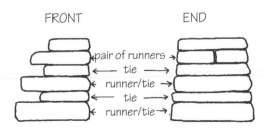

In effect these heads comprise almost entirely of tie stones. From the side the wall appears to have runners, but these completely straddle the wall and so also act as ties. Some pairs of runners are mixed in.

Grade the slabs with the largest at the bottom. The size difference in the slabs means it's difficult to achieve smooth faces to the head, but as long as the overall 'A' shape is maintained the structure is sound, and a lot of movement would be required to displace any of the stones. A drawback is that the flatness of the slabs may require some pinning to prevent them rocking.

Combinations

With some walls it may be necessary to combine two, or even all three, of the previous methods. 'Standard' and 'overlapping' can be satisfactorily combined, but when mixing the 'L shaped' method with any other, care has to be taken to avoid running joints, or only slightly overlapping joints. Problems arise because you will either be placing a runner on top of another runner, or 'broken tie' on top of a tie, or vice versa.

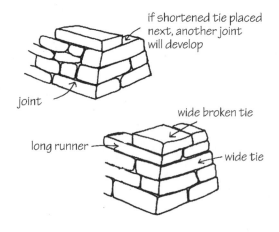

if shortened tie placed next, another joint will develop

joint

long runner

wide broken tie

wide tie

Consequently it's important to overlap the stones as much as possible. This necessarily involves having either much shorter or much longer runners, and wider tie stones as shown.

Single stones

Occasionally one comes across heads made of a single large stone or boulder, such as the milestone heads of Little Langdale in the Lake District.

The diagram shows head stones in a gateway at Mains of Murthly, Aberfeldy, Perthshire. Normally such stones are set in only about 4-6" (100-150mm), although stones used to hang gates may be set in 2-3' (600-900mm). The sheer weight and bulk of the stones keeps them in position. In this example the taller, thinner stone has been leant back into the wall, which compensates for its smaller base size.

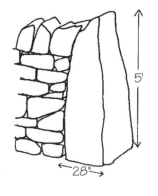
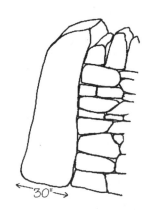

Thinner slabs can also be used, and are surprisingly stable if set well into the ground.

With these types of single stone heads, care is still needed with the construction of the wall up to the boulder or slab, as a running joint is created. The end stones must have length into the wall, in effect building a rough head behind the single stone.

It is generally advised that a gate should be hung on a separate gate post, whether of stone or wood, set about 2" (50mm) from the head of the wall. If the post gets knocked or moves with use, the wall is not affected. However, single stone heads do get used as gateposts, especially where there is a shortage of suitable ties and runners to build a separate head.

Changes in direction

CORNERS

Corners frequently collapse through poor construction or lack of suitable stone. When dismantling a corner, sort the stone carefully, and try and gain some additional long stones by using throughs from just along the wall. As with heads, the result is likely to be stronger if you sacrifice a few throughs and use them to strengthen the corner. Take care when dismantling the inside corner as space is limited, and you will need to spread the stone out further than normal to give you space to work.

Batter frames or line bars should be set up 2-3' (600-900mm) beyond the ends of the two sections of wall, so they don't interfere with placing the stones.

The method of construction is similar to 'L shaped' heads (p91) with each layer overlapping the other below, crossing all the joints. Use large stones with two good outside faces if possible.

As the drawing shows, the face of one section of wall forms the head of the other, and vice-versa. Pack the centre with fillings at each layer in the usual way, and check that each stone in each layer binds well with the stones that touch it. Where the corner stones are 30" (750mm) or more, it is advisable to also secure them with throughs as they are effectively traced stones.

It is important that the inside of the corner should be built following the same principles, ensuring that there is good overlapping within the wall. Just because the extent of the overlapping cannot be seen from the outside is no reason to skimp on it.

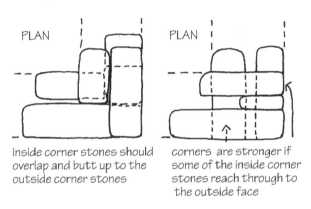

inside corner stones should overlap and butt up to the outside corner stones

corners are stronger if some of the inside corner stones reach through to the outside face

Wherever possible the inside runners should butt up against the inside edges of the face stones on the other side of the wall as shown above left. In addition, where there is suitable stone, try to fit some stones in the inside corner which are effectively long through stones, as shown above right.

Finally, do not build a corner as a junction with two wall heads. As the wall settles, the seam is almost certain to widen, especially if the ground slopes in any direction.

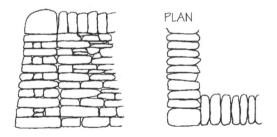

T-JUNCTIONS

Where two walls meet at a T-junction, you sometimes find that one wall has been simply butted up against the other with a head, or worse, just built up against it with few, if any, tie stones. Either method creates a serious weakness.

A T-junction should be built as effectively two inside corners, following the principles outlined above. It is best to alternate the L shapes as shown. This makes it easier to overlap, especially where longer stones are available to butt up against each other in the higher part of the wall.

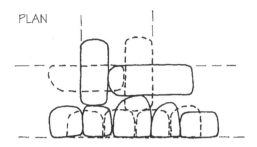

Where available, complete throughs or tie-stones should also be incorporated in the junction, either to tie the joining wall into the other, or to tie across the join.

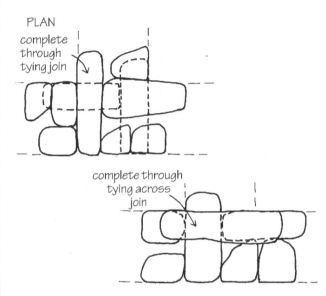

Four way junctions are rare, but the method of construction is as above, trying to apply the principles for T-junctions wherever possible.

Cripple holes and smoots

Walls often contain a variety of openings. Margaret Brooks (1973) considers these in some detail for the West Riding of Yorkshire. Apart from gateways and stiles, there are two main types of openings. These are the small 'water smoots' or 'rabbit smoots', and the larger 'cripple holes'.

Cripple holes, also known as 'hogg holes', 'thawls', 'thirl holes', 'smout holes', 'sheep runs', 'sheep creeps', 'sheep smooses' and 'lunky holes', are built large enough to let sheep through, but are too small for cattle. If located carefully, they increase the flexibility of the grazing enclosed, as sheep can be allowed to graze through fields which contain cattle, without opening any gates. At other times they can be blocked off to make them impassable. For moving a big flock more quickly, two cripple holes are sometimes built side by side.

Another interesting use for cripple holes is found on the Isle of Noss, Shetland. Here the holes are designed to let sheep through to graze the cliffs, while being impassable to Shetland ponies.

Smoots allow water to flow freely through walls which are built in hollows, or along the contours of a hillside. Smoots not obviously sited for drainage may have been constructed to allow rabbits through the wall. This may have been to discourage burrowing and damage to the wall, or for the purposes of snaring or trapping. Another theory is that in some cases the holes had to be built to allow rabbits free access to properties which held pre-Enclosure game rights. Rabbits formed an important part of the rural diet up until the mid 20th century. Many walls contain rows of smoots often only a few metres apart. A good example is a wall at the top of a slope near Barnsfold Farm, Hayfield, where once a year rabbits were driven up the slope and through the smoots into nets.

Rollinson (1972) shows a diagram of an interesting rabbit smoot and trap at Ayside, Cartmel, which has a stone lined pit to one side of the smoot. The pit would have been covered with a counterweighted wooden trap door, which swung as the rabbit stepped on it, trapping it in the pit.

Other smoots for trapping animals were built either diagonally through the wall, or offset, to prevent the animal seeing the trap on the other side. These are more complicated to build than straight smoots, because good stonework is needed to provide a strong inner face to the smoot and hold the hearting in place. Unless the walling stone is very regular, such as Cotswold stone, offset smoots are best built using single large stones, which form both the face of the wall and the inner face of the smoot.

Today's smoots are most likely to be built to enable wildlife to pass through the wall, or to maintain a tradition. New smoots are still built for trapping on shooting estates. These are usually about 7" (180mm) square to trap weasels or stoats, or 12" (300mm) square to trap foxes, and offset so the fox cannot see the trap through the smoot.

Other unusual openings are sometimes found for which there is no easy explanation. Margaret Brooks (1973) describes the 'mystery holes' which occur along several walls at World End, near Keighley. These are identical to smoots, but located midway up the wall. Among the ideas offered by wallers and country people for these holes is that they were built to shoot through, to relieve the walls of wind or water pressure in times of storm or flood, to allow rabbits to run through on top of drifts of snow, to allow snowbound sheep to breathe through the wall, to provide a place to lodge blocks of salt or the farmer's lunch or wooden beams for a low structure. None of these explanations, serious or not, seems satisfactory for the number of holes concerned.

Raised smoots are sometimes found opposite each other on either side of a road. A suggestion that these were constructed by the Home Guard during the war to take poles to block the road is likely to be another apocryphal story.

It is not always easy to be sure why an existing smoot has been built, and the local name does not necessarily determine the original purpose. The location is the best clue. Holes in walls up and down slope have no drainage purpose, so were probably built for animals. Holes in walls across slopes were probably constructed for drainage, especially in high rainfall areas such as the Lake District. In limestone country, drainage into the subsoil is so fast there is little need for water smoots, whatever the alignment of the wall.

Small smoots are also built to bridge tree roots, which may otherwise damage the wall (p71).

CRIPPLE HOLES

Cripple holes, built to control the passage of sheep through the wall, are constructed in the same way as large water smoots. Dimensions are normally about 1'6"-2' (450-600mm) wide by 2' (600mm) high, but there can be considerable variation. As sheep breeds tend to be larger than they used to be, traditional cripple holes may not be big enough. When rebuilding an existing cripple hole, the size will probably be limited by the length of the original lintel.

In Scotland, according to Prevost (1957), these holes are often built narrower at the base than at the middle and top.

The following drawing (adapted from Wood, 1973) shows an unusual hole in a wall in Grassington, North Yorkshire. The wedge-shaped opening is built so that lintel stones can be placed securely across to form an ordinary cripple hole. The stones above are added loosely so that they and the lintels can be removed when necessary to form a full-height 'cattle creep'.

Occasionally you may even come across a cripple hole that has been bridged with an arch, in the absence of suitable lintels. Arches are described further in chapter 10.

As cripple holes do not provide convenient access for shepherds, stiles are sometimes built alongside.

Procedure

A cripple hole is effectively two low wall heads or piers, with a single slab or pair of narrower lintels forming the roof. Hence any of the patterns for building a wall head can be used.

Care needs to be taken in selecting lintels. They should be as long as possible, to bind well into the wall on either side, and at least 4" (100mm) thick in order to support the wall above. Many old cripple holes have failed because the lintel has cracked. If a thinner lintel has to be used, or the wall above is over 6' (1.8m) high, you may need to consider some of ideas given below (p96).

There are a number of ways to floor a large opening. Turf is quick and easy, but with frequent use may get worn away, causing the sides of the opening to settle or collapse. A better option is to continue the foundation trench through the smoot or cripple hole, and floor it with large flat footings or slabs to ground level. You need to choose and position the slabs with care, pairing them as necessary, so that the weight of the wall is distributed evenly.

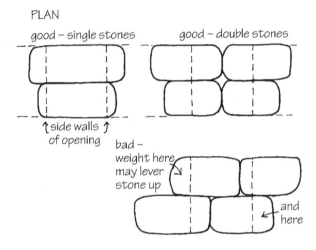

PLAN

good – single stones   good – double stones

↑ side walls ↑
of opening

bad –
weight here
may lever
stone up

and
here

If large, slab shaped footings are not available, the rest of the floor can be filled with smaller stones, which should be set with their long axis down into the ground, and tightly wedged together. Use the biggest stones across the opening on the downhill side, to protect it from erosion by water and stock. The stones should be set with the flattest face upwards, to create a reasonably level surface. This technique, called pitching or cobbling, is fully described in *Footpaths* (BTCV, 1996).

Construct the wall heads the required distance apart, keeping the inside faces as smooth as possible so there are no projections on which stock could catch, destabilising the wall. There is some debate as to whether the piers should be finished with runners or tie-stones. Each can present problems, and the choice is usually dictated by the stone available.

If you are using two narrow lintels it is probably best to end the piers with tie stones, so that you are not placing one 'traced' stone on top of another. Select tie stones which will not form running joints with the ends of the lintels. If you are using a single slab lintel, end the piers with two runners, as the lintel will act as a tie, and the problem of running joints will be avoided.

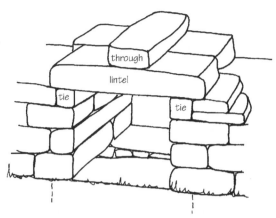

Place the lintel or lintels on the two piers, with an equal overlap on either side, and taking great care not to dislodge the top layers of the piers. Place one end on one pier first, and gently lower the other end into place. Larger lintels may require three or more pairs of hands. For information on manoeuvring large stones, see page 23.

Where a pair of lintels has been used they should touch along the centre of the wall, and be tied together with at least one through directly on top of them. If there are any gaps, they should be well bridged with flat hearting, to prevent other hearting falling through. Don't simply plug the gaps with hearting, as it will get pressed down by the weight of the wall above, forcing the two lintels apart.

SMALL ANIMAL SMOOTS

Small animal smoots vary greatly in size, depending on their purpose and probably also on the available stone. There are set sizes for traps (p94), but for wildlife conservation it's probably best to consult with local wildlife experts about requirements for the locality. Small smoots for rabbits, hares and other small animals are normally about 4" (100mm) wide and from 10-18" (250-450mm) high. Badger smoots should be about 7-8" (180-200mm) wide and 12" (300mm) high.

Procedure

1   Lay the foundations for the wall, choosing footing stones for the smoot which form a complementary pair, are even topped and set to finish at ground level. Ideally they should be about 6" (150mm) wider than the smoot, to allow a 3" (75mm) overlap on either side to help prevent erosion.

2   Build up the sides of the smoot as miniature wall heads, which requires just one or two good stones on either side, which should have good length into the wall. Don't construct the smoot by simply omitting a few stones from the base course, as this exposes and weakens the wall's centre.

3   Bridge the smoot as described for cripple holes. This will normally require two lintels, as the wall will still be

quite wide at this height. They must be at least 6" (150mm) thick to support the weight of stone above. Methods for 'strengthening' lintels are described below.

4 Tie the lintels together and bridge any gaps as described for cripple holes, and then continue the wall to the top.

WATER SMOOTS

Water smoots are built to allow the passage of streams or ditches through dry stone walls. Finding suitable lintels to span the width of the ditch can be a problem. The size of the available lintel stones largely determines the width of the watercourse that can be spanned, and consequently you often find heavy iron bars or old axles, or wooden rails or sleepers used instead. The results tend to be short lived. Sheet metal should definitely not be used as it quickly rusts and bends. Sections of large diameter concrete pipe can be used, turning the smoot into a culvert. For more details on culverts, see *Footpaths* (BTCV, 1996).

Water smoots are built in the same way as cripple holes and smaller smoots, but bear in mind the following:

a Make sure that the foundations of a large water smoot extend to the bottom of the ditch or stream, or erosion will occur, causing collapse of the smoot.

b The width will be limited by the lintels available, although double smoots can be built as shown below. The height should give sufficient clearance for seasonal flood levels. Exceptional floods may well cause damage.

c Smoots require checking from time to time to clear any accumulated debris. Smoots which incorporate a water gate or bars (p103) require more frequent checking.

d Large boulders set into the bank on the upstream side of the smoot will help protect the sides of the smoot from erosion. If there are sufficient boulders, protect the downstream side in the same way.

Wide spans

For wide shallow streams, a series of piers or pillars (p107) can be built, bridged by separate lintels. The pillars must be set on deep and solid foundations to resist erosion.

Smoot and bar

Another method of increasing the capacity of the smoot is to build a high smoot with a stone slab or bar through the centre of it. This permits extra flow, while still being sheep proof.

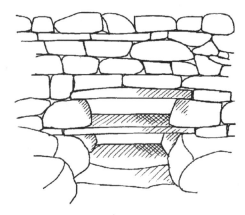

This example, using a thin slate across the centre, is in a single stone wall (p139) at Blaen y Nant Farm, Nant Ffrancon, North Wales. As it is not weight bearing, the thin stone is not a problem, and it is less of an impediment to water flow. This technique can also be used where you need to make a smoot, but don't have a sufficiently strong lintel to carry much weight of stone above. Note the boulders that have been dug in to protect the smoot.

STRENGTHENING LINTELS

Triangular lintels

This is a method of strengthening a lintel where the lintel itself is rather thin, or where the weight of stones above is heavier than normal. The use of triangular stones to displace the forces over lintels is an ancient technique, used by the Mycenaen Greeks over 3000 years ago.

The Lion Gate, Mycenae, Greece

Triangular lintels were also used by the builders of some of the Scottish Brochs, which are fortifications that date back to the Iron Age. The example shown, at Dun Dornaigil,

Scotland, still has around 20 foot of stonework remaining above it.

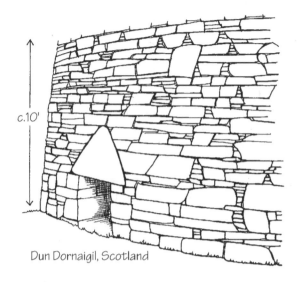

Dun Dornaigil, Scotland

To use this technique over a smoot in a dry stone wall requires a triangular stone. Ideally the stone should be regular and overlap the piers, but narrower or less regular triangular stones will help to a lesser extent. As the triangular stone takes the place of a through which would normally link the lintels, throughs should be placed adjacent to the triangular stone to compensate.

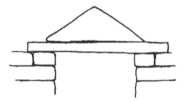

The smoot with a bar, shown above (p96), is another way of improvising where you don't have a strong enough lintel to support the full weight of the wall above. A weaker lintel, sufficient to support a few upper courses is used, higher up than required for the smoot, which is made stockproof with a slab or bar.

These techniques are not common, but are methods which can be borne in mind and added to a waller's problem-solving arsenal.

Cantilever lintels

Another method of strengthening a lintel is to place further long stones bridging from the main body of the wall over the lintel.

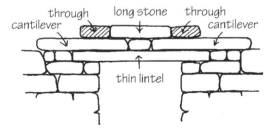

The cantilever lintels should be anchored into the wall by at least half their length. If possible they should meet in the middle, but if not, use a suitable stone to fill the gap. Another long stone can then be placed on top to further dissipate the forces.

As with triangular lintels, this method compromises the use of throughs. It also has the drawback that traced stones are used on top of each other, and if these are narrow an unstable structure may result. Place throughs at the first opportunity.

Stiles

Stiles are designed to allow people to pass through or over walls, but to be inaccessible to livestock. In the past, their main purpose was to provide access in a way which did not damage the wall, and so maintained the livestock barrier. Ease of use for the person was not the main design criterion. With the increasing importance of access to all in the countryside, the emphasis is now much more on providing access through the wall in a way which is appropriate for all likely users, whilst still being proof against livestock if necessary.

Depending on the location of the wall and the type of use the area receives, gates may need to be provided instead of, or in addition to stiles. In more remote locations, which can only be reached by people who are fit and agile, the more traditional designs of stile may be appropriate. Stiles are in effect a barrier erected by the landowner across a public right of way, and must be of a standard which does not make an unreasonable interference to the rights of users, and must be maintained by the landowner in a safe condition. However, stone stiles are a traditional feature which should be preserved, rebuilt or created where suitable stone is available, even if a gate is needed alongside. There are few children who, when presented with the choice of a gate to walk through or a stile to climb over, will choose the former!

Stiles need to be robust and easy to climb or pass through, without the person needing to use the coping or other parts of the wall as a handhold or step. Wooden ladder and other stiles should not have steps or strengtheners running into the wall, as the resulting vibration will disrupt the stonework. 'Built-in' stone stiles are much more robust and durable than wooden or metal stiles, which are more appropriate for hedges and fences, and are fully described in *Footpaths* (BTCV, 1996).

The pattern of stone stiles varies considerably from area to area, according to the available stone, local tradition and the whim of the builder. The examples below give an idea of the variety to be found, and of the careful yet ingenious use of stone which they illustrate. The examples are somewhat biased towards Yorkshire, probably because it not only has the advantage of geographical size, but of the ready availability of large pieces of sandstone. Similar types are found in many other areas.

There are three basic types of built-in stiles: step stiles, through stiles and step-through stiles.

STEP STILES

The most common type uses long throughstones, built into the wall so they protrude at right angles and form a diagonal series of steps. Where very long stones are available they can protrude on both sides. Stones which are long enough to protrude on one side only should have at least twice the length of the step embedded in the wall. They can either be set in pairs as shown below, or set so they run up one side of the wall, and continue in the same direction down the other side.

Steps should protrude a minimum of 12" (300mm) from the wall. The vertical spacing is more problematical. The British Standard for Stiles and Gates (5709: under revision) recommends a minimum 'step up' of 12" (300mm) for all stiles. Many stiles, both old and new, do not conform to this standard, and it may be difficult to do so when building within the limitations of the stone available. As discussed above, a pragmatic approach has to be taken, building to a standard which does not create a hindrance to walkers who are likely to be in that particular location. A fit and agile walker could easily climb a step stile with a vertical spacing of 1' 6" (450mm), and this seems a reasonable dimension to build to. A smaller vertical spacing not only requires extra stones, but does not necessarily make the stile more easily negotiable for the less agile. Where the location indicates a problem, a gate will be needed anyway in addition to the stile.

Step stiles are most often built in areas where suitably shaped stones over 3' (900mm) long are available, but stone may be brought in from elsewhere. Ideally stones should

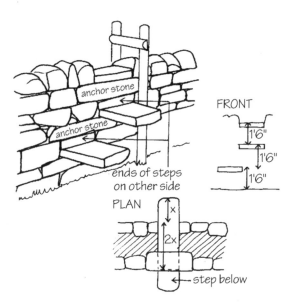

FRONT

1'6"

1'6"

1'6"

ends of steps
on other side

PLAN

x

2x

step below

be 3-4" (75-100mm) thick, at least 12" (300mm) wide, and regularly shaped with good, flat surfaces. Step stiles can also be built of railway sleepers or reinforced concrete posts, but are usually less satisfactory than slabs, and decay with time.

The top of the wall has been brought to small heads with a sill between to make the top step. This slightly lowers the height and avoids the chance of coping stones being knocked by people climbing over. Where three or more steps are fitted, the top step should be high enough to allow the coping to be carried across the top.

Hand holds can be a useful addition, but are not easy to fit securely. A short wooden post can be mortared into the top of the wall, but needs to be checked frequently to make sure it is secure, or it may itself present a hazard. Alternatively, a post can be knocked into the ground just to either side of the wall, to finish at a height to make a convenient handhold. If the lack of hand holds is making an 'unreasonable interference' at a particular location, it's likely that a gateway may be needed anyway.

Note the following:

a If, as is often the case, you must leave some steps shorter than others, grade the steps from biggest at the bottom to smallest at the top.

b The stepping stones must be securely anchored in the wall, or they may prise it apart instead of strengthening it. The best stones protrude both sides, but only exceptionally long stones, of 5'-5'6" (1.5-1.7m), are long enough to use in this way low in the wall. If the stone only protrudes one side, at least twice the protruding length must be embedded in the wall.

c Build up around the steps in the same way as for throughstones (p55), carefully crossing each joint, and be sure to use large face stones at this point to spread the wall's weight as evenly as possible. The stepping stones must be absolutely solid, whatever the weight put on them. Where available, a large anchor stone, about twice the length of the step, should be used over each step, or over the upper step of a pair (see diagram left).

d When using paired stones, take care that there is sufficient weight of stone above the top pair of stepping stones to hold them securely.

Where long, blocky stones are available, the staircase design can be used, with each step slightly overlapping and resting on its predecessor. This makes a very strong structure. The example shown is 6' (1.8m) high with seven steps, the top four being throughs which protrude on both sides. A notable feature is the top stone, which is about 3' (900mm) long, 8" (200mm) deep, and completely spans the wall at a width of about 14" (350mm).

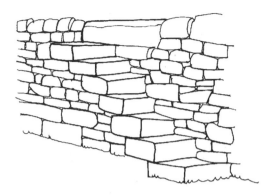

SQUEEZE STILES

Squeeze stiles are found in a variety of designs and materials. They are generally more accessible for users than step stiles, and can make use of various shapes of long and large stones. The main design requirement is to make a gap which is wide enough for people, but too narrow or difficult for stock. An extra barrier may be needed at lambing time. Squeeze stiles may incorporate a low step or sill to protect the ground in the gap, or to make a step between different ground levels.

This stile, one of a pair either side of the road in Arkengarthdale in Yorkshire, tapers out from 8" (200mm) at the base to 11" (280mm) at its top. On the field side, both these dimensions are about 2" (50mm) smaller, in order to discourage stock.

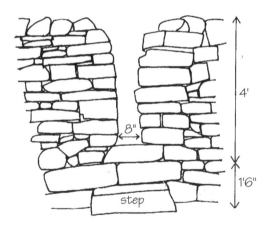

These stiles can be awkward to negotiate, as they are not only narrow, but deep. It is also fairly easy to dislodge stones. Squeeze stiles are better made of large stoops or slabs, which are narrower and smooth surfaced, so easier to squeeze past. They also protect the wall head.

PLAN

Wall heads – deep gap
Difficult to negotiate

rough stone surfaces

Shallow gaps – easier to negotiate

stoops

slabs

Trimmed stones are quite often used in squeeze stiles, as they allow the structure to be made to accurate dimensions. They will normally need mortaring.

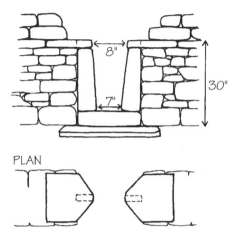

PLAN

The following example, one of several in the Askrigg area of Swaledale, Yorkshire, has been very carefully constructed from small stones accurately trimmed to shape, and secured without mortar. In this case the shape of the gap and the skilled use of trimmed stones successfully combines wall head with squeeze stile.

Where long stone stoops are available, these can be set into the ground to make a simple but very robust stile, which also protects the wall heads. The stoops should be set in a minimum of 24" (600mm), leaving a gap of no more than 10" (250mm). Carefully select a suitable stone to wedge between them and form a sill.

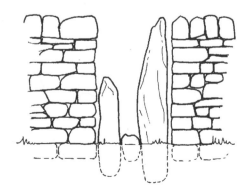

This example at Ashford, Derbyshire, shows the fairly widespread technique of using a tapered piece of stone to make a splayed gap.

These two examples from Derbyshire show the use of shaped stone. The stile at Monyash uses shaped limestone stoops, now worn and polished with use. The sandstone slabs at Newhaven are elaborately shaped for the leg and foot, but unfortunately are too closely set at 5" (130mm) minimum, so have to be stepped over by most users.

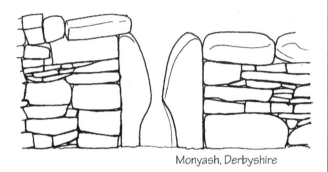

Monyash, Derbyshire

Newhaven, Derbyshire

STEP-THROUGH STILES

Step-through stiles combine steps with a squeezer or narrow gap. The steps discourage stock, while the narrow gap allows the walker to step through, rather than climb over, the upper part of the wall. If the wall heads are not strong enough to use as hand holds, separate wooden posts may be needed.

This simple design requires no special stones, apart from a flat throughstone to form the base of the stile.

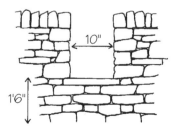

This example from Malham, South Yorkshire, has three throughstone steps, and additional handholds.

This more elaborate version has a slab set in the gap. The slab and blocks are not tied into the wall and should be mortared to secure.

OTHER PATTERNS

There are other patterns of stile which further illustrate the wide variety to be found.

In the Cotswolds, many stiles incorporate a large upright slab. This example at Swinbrook, Oxfordshire has a sill and step, with flat wall heads so the walker can sit and swing the legs over.

This example at Great Haseley, Oxfordshire, has an additional wooden cross beam to bring the barrier to a suitable height, but needs a step to make it easy to negotiate.

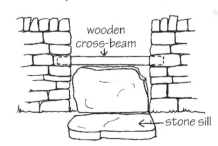

Sometimes a slab is simply set in the ground between wall heads to make one or two narrow 'squeezers'.

Slabs can be incorporated into staircase type stiles, as in this well-worn example in a churchyard wall. This is not stockproof against sheep.

Stone faced earth banks normally have step stiles (p86), with steps or 'staircases' built into retaining walls.

Three-way stiles

Occasionally the need arises for a three-way stile, where paths and walls meet at a T-junction.

This example has three heads built to form a three-way squeeze stile, with steps a further deterrent to stock.

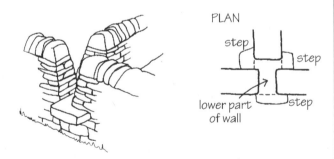

PLAN

step

step

lower part of wall

step

An alternative method is to build the junction as normal (p93), incorporating two or three projecting steps on each of the three sides. The top of the junction should be finished with a large slab to make a platform for access between the sets of steps.

Gates

Traditionally, gates in stone walls were hung on monoliths of stone called stoops, of hewn granite, mica schist, slate, gritstone, rhyolite columns or any other stone which does not readily split or crumble. Metal, reinforced concrete or wooden posts are the usual modern equivalent. The construction of dry stone and mortared pillars for gate posts is described in chapter 10 (p111).

DESIGN AND METHODS

Stoops

Normally it's better to set the stoop or post in the ground before completing the wall head, as it's difficult to dig right up against the wall head, and may disrupt the foundations. Check carefully the dimensions of the gate which is to be hung, together with the method of hanging, so you get the hanging and closing stoops or posts in exactly the right position. Allow about 2" (50mm) between the stoop and the wall head, so that if the stoop gets knocked by a vehicle, it will not disrupt the wall head.

The hanging of field gates on wooden or metal posts is described in another handbook in this series, *Fencing* (BTCV, 1985). Suppliers of gates will advise on appropriate hanging and shutting posts, which are normally set in the ground to half their length, or about equivalent to the height of the gate. Stone stoops are not often this long, and are set in the ground to about one third their length, so that a stone stoop for a 3'9" (1.15m) high gate would need to be about 6' (1.8m) long, set in the ground about 2' (600mm). Posts and stoops can be set in concrete as considered necessary.

Loose rail

The simplest traditional gate is made of loose rails, set into holes or grooves in the stoop. These are easily displaced by cattle and are not effective against sheep, so their practical use today is limited. However, stoops with sets of three or four holes are quite frequent, particularly in sandstone country, as sandstone is easy to work. Usually the holes are round, but an improved method uses square holes on one stoop to take the trimmed butts of the rails, and smaller round holes on the other stoop to take the thin ends. The rails are set in position by placing the butt ends in first, and then flexing the thin ends to fit into the correct holes.

Another design has deeply curving grooves, known in North Yorkshire as 'yat steads' (Ogilvie, E, 1996). Sometimes the grooves were cut in opposite directions, to make it harder for cattle to nose the rails out of place.

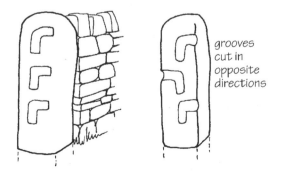

grooves cut in opposite directions

Four or five grooves or holes are the norm, but an example at Farndale, Yorkshire (Ogilvie, E, 1996), has seven L shaped notches, remarkably cut in a limestone post, which is far less easy to work than the more common sandstone posts.

A variation on this idea is to build recesses into the wall head, between the runners. The recesses are normally around 8-12" (200-300mm) deep on one side, and about 4-6" (100-150mm) deep on the other. Rigid wooden rails are used, inserted first into the longer recess and then pulled back into the shorter recess. This example is from the National Trust's Ysbyty Ifan Estate in North Wales, where there are also gateways with recesses at one side and a stoop with holes at the other.

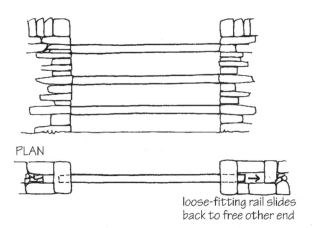

PLAN

loose-fitting rail slides
back to free other end

Harrhanging

According to Evans (1957), the most primitive type of swing gate uses the 'harrhanging' method found in Ireland, Scotland, the Lake District, Cornwall and Brittany, and traced back as far as 5th millennium BC Mesopotamia. The gate swings not on hinges, but on what Raistrick (1966) calls a 'creak' or hook near the top of the post, and a socket stone (Evans' 'spud stone') at the bottom. The heel of the gate post has a projecting iron stirrup and peg or spud, which swivels in the stone socket.

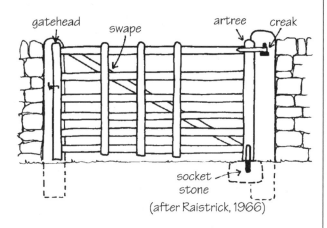

gatehead   swape   artree   creak

socket
stone

(after Raistrick, 1966)

Generally the gate is hung against the front of the stoops, as shown, and is balanced so that if left short of the fully open position it swings shut by itself.

Rare variations on this method can be found in parts of the Lakes, where in addition to the socket stone, a runner protrudes from the wall head and has a hole drilled in it to take a pin from the gate.

Harrhanging was a method favoured by the Romans, as seen in the socket stones still remaining at forts such as Housesteads, on Hadrian's Wall.

Wall heads

Small gates can be hung directly from wall heads, although this is not as good as hanging from a stoop. Use steel hinges with long flat shafts, which are set into mortar in the wall head as it is built. Select a large boulder, trimmed as necessary, to make the base of the head immediately above the footings. This will help protect the wall head from damage, and give a solid base for the lower hinge, which should be secured immediately above it. Alternatively, the hinges can be leaded or cemented into holes drilled in an existing wall head, provided there is a large boulder at the base.

SETTING IN HINGES

Methods are similar for fixing hinges, posts and other fittings into stonework. In each case, the hole should be drilled deep enough to hold the hardware securely. Drill the hole as explained on page 41, and make it about a quarter inch (6mm) bigger in diameter than the item to be fixed. Enlarge the hole at its base, so that the hardened metal or cement forms a plug which cannot be pulled out through the opening. For vertical holes, flare the top of the hole slightly, to ensure that the fixative will flow in easily.

flared top to vertical hole

Glue

Epoxy resin glue is the easiest, quickest and most effective way to fix metal into stone, and is suitable for gate fixings and other small jobs, but may be too expensive to use for fitting posts or other items in quantity. Various makes are available from specialist building suppliers, including 'Chemfix', 'Fischer' and 'Ramset'. The setting time depends on temperature, and you may find that particular brands are more suited to particular times of year. If you need to drill a new hole for the hinge or other fixing, you can sweep up the resulting stone dust and then sprinkle it on the top of the setting glue, to give a 'stone' finish.

Lead

Lead is a traditional method of setting fixtures into stone, and is very durable, but is a time-consuming process compared with using glue. Great care must be taken in handling, heating and pouring lead, and the work should only be done by suitably experienced persons. For ease of pouring, lead works best in holes which are more or less vertical. They must be fairly clean and absolutely dry, and even a trace of water causes lead to spit explosively. Scraps of lead can be used, provided they are not too encrusted with mineral deposits. Most of the impurities stay in the ladle if you pour gently, and a small amount reaching the join should not cause problems.

1 Clean out the hole, using a cycle pump to blow out debris, or a piece of plasticine to which dust and rock fragments will stick.

2 Position the hinge bolt or fence post securely. For the post, it's best to wedge it in place with one or two small pieces of steel forced into the hole beside it.

3 Heat an adequate amount of lead in a crucible over a fire or calor gas burner until it melts, and then pour it in using a long-handled ladle. For small amounts, you can melt the metal directly in the ladle. Pour the lead into the near side of the hole. This forces any debris in the hole up and out the far side, and so directs any spitting away from your face. Keep pouring in the lead until it fills the hole and is flush with the surface of the hole all round.

4 Pound the surface of the metal flat and fully firm all around the hinge or post, using a lump hammer and a wedge with a flattened end.

Cement

Cement can be used to fix hinges or posts into rock in any situation, but is most appropriate where the hole is not vertical, or where it cannot be made clean and dry. The disadvantage of a cement fixing is that it is less secure and durable than a glue or lead fixing.

1 If possible, prepare the hole in advance and leave it filled with water to soak for several days, before cementing in the hinge or post. This ensures that the cement sets properly, as if the hole is too dry when the cement is poured, the stone absorbs water from the cement and causes it to become weak and crumbly. If you cannot prepare the hole in advance, at least wet it thoroughly before cementing in the hardware.

2 Secure the hinge or post in position, using small wedges as necessary.

3 Mix up a thin mortar or grout of cement and water, using enough water to form a smooth creamy paste which pours readily into the hole.

4 Pour in the grout, making sure that it flows into all parts of the hole, and tamp it down. If the poured grout seems too watery, stir in a little dry cement to absorb the excess moisture.

To pour cement into an angled hole, follow the same method but form a small cup of putty or plasticine around the underside of the hole to help direct the cement and to contain any overflow.

WATERGATES

Large water smoots are often built with gates to prevent livestock from getting through. A simple but ingenious design can be found at Stephenson Ground in the upper Lickle Valley, where there are two or three water smoots with hexagonal columns of rhyolite to prevent sheep passing through.

Other examples of this method can also occasionally be found where wooden rails, such as split oak, have been used rather than stone.

This wooden watergate is suspended on short chains from iron bolts set in the lintel stone on the downstream side of the smoot. In this example, the gate only needs to be stockproof from the downstream side, where boulders prevent it being pushed open. In times of flood, the gate will swing open to allow water and debris through.

Watergates can also be secured between wall heads or across a smoot, if holes are made at the appropriate level to take a fixed or moving pole as shown.

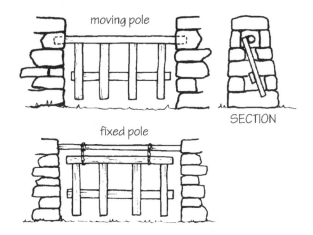

For one-way opening, build projecting stop-stones into the wall heads.

Walls with fences

Occasionally walls are built too low through poor workmanship or a mistaken effort to save time and money, or the wall's purpose may have changed, for example from fencing cattle to sheep, requiring it to be higher. The best solution is to remove the topstones and add more courses, but the wall may be too narrow at its top height to allow this, while maintaining the correct batter. If the coping is of locked top construction (p133), and you have sufficient topstones available, you might be able to simply add another coping to bring the wall up about 1' (300mm).

Walls with fences are a compromise solution, and are not usually particularly attractive. The fence is also likely to have a shorter life than the wall, and is not easy to replace. Where a high barrier or windbreak is needed with only a limited supply of stone available, an alternative solution may be to build a stone faced bank with a hedge planted on top. For stock control purposes, a separate fence alongside, possibly of temporary electric fencing, may be the easiest solution, though this will not encourage repair and maintenance of the wall.

POST AND WIRE FENCING

To make a wall stock proof, you can increase the height by erecting a 'flying' fence on 7' (2.1m) poles, placed about 15' (4.6m) apart and leaning against the wall, with two strands of barbed wire stapled to the posts above the wall top. Larch thinnings or coppice poles will do for the short term. Dig or knock the poles in a short way. In rocky ground where the posts can only be driven in a few inches, set the posts alternately on opposite sides of the wall to make them more secure.

A more durable solution is to wire the posts to the wall. With most walls this can only be done if the wires are put in place as the wall is rebuilt, although with single thickness walls (p139) it may be possible to thread the wires through the standing wall. This technique is also necessary if the fence follows the inside curve of a wall, where the tension of the wire would pull the posts away from the wall.

At a suitable height, place a length of wire sufficient to go across the wall, around the post and back again, leaving enough to twist together over a wooden batten. Don't sit stone directly on the wire or you will trap the wire. On completion of the wall, push a post down through each loop and into the ground, and then use fencing pliers to tighten the wires over the batten.

This can be used to extend a 5-6' (1.5-1.8m) wall the extra 1-2' (300-600mm) necessary for fencing deer. Always bring the stonework up to a uniform level before adding any wire fencing.

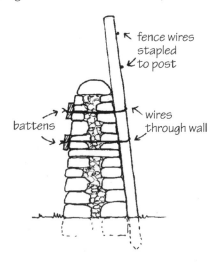

Occasionally, lower walls of about 3'3" (1m) height have a 'flying' fence of sheep or stock netting. Either C8/80/15 (80cm/31" high) or C6/60/15 (60cm/24" high) netting is used. The former is usually set with the bottom wire level with the base of the topstones, and the latter set only slightly overlapping the topstones. A strand of barbed wire 2-4" (50-100mm) below the netting will block the gap, caused by the thickness of the post, between the netting and the wall. This type of fencing looks unattractive, but does make a low wall proof against sheep from both sides.

The fence posts can be thinner and set further apart than for a standard stock fence, as the fence does not come under the same pressure as a fence at ground level. Posts of 7' (2.1m) height and 2-3" (50-75mm) top diameter are suitable, set at 10-12' (3-3.6m) intervals, with every third or fourth post tied back across the wall as described above.

An interesting variation found at Lough Rigg Terrace, Grasmere, in the Lake District, is a wall with throughstones which project every 6' (1.8m) on the stock side, and are drilled to take wooden posts. The holes in the upper throughs are about 4-6" (100-150mm) diameter so a post can be dropped through, with the holes in the lower throughs smaller, so the point of the post wedges into them. Some of the posts are wedged into the lower throughs with small slivers of stone. The posts are simple to replace when necessary.

Occasionally you will find a wall with wooden posts built into the top layers. This is not recommended, as the posts will rot long before the wall should need rebuilding, and trying to replace them will inevitably destabilise the wall.

A very simple method of keeping stock from jumping a wall is to fix a strand of barbed wire along the top, secured every 15' (4.5m) by a loop of wire around a block of stone about 10" (250mm) square, placed on top of the coping.

STEEL BARS

In areas where suitable stone was available, the traditional method of additional stock proofing was to fit large blocks at regular intervals in the coping, into which iron or steel bars were leaded.

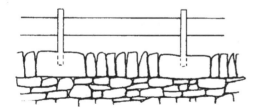

A similar but more troublesome method was to set the bars into the wall itself, as is often seen in road and rail-side walls in Scotland. Flat steel standards 2'6"-3' (760-900mm) were used, drilled to take one or two strands of wire, with the top strand about 1'6" (450mm) above the top of the coping. The standards can be mortared into the wall, or fixed with lead or glue to holes drilled in the throughstones or coverband. In either case, start by installing the two end posts. Once these are secured at the correct height, run a guideline between them for positioning the intermediate posts.

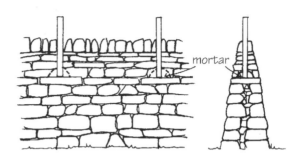

When using mortar, the standards can be cut and bent to a T shape to give a more secure fixing. Position and temporarily wedge the standards before building up the wall around them.

When repairing a fence with standards, if you find that the wire is still good, but that one or two standards are bent or broken, you can replace them without cutting the wire by sawing slits in the replacement standards.

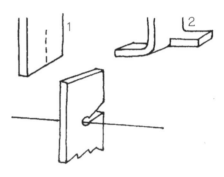

SLATES

In slate districts one sometimes sees walls where some of the slate top stones are taller than the others, and are drilled to take fence wires. Such slates must be very secure, and should be spaced fairly closely, about every 4' (1.2m).

A similar technique uses slate standards set into the body of the wall. These normally project about 18-24" (450-600mm), with holes drilled for two or three strands of wire. Their length varies considerably from one wall to another, with some as long as 5-6' (1.5-1.8m), although around 4' (1.2m) is the norm. They should be set at least 12" (300mm) into the body of the wall, with 24" (600mm) preferable.

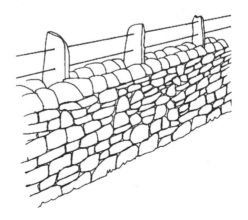

The procedure for building is as follows:

1   Level the wall to the planned height for the base of the slate.

2   Build the next layer, leaving enough space between the face stones for the slate to stand wide end down. Place the hearting, leaving a gap for the slate.

3   Set the slate in position, and then one person should hold it vertically, while another person wedges it tightly with hearting.

4   Use half or three-quarter throughs, two each side of the slate, to hold it firmly in position. It's a good idea to select these stones before you start building. Check that the slate is vertical.

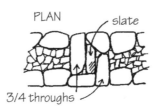

PLAN · slate

3/4 throughs

5   If the slate is not quite secure, temporarily place blocky stones alongside it while you continue the rest of the layer.

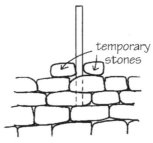

temporary stones

6   As you build up, place as many half or three quarter throughs as possible alongside each slate, and make sure the hearting is jammed in really tightly against it. The slates must be very secure, as any movement is likely to destabilise the wall in the long term.

7   Some stones will have to be 'traced' alongside the slates, and should be tied with half or three-quarter throughs above.

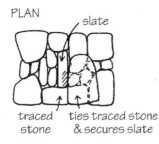

PLAN

slate

traced stone   ties traced stone & secures slate   triangular stones give poor contact

8   Triangular stones can also be used at intervals, although the stone to stone contact is poor.

Height and line

In common with other posts set in walls, care must be taken to get the holes aligned so that the wire runs straight or at an even gradient. This not only improves the appearance of the wire fence, but is important structurally. If one slate or post is too low, the wire will act to lift and loosen it. Conversely, a post that is too high will cause the wire to exert a force on the adjacent posts.

Use the longest slates at each end or at changes of direction or gradient, as these will take more strain than other slates. When using metal posts, larger posts may be needed for the strainers.

The general procedure is to work on a section of about five or six slates or posts. Carefully position the posts at each end of the section, so that the holes for the wires are at the correct height, and the posts are vertical. Run a line between the tops of the slates or posts, tightening it with pins or stones.

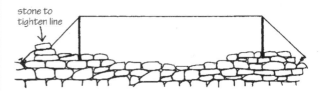

stone to tighten line

Set each intermediate slate or post so that the top just brushes the line.

Further details on the use of strainer posts and all other aspects of fencing are given in *Fencing* (BTCV, 1985).

RAILS

The use of rails for additional stock-proofing of walls is not common, but interesting examples are found in parts of Scotland, including the Aviemore area. The 'Inshriach Dyke' consists of a low coursed wall of granite with throughs and coverband of mica-schist. The topstones are granite, with long slabs of mica-schist set at 6' (1.8m) intervals, which are drilled to take timber poles of 3-4" (75-100mm) diameter.

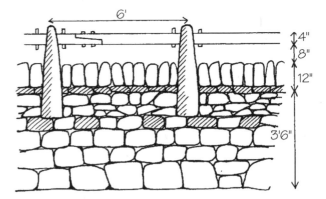

6'

4"
8"
12"

3'6"

Other variations have the extended topstones notched to take the rails, rather than having holes, and the extended stones sit on the coverband, instead of being built into the wall. These examples probably pre-date the use of wire, as later walls have extended stones drilled to take fencing wire.

10   Dry stone features

This chapter describes some of the many features which can be built out of dry stone. Some are traditional features of the countryside, such as cairns, pens and niches in walls, while others such as arches and pillars are more often associated with gardens. Dry stone can also be used for purely aesthetic structures, which have no practical use.

Whatever the purpose of the dry stone feature, a valuable wildlife habitat is created. The process of designing and building dry stone features also develops the skills of dry stone work beyond those of traditional walling, and in ways which can be used in wildlife gardens, parks, alongside transport routes and other open spaces in both urban and rural areas.

Pillars

Square, or less commonly rectangular pillars tend to be built in areas, such as those of sandstone, where there are plenty of square stones, called quoins, for making the corners. Round pillars require lots of small stone, or stone which can be shaped easily. Even given good stone, both types require time and patience to build successfully in dry stone work, and frequently a mortared structure is built instead.

Pillars are used as an attractive way to end a wall, to frame a gateway or to hang a gate. Occasionally they are also seen free-standing, as memorials or cairns. Pillars used for gate-hanging are usually mortared, as the pillar has to take the weight of the gate, as well as providing a secure fixing for the hinge. See page 111 for details of pillars and gate hanging.

FOUNDATIONS

A pillar is one of the least stable forms of dry stone work, so it's normally best to build on a concrete foundation, as any uneven settling may cause the pillar to topple. Use a mix of 6:1 aggregate:cement, tending to 4:1 for wetter conditions. The foundation should be about 6" (150mm)

thick, with the top finishing about 8" (200mm) below ground level. Some wallers use the frame (see below) as formwork for the concrete, so the area is exactly the same as the pillar. Others maintain that the concrete base should be larger in area, to help spread the load, but this makes it less easy to secure the frame assembly. This is explained further below.

When building on bedrock, or in a remote location to which materials for concreting cannot easily be transported, make foundations as for a dry stone wall, using large, blocky stones. Make the foundation larger in area than the pillar, by perhaps 6" (150mm) all round, with the exact dimensions dependent on the stone available.

FRAMES

Specialist frames can be used to construct pillars, although these are expensive to make for a single use only. Methods for constructing pillars without frames are outlined on page 108.

Design

A simple frame for constructing square pillars can be made of 2 x 1" (50 x 25mm) timber, joined with metal brackets. The frame is supported by four metal rods, about 1" (25mm) diameter, slightly thicker than those used for line bars (p33). The bars should 18-24" (450-600mm) longer than the height of the pillar, and pointed at the base. The bars are secured to the frame with an adjustable clamp, as shown on the circular frame below. These clamps may need to be specially made by a local metalworker. An alternative is to have the frame itself made of 4-6mm x 50mm (2") steel, welded at the corners rather than bent to shape, to give exact square corners. Any internal welds must be ground flat. A circular frame can be made similarly.

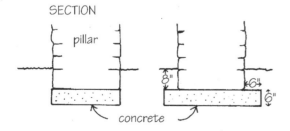

SECTION

pillar

concrete

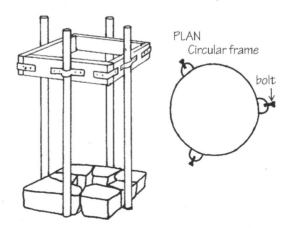

PLAN
Circular frame

bolt

Installation

1 Place the frame, without the bars, on the completed concrete or stone foundation. If the foundation is exactly the same area as the pillar, the bars can be driven down into the ground beside the foundation. If the foundation is bigger, you will need to first build one or two layers to bring the stonework up to ground level. Backfill around the stonework and tamp down well to give yourself a firm base to work from. The bars can then be knocked into the backfill to secure.

2 Place each bar in position through a clamp, and drive at least 6" (150mm) into the ground, until fairly stable.

3 When all the bars are in position, raise the frame to near the top and check that all the bars are vertical, making minor adjustments as necessary.

4 Lower the frame back down to the base, and if the bars are outside the foundation, drive them in another 6" (150mm) or so, until fully secure.

5 Raise the frame again for a final check.

Use

1 Set the frame on the base to place the first layer of stone. Each stone should just brush the frame, without butting up tightly or the frame will be difficult to raise. If the stones do not brush the frame an accurate shape is difficult to achieve.

2 Raise the frame for each subsequent layer, so that its base is level or just above the top of the previous layer. Experienced wallers may prefer to raise the frame in increments of 12-18" (300-450mm), judging the layers between by eye or by using a spirit level. Check that the frame is level, using a spirit level, and ensure that the bolts just nip the bars to reduce the chances of distorting the frame.

3 As the pillar gains height, check every 12" (300mm) or so that the bars are still vertical.

ALTERNATIVE METHODS

Where frames and bars are unavailable or inappropriate, alternative methods can be used to build an accurate pillar.

Square pillars

Some wallers use the frame without the bars, initially using the frame to mark a square in the mortar for the foundation, or as a template for setting the foundation stones. If not using a frame, some form of square is essential to accurately form the right angles. Check that the square is accurate by measuring both diagonals, which should be the same length.

Once the foundation stones are set correctly, you can follow these for subsequent layers, making frequent checks with a spirit level. You will need a long spirit level, preferably at least 3' (900mm) long. Check the outside of both sides of each corner, and don't be misled by just placing one stone up to the edge of the previous stone.

Once two adjacent quoins have been set, the stone or stones between them can be set in line by eye, and then checked with the spirit level.

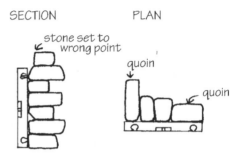

Also check the width of the pillar as work progresses. Variations of up to 5mm on either side are acceptable, provided they are the exception rather than the norm, and that the pillar remains vertical. Use the frame every 12" (300mm) or so to check that the pillar is square. Frequent checks on accuracy are essential when building pillars, as it is impossible to judge precisely by eye, because due to perspective, a pillar always looks wider at the top than the bottom.

An alternative method is to set four line bars at each corner. To ensure they remain vertical, use clamps (p33) to secure.

Round pillars

A fairly simple method of ensuring an accurate shape is to set a metal rod securely and vertically in the exact centre of the sub-base. Attach a string to a washer of only slightly larger diameter than the rod, and make a knot at the required radius. You can just tie a loop rather than using a washer, but this tends to be less accurate.

As you use the string to measure, make sure you are holding it level.

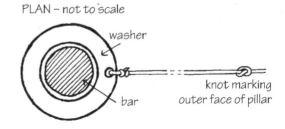

PROBLEMS

When you step back to check that no running joints are developing, look very carefully because the frame and bars tend to obscure the stonework and mistakes are easy to overlook.

Square pillars

Ideally, quoins should be flat with precise right-angled corners, but with uncut stone, this is not the case. There are various problems relating to quoins:

a The long axis of the quoin should be set level. If the stone is slightly tapering, set its base level, compensating for any slope when building the next layer. Severely tapering stones should only be used as quoins if there is another of complementary shape to sit on it. Use a wedge rather than place a sloping quoin, but avoid wedging if possible. Sloping quoins are not only structurally unsound, but will greatly mar the appearance of the pillar.

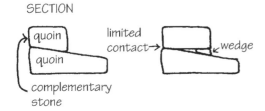

SECTION

b Avoid using wedges on the outside corner of the pillar, as the wedge is effectively the corner stone.

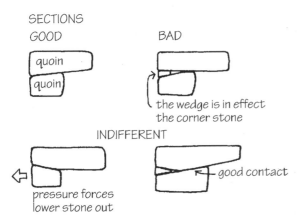

c Where the angle of the end of the quoin is not 90°, and cannot be trimmed accurately, the longest axis should still be set in line as shown below. Set the stones, as 1 and 4, with the furthest point in line with the outer face of the pillar.

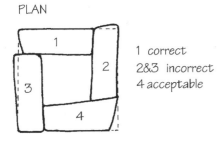

PLAN

1 correct
2&3 incorrect
4 acceptable

d However, if the angle is such that the stone above is largely unsupported at the corner of the pillar, you will need to trim the projecting point as shown.

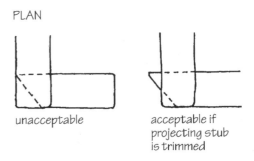

PLAN

unacceptable   acceptable if projecting stub is trimmed

e End stones with a rounded profile can either be set back, or with the 'nose' protruding to make a feature. Setting the stone back makes it easier to keep building to the vertical. Protruding stones can look out of place unless they are a design feature, set at regular intervals, and they also make it more difficult to keep to the vertical.

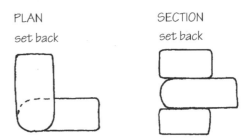

PLAN   SECTION
set back   set back

furthest point of curved face in line

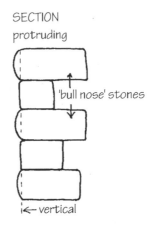

SECTION
protruding

'bull nose' stones

←vertical

The need to build four corners close together also causes problems. Ideally the quoins should alternate and tie each other in, but in practice they rarely fit this well. Normally you should place the quoins first, and then fit the stones between, which must be tight, but not enough to move the quoins. You need to leave gaps which can easily be filled. If a frame is not being used, you can work sequentially around the pillar, trimming the quoins to fit as necessary. A lot of forethought is required, and when mortaring, a 'dry run' may be needed for each layer in order to get it right.

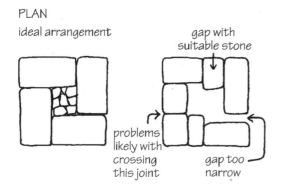

PLAN
ideal arrangement

gap with
suitable stone

problems
likely with
crossing
this joint

gap too
narrow

You also need to think ahead in order to avoid running joints. The joints must be well bridged, and not just overlap by an inch or so.

Ideally, stones should be set in even courses, as a further problem occurs where the quoins are of differing height. As careful study of the diagram below will show, as you proceed from a level course upwards using quoins of differing height, at the height where the courses 'catch up', the quoins will be running in the same direction. In addition, you will have to use thin stones to even up the courses and a running joint is hard to avoid.

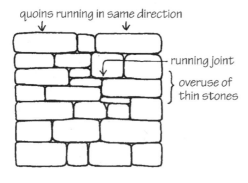

quoins running in same direction

running joint

overuse of
thin stones

To solve this problem, level the pillar off at intervals and start again with alternating quoins. Some wallers level every two layers, others every 12" (300mm) or so, but you are likely still to have a point where the quoins are not running correctly.

When levelling off, avoid using thick square quoins, as you will create poor overlaps as shown. A longer than normal quoin should be used instead. Alternatively, use wider and longer stones, even if they are thin, to level off. Plan ahead and save any suitable stones for this purpose.

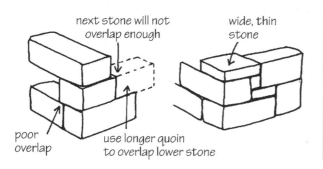

next stone will not
overlap enough

wide, thin
stone

poor
overlap

use longer quoin
to overlap lower stone

Round pillars

Problems with round pillars are similar to those of curves (p67). As the curve of a pillar is tight, small stones must normally be used. Larger stones need dressing to avoid the formation of large gaps, and mortaring is usually required.

Care must be taken to build accurately, with frequent dressing necessary, even for smaller stone. Instead of a frame (p107), a template can be used, cut out of thin sheet metal or 6-8mm plywood. Some wallers make a template with a second sharper curve along one edge for use when constructing the inside of circular features such as wishing wells, which are effectively hollow pillars. Use the template to mark out the foundation, and then to check each quarter layer of stonework as you build.

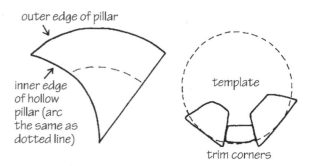

outer edge of pillar

inner edge
of hollow
pillar (arc
the same as
dotted line)

template

trim corners

For really accurate work, put the stone in position with the template over, and mark the stone with a nail or similar to give a line for trimming.

Most of the dressing of smaller stones will be of the inside edges, so they butt together well. Check frequently with a spirit level that the pillar is vertical, and also use the level to check that the layers are horizontal, or spiralling may develop.

CAPPING

There are various methods for capping pillars. Single slabs are the easiest, although for round, and most square pillars, slabs will have to be specially cut at the quarry. Smaller slabs will need weighting with a block, or with a series of slabs in diminishing sizes. Sometimes the initial slab is cut to project evenly all round, and an ornamental top is used to finish.

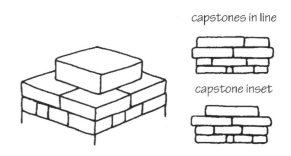

capstones in line

capstone inset

Vertical top stones are also used, although mortaring is usually needed to secure them. Square pillars need four square corner stones, and careful selection of other stones to fit in the centre. Round pillars require wedge-shaped top stones.

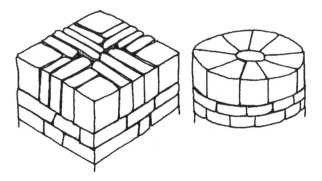

Because of the difficult of fitting vertical stones, square pillars frequently have two or four large and heavy stones for capping. These may be topped by another block, slab, or a series of slabs.

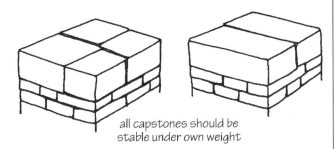

all capstones should be stable under own weight

TYING PILLARS INTO WALLS

Square pillars tend to be built independently of walls, with the wall butted up to the pillar. This saves damage to the wall if the pillar moves, although tying the pillar into the wall can help stabilise it so movement is less likely. If the pillar is built on a concrete base then it is definitely better as an independent structure, as the settlement rates of the pillar and the wall will be different.

It's also difficult to tie the stonework together unless the pillar is at least 12" (300mm) wider than the wall at the base, or there isn't sufficient space to fit the quoins. It becomes easier with height as the wall batters in, and the gap between the face of the wall and the corner of the pillar increases.

An unusual variation is to build a square pillar with sides battered to the same slope as the wall, which makes joining easier. In this example, on one side the pillar is simply an extension of the wall, and on the other side is about 12" (300mm)

wider than the wall, creating enough space to overlap the stones which form the join. As the pillar only has three corners, the number of quoins is reduced. In this case, the battered design was partly chosen as the pillars were subject to pressure from cattle, and it was felt these would be more stable than vertical-sided pillars.

Round pillars are much easier than square pillars to tie into walls, as there are no quoins to worry about. Don't simply butt the pillar to the wall head, as an ugly gap will occur where the curving face of the pillar meets the flat face of the wall head. The technique for tying the two together is basically the same as used at wall corners (p92).

SYMMETRY

In formal situations the symmetry of a pair of pillars can be quite important. If there are any notable stones, such as long quoins which act as ties running across the face of a pillar, try and place them to match on each pillar, to increase the appearance of symmetry.

Make sure the pillars match exactly for height by using a spirit level on a long piece of timber set on edge, spanning the gap. Alternatively, a special small level called a line level can be suspended from a taut line.

To fit a light on top, build the pillar up around standard 16mm copper piping with an elbow joint, through which the wire can later be threaded.

GATES

Pillars used for gate hanging need to be vertical, and a small amount of settling can create instability. They should be set on a concrete foundation.

Pillars which are used for gate hanging are normally mortared for strength. Use a 4 or 5:1 sand:cement mix, or a 7 or 8:1 aggregate:cement mix for the core of the pillar, in place of hearting. Use hooks or pins with long flanges, mortared in to secure. Alternatively, a metal post with long pins can be set into the pillar as it is built, as shown. This post will need to be specially made by a metalworker.

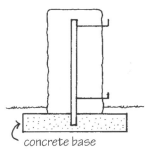

concrete base

Dry stone pillars are usually only suitable for hanging small gates. Large stones should be built in at the appropriate heights to take the pins, which can be fixed into drilled holes using epoxy resin glue (p102).

This pair of stone pillars on the Calf of Man have built-in recesses to take the gate, so leaving unspoilt the smooth curving faces of the pillars.

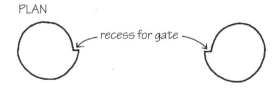

PLAN
— recess for gate —

Cairns

Cairns come in a variety of shapes and sizes, from simple piles of stones through to formal pillars and spheres. Cairns have been used for centuries to mark hilltops, mountain passes and routes across rocky terrain. They are also used to mark significant sites such as burials, battle grounds and memorials.

This cairn, near Askrigg in the Yorkshire Dales, is typical of those marking paths across mountain and moorland. Whilst roughly built, it is more than just a heap of stone, and some care has been taken to produce a symmetrical structure. The top 14" (360mm) or so is made of stones roughly piled on a layer of flat slabs, indicating that the original cairn has possibly been added to by passers-by. The cairning of paths across open country is controversial. Some walkers view them as helpful path finders, especially in misty conditions, whilst others see them as marring a wild and unspoilt landscape. Cairns can also become a focus for erosion.

height approx. 5'

Cairns used to mount viewpoint indicators, plaques or memorials need to be more carefully constructed, as in the example right. This is probably the easiest formal shape to construct.

height 3', diameter 3'

CONSTRUCTION

Dimensions

A scale drawing or plan is essential for most cairns. While dimensions of less formal cairns don't need to be exact, the general dimensions of base and height still need consideration. If the base is too small, you will end up with a needle rather than a cairn. If the base is too wide for the height, to quote one waller, 'it will look like a giant cow-pat'.

Materials

The style of cairn and the neatness of the stonework depends on the type of stone available, as well as on the skill of the builder. More formal and technically complex cairns tend to be built out of level-bedded stone such as some sandstones or slates. Rougher stone is more suited to larger diameter and less complex cairns. The larger the cairn, the greater the scope for disposing of poorer stone, as the hearting space can be enormous.

Estimating the materials required can be complicated, and it's always best to over estimate so that you have plenty of choice. For tapering pillars, bell-shaped and conical cairns, get at least enough stone to build a solid cylinder of the same height and base size. For shapes such as pine cones, estimate by using the diameter at the widest point, rather than the base, and expect to have quite a bit left over.

Batter

While most cairns are circular in cross section, their profiles can vary from conical to bell-shaped and other shapes.

If the batter is constant, as in the lower section of the cairn below, line-bars (p33) can be erected in a tepee-like structure. However, apart from the difficulty of setting the bars precisely to the right angle, the number of bars required means they get in the way of building, particularly as you gain height. Sooner rather than later you will find you have to remove the bars, and work by eye.

FOR ALL THOSE WHO HAVE CARED FOR AND LOVED THIS LAND

height 12'

7'

Brora, Scottish Highlands

112

For shapes without a constant batter, you can either work entirely by eye, or rig up a central post with a washer and string as shown above (p108). For each layer, fix a peg or some moveable marker on the string, to mark the appropriate radius for the height.

When building by eye you must keep standing back and checking the shape at frequent intervals, and from various angles. Even then smaller bulges and 'flat spots' tend to become obvious only after they have developed for two or three layers. Frequent dismantling and reconstruction of parts of the face may be necessary. Whilst perfect symmetry is difficult to achieve, and not appropriate for an informal cairn, it should be borne in mind that structural integrity is closely related to symmetry.

Topping

The problems associated with topping cairns are similar to those of pillars (p110).

The smaller the top diameter of the cairn, the less stable the top layers and top stone are likely to be. The simplest method of topping is to use a suitably shaped flat stone, which ties all the face stones together. This can either be left to give a flat top, or topped with a few more stones to improve appearance, as in the Brora example above.

If the cairn tapers to a point, building becomes increasingly difficult and stone size necessarily decreases. A suitable conical capstone to finish may need to be specially cut. One option is to create the point with a series of flat circular stones, gradually decreasing in size, as in the pine cone cairn below. If you are skilled, patient and have an ample supply of stone, you may be able to dress them yourself.

Cairns under about 8' (2.4m) total height, where the top can easily be displaced, may need to have the upper layers and topstone mortared or glued to secure.

Plaques

Commemorative cairns frequently have plaques built in or attached. For the former, build alongside and over the plaque as if it were bedrock (p70). Ensure there is good stone length into the wall around the plaque, especially on top, so that it is tied in well. The stones behind the plaque should be properly placed building stone, and not just hearting, so that the plaque itself is not an essential part of the structure.

Plaques can be attached by drilling into suitable face stones, and setting the fixings into epoxy glue.

CONICAL CAIRNS

Conical cairns are those with a constant batter, either ending in a point, or 'cut off' and topped with a slab.

Normally line bars are used to give accurate dimensions (p33). In the example below, another method was used, taking advantage of the trig. point which the cairn was being built to disguise. A pipe flange was attached to the trig point, with a rotating arm of angle iron set level with an adjusting screw, which also served to counteract the weight of the line bar. Care was taken to set the first layers at a true circle, and then the bar was rested against the stone, and rotated as necessary around the cairn. To avoid spiralling, the level of each course was chalked onto the line bar.

The face stones were secured into a core of mortar, as the cairn is of climbable height. The cairn incorporates an information board.

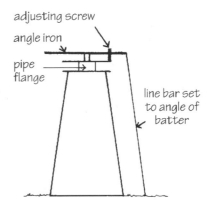

PINE CONE CAIRNS AND SPHERES

This limestone pine cone cairn is one of a series built by the sculptor Andy Goldsworthy in Nice, France. The base requires long, wedge-shaped slabs, with each layer projecting a little further, or 'corbelled', to the widest point of the cone. The top is finished by a series of concentric circular slabs.

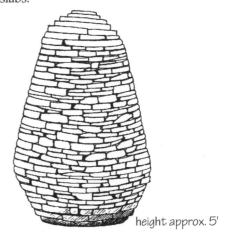

height approx. 5'

FRONT   SECTION

Spherical cairns are built in a similar way to pine cone cairns, using thin layered stone, corbelled out from the base.

Spheres and pine cone shapes can also be constructed hollow. These, at Portrack House, Dumfries and Galloway, are mortared inside and used for storage.

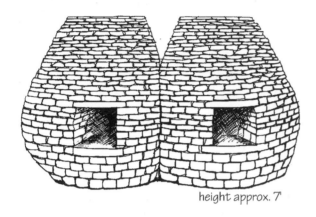

height approx. 7'

DOMES

The dome cairn below is to be found near the A82, about 4 miles east of the National Trust for Scotland Visitor Centre at Glen Coe.

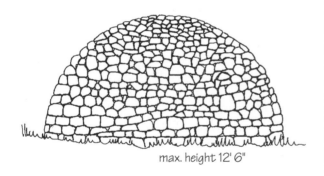

max. height 12' 6"

The dome has a diameter of about 17' (5.25m), with a maximum height of about 12'6" (3.8m). It was rebuilt in the early 1990s, to replace an earlier cairn to which various stories are attached. One story is that it was originally a much smaller 'coffin cairn', used to rest a coffin on its way to wolf-proof consecrated ground, which could involve a long journey in earlier centuries when wolves were numerous.

There are three similarly shaped but smaller dome cairns on the A623 between Wardlow and Stoney Middleton in Derbyshire, of which the largest is about 8' (2.4m) tall and 13' (4m) across.

Arches

An arch is any curved structure which spans an opening. The most common dry stone forms are semicircular (Norman) arches, with pointed (Gothic), and flattened

(elliptical) arches also found. Other more ornate forms require ornamental mouldings or tracery, and are normally only found in buildings.

In the construction of arches, extra attention must be given to safety considerations (ch4), both during building and in ensuring the stability of the final structure.

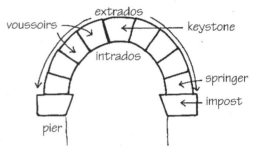

The various parts of an arch have specific names as shown.

In walling terms, the pier may be a wall head, square pillar, the side of a smoot, or even the main body of the wall itself, in the case of arched niches. The impost is the upper course of the pier, and does not necessarily project. The intrados, also called the archivolt, is the inside curve of the arch. The extrados is the outside curve.

Arches can be used in place of lintels either for ornamental purposes, or where lintels of a sufficient size cannot be found, for example where a wall crosses a stream.

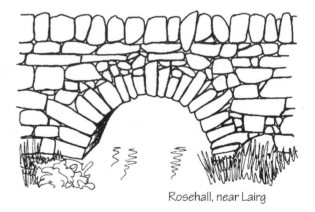

Rosehall, near Lairg

Stone arches are also used to build packhorse or footpath bridges across streams, although modern versions usually incorporate mortar.

Gothic arches tend to be used for more decorative purposes, or to make better use of flatter voussoirs. The example below is a reconstructed bread oven at Hutton Roof, near Penrith, Cumbria.

The structural theory relating to arches is quite complex, but put simply, 'the arch creates an opening, while transferring to either side the weight of thrust that tries to fill that opening' (McRaven, 1989). Semi-circular arches are the most efficient at doing this, with Gothic and elliptical arches less so.

Hutton Roof, near Penrith

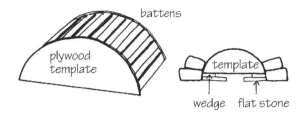

Arches can be built out of a wide variety of stone types, although stone that is workable to some degree is preferable. A good supply of slightly tapering stones is helpful.

FORMERS

All arches need temporary support below the intrados to support the stones during construction, which is provided by a 'former' or 'form'. For smaller elliptical arches the former can simply be a thin sheet of plywood, wedged between the foundation stones as shown. The plywood should be the width of the wall at ground level.

Raised arches, or arches of a specific shape such as semicircular or Gothic arches generally require a more accurate former. Cut two templates of the required shape from quarter-inch (6mm) plywood. Battens, 1" (25mm) thick are then nailed between the two templates. Start with the battens at either end and at the apex, and then space the other battens evenly around the arch, making sure the gaps are smaller than the thinnest voussoir. If you are using very thin stone, it's best to use battens only at the edges and apex, and use plywood elsewhere to make a solid former. Mark the apex on the former, as this will help with accurately positioning the keystone.

Rest the former on thin wooden wedges when setting it in position, to make it easier to remove the former on completion of the arch. If working on soil, first place flat stones under the wedges to stop them being forced into the soil.

For raised arches, the former should be raised on 4 x 4" (100 x 100mm) timber legs, braced and supported as shown.

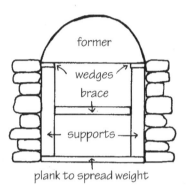

plank to spread weight

Alternatives to these simple wooden formers for small arches have been known to include tractor tyres and whisky barrels. However, safety is an important issue with larger arches, and advice should be sought for any structure requiring scaffolding.

CONSTRUCTION

Piers

Generally the piers are either pillars (p107), wall heads (p89) or the sides of cripple holes (p93). If the pier is set on a concrete foundation, it must be strong enough to also support the weight transferred onto it by the arch. If set on stone footings, you must choose the largest, most regular stones for the footings, as they will support more weight than normal.

Where the arch forms the roof of a niche, set the piers on the slab which forms the base of the niche.

Basic procedure

The basic procedure is similar for all shapes of arch.

1 Place the springers at either end so that they have level bases and their ends touch the former.

2 Place the first voussoir against each springer.

3 Continue placing voussoirs, alternately one side and then the other.

4 Jam the keystone into place at the apex.

A shallow arch may be spanned with one or two rows of voussoirs. With deeper arches, three or more rows of voussoirs will be needed (see below).

Stone placement and alignment

Selection of good springers is important. They must have a flat base to sit on the pier, with an angled top surface which points towards the centre of the base line of the former. Getting this angle correct sets up the subsequent placement of the voussoirs. In semicircular arches each voussoir should point along a radial line as shown. Mark the centre point clearly on the former.

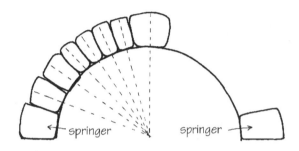

springer   springer

Other arch shapes are not so simple. The voussoirs should be set with their middle line at 90° to the tangent at the point where they touch the intrados. This principle holds true for each voussoir on any curve,

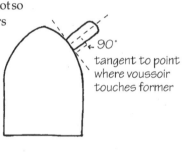

90°

tangent to point where voussoir touches former

whatever its shape. The angle can be checked using a square, or by eye.

When building out of uncut stone, some wedges may be needed on the extrados (outer edge), but keep use to a minimum as stone contact between the voussoirs is reduced.

Maintaining alignment and contact can be a problem with flat, level bedded stone. Take care not to reduce the contact between voussoirs to a single point, or the arch is likely to

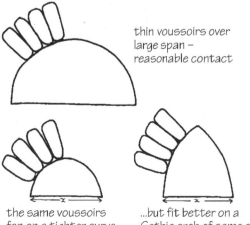

thin voussoirs over large span – reasonable contact

the same voussoirs fan on a tighter curve...

...but fit better on a Gothic arch of same span

collapse. This type of stone is best suited to larger radius semicircular arches, or to pointed arches, as shown.

Slightly rounded stone can be used for a semicircular arch. Although contact is limited, even if a stone slips slightly it should not fall out, and although the arch may become misshapen, it shouldn't collapse.

Whatever the shape of the voussoirs, you must always place each one with the thickest end at the extrados. If you place any the other way round, they will be forced out as the arch settles.

Keystones

The shape of the keystone must accurately match the remaining gap. It can be a few millimetres wider, but must not be narrower or it will slip through. If it is too wide it will be impossible to hammer in, or may move some of the voussoirs out of line.

The last two voussoirs on a pointed arch should just touch each other at the apex. The wedge-shaped keystone should be placed rather than hammered in. The keystone should be at least the same height as the voussoirs, or protrude above them, so that the weight of the

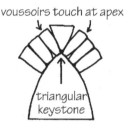

voussoirs touch at apex

triangular keystone

wall is transferred down through the voussoirs. As the keystone cannot slip through the apex of a pointed arch, it's permissible to use small wedges if necessary between the keystone and adjacent voussoirs, to get a tight fit.

Depth of arch

An arch in a narrow wall may be constructed of voussoirs which span the wall. This is the simplest type of structure. Normally, two sets of voussoirs will be needed, making two matching arches which are tied together. A deeper arch will need a third set of voussoirs in the middle.

Try to interlock the voussoirs where possible, eliminating voids from the centre of the wall. This is easier to achieve if the arches are constructed at the same time. When building three arches you must work across the wall, rather than building each arch independently.

Ideally the voussoirs should interlock as shown, but in practice a few voids are likely. This is not a problem provided there is good contact between adjacent voussoirs in any one arch. Once each arch has been tested for strength, these voids should be wedged from the top.

Stones of a more triangular profile can be used, provided

PLACEMENT OF VOUSSOIRS – DOUBLE ROW

PLAN VIEW

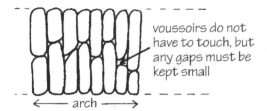

voussoirs do not have to touch, but any gaps must be kept small

← arch →

PLACEMENT OF VOUSSOIRS – TRIPLE ROW

PLAN VIEW

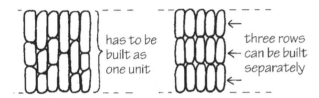

has to be built as one unit

three rows can be built separately

that good contact is maintained with the adjacent voussoirs in the same arch. A temporary wedge can be used, which will fall out once the former is removed.

Note in the diagram that it will often be necessary to trim the faces of the voussoirs to match the batter of the wall. If it's not possible to trim the whole face, then round off the top edge so that the voussoir blends better with the wall.

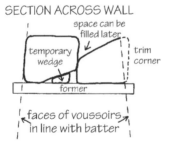

SECTION ACROSS WALL

space can be filled later

temporary wedge

trim corner

former

faces of voussoirs in line with batter

Gaps at the top of the voussoirs should be wedged when the arch has been completed, with small gaps wedged to help lock the arch. Each wedge should be only marginally thicker than the gap, to squeeze the voussoirs together, rather than forcing their tops apart.

Finishing

When both sides of the arch are completed you can test it by sitting on it at the apex. It should not move, although a small amount of settlement against the former shouldn't be a problem. Check each voussoir by trying to rock it, and remedy any slight movement with wedges. If any voussoir can be easily displaced you will need to dismantle the arch to this point, possibly substituting some different stones or the keystone, and rebuild it.

The weight on the arch locks it together and strengthens it.

A long traced stone placed on top of the keystone helps transfer the weight through the keystone to the voussoirs.

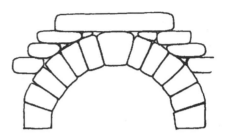

Where the arch forms a simple top to a gateway, with or without topstones above, the lack of weight means that the arch must be mortared to hold it together.

The matter of weight dispersal leads to some debate over the best time to remove the former. Some wallers prefer to leave it in place until the arch is complete and under full stress. Others prefer to remove the former once the arch is complete, or after the first layer above is completed. If the arch is solid there should be no problems, and any small movement will only lead to minor distortions. If there is a major disaster you have less to rebuild than if the arch had been completed!

It's best to use voussoirs of similar height, dressing them as necessary, as it is then easier to fit the face stones above the arch, and they won't interfere with the transfer of weight through the arch. If occasional longer voussoirs are used, they look better if they are placed symmetrically.

Niches and boles

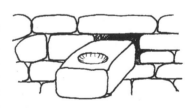

Niches and boles are various types of recesses within a wall. The thick walls surrounding many old Irish farms, for example, often contain various recesses and cavities (Evans, 1957). Some were used as dog-kennels, duck-houses and storage places. Smaller niches in sheep pens were made for keeping clippers ready to hand. Some cavities were specially designed as safes, with a 'money safe stone' that was impossible to distinguish from other stones. These are sometimes known as 'vinegar stones', following the practice of filling them with vinegar to disinfect the money during the time of the Black Death.

Niches also serve a decorative function in garden walls to house pots or statuary, or as seats. Niches without a back in a retaining wall are used for planting holes, or to facilitate drainage.

Constructing a niche

This is essentially the same as for a smoot (p93). The base is normally formed with one or two large flat stones, which are held in place by the sides and back of the niche. The roof of the niche can be formed by an arch, or by fitting a lintel.

The back of the niche is the most difficult part to build.

SECTION

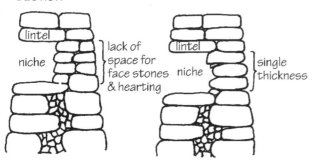

A double thickness of face stones is difficult to fit in. A single thickness of stones can be used, but the stones have to be very regular to fit together without wedging, as any wedges would be likely to fall out.

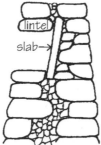

One possible solution is to use a slab for the back, and this will hold the hearting and any wedges in place.

Constructing a bole

In the wetter and windier parts of Britain and Ireland, boles were built in walls to provide shelter for straw bee skeps. The skeps were packed around with straw in frosty weather. Bee boles are typically found in sets of three or four, about 2-3' (600-900mm) above ground level to ease working, 18" (450mm) square and 15" (380mm) deep. Most are topped with lintels, although arched tops are also found. Sometimes the lintels project to help shed rainwater. On some boles the base also projects, to provide a landing place for the bees.

The spacing between boles varies, from a length of wall down to a single upright stone. Such stones should have good square bases and tops, and preferably be built into the back wall of the bole. Mortar may be needed to secure the pillars.

An interesting set of ten boles can be found at Penrose Farm, St. Ervan, Wadebridge, Cornwall, built into a stone hedge of vertically set stones.

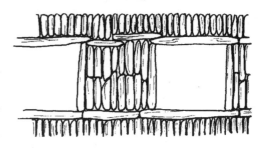

Interesting bee boles can be found in all sorts of locations, and are particularly numerous in the Lake District. The International Bee Research Association conducted a survey, and had recorded 836 sets of boles in Britain by 1994, although these included some brick-built and other types of boles. For further details on boles see Wood (1973)), and the Dry Stone Walling Association leaflet 'Bee Boles'.

Holes and apertures

Raised holes in walls occur in a variety of shapes and sizes, and for various purposes. Simple square and rectangular vertical slits are built in the same way as smoots (p93). Round, triangular and cross-shaped holes are normally for decorative purposes.

ROUND

Round holes are also known as bull's eyes, and basically consist of two semi-circular arches. The example here has four large keystones, but only the top one is essential.

To build a bull's eye:

1 Level the wall off to the height of the lowest stone in the bull's eye, and then build up either side to the mid-point as shown. Place a 2 x 1" (50 x 25mm) batten across the gap, ensuring it's level. Pin a thin, pointed length of wood, called a trammel, to the centre point of the circle.

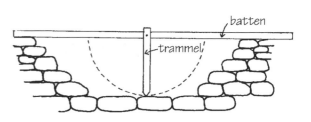

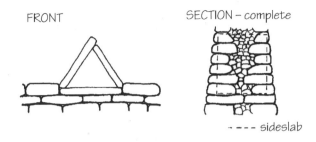

FRONT   SECTION – complete

- - - - sideslab

2   Extend the wall on either side as shown. The exact size of the hole and the 'smoothness' of the finish will depend on the size of stones being used, both for the wall and for the bull's eye. Small walling stone will give a smoother finish, better suited to using regular shaped, smaller stone for the bull's eye. Larger walling stones will leave steps, which can be filled using larger and irregular length stones for the bull's eye.

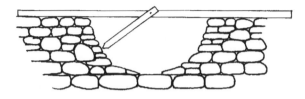

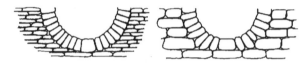

3   Starting at the centre bottom, work out on alternate sides as if you were building an upside-down arch, angling the stones towards the centre of the circle.

4   Complete the lower half of the circle. If they are part of the design, set 'keystones' at the horizontal, which will act as springers for the upper arch.

5   Set up a former for the upper arch. For smaller bull's eyes this can be supported on a pile of bricks set centrally. For larger bull's eyes, a length of timber should be wedged in place, carefully set level.

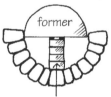
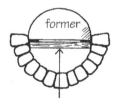

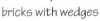

bricks with wedges   timber with wedges

6   Complete as for building an arch. As with arches, the stones may span the wall, or a second bull's eye may need to be built on the other side of the wall.

TRIANGULAR

Triangular apertures can quite easily be built using the technique of corbelling, in which successive stones protrude a measured amount beyond the stone below. However, you do need a sufficient supply of long stones.

If enough stones are not available, you can instead construct a triangle using three flat slabs to line the aperture. These should lap onto each other as shown, to give good stone contact. Some trimming may be required.

Take care with placing the first couple of layers, until the triangle is firmly gripped by the stones. Build the wall alongside the slabs as if you were butting up to bedrock (p70), using the longer stones in the style of corbelling, although strict corbelling is not necessary as they will be held in place by the slabs. Finish with a stone sitting on the apex, as with an arch, to help lock the structure.

Whilst it is useful if the side slabs match the batter of the wall on both sides, it's not essential. As long as the stones alongside the slabs overlap into the wall, all should be secure.

CROSS SHAPED

X shaped crosses cannot be built out of dry stones, but 'plus signs' and crucifixes are relatively simple, provided you have plenty of long stones. The major limiting factor on size and shape are the stones available to form the top of the horizontal slits, and the dimensions should be planned with these in mind.

1   Build the lower slit to the required dimensions as two mini wall heads (p89). Finish the heads with either a slab or two to three matched stones which are longer than the proposed length of the horizontal slits.

2   Build up the two ends of the horizontal slits, preferably ending with a tie rather than a runner.

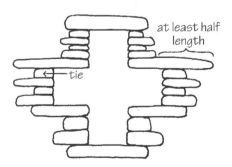

at least half length

tie

3   Level up the wall, and place the two slabs to form the top of the slit. More than half the length of these slabs, and preferably two-thirds, should sit on the stones below.

4 Start the next layer of stones as shown, to anchor the slabs in position, creating a cantilever.

5 Construct the heads on the free ends of the slabs, ensuring there is always sufficient weight on the fixed end to counterbalance. This means building the wall and then the head, contrary to normal practice, and a little care is needed to ensure a tight fit.

6 Finish the feature with a lintel.

Seats

CONSTRUCTION

Free-standing seats

Free-standing stone seats are relatively simple to construct. The height should be about 14-16" (350-400mm) for general use, and slightly lower for children. The other dimensions are a matter of personal choice, and the availability of the top stone or stones.

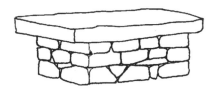

The base is essentially a stone box, built using the principles of building a corner (p92). The top stone or stones need to be heavy enough that they cannot be displaced by someone leaning on them, and for improved appearance and comfort they should overlap the base by 2-3" (50-75mm). If using a pair of stones, match them carefully for height and width. The top stones should be so heavy that more than one person is needed to move them. Note the details on moving heavy stones (p24).

If suitably heavy top stones cannot be found, lighter ones can be set on a 10-20mm deep bed of mortar, of 5:1 sand:cement.

In the curved example below, a heavy wooden slab has been used, because this was easier and cheaper to cut than a stone slab. The wooden slab has metal brackets beneath, which are anchored into the concrete core of the base, by

being placed in position before the concrete set. This holds the top securely and prevents it being removed by vandals.

A simple variation on this type of free-standing seat is to sit a large slab or slate on two regularly shaped support stones, each one placed a sixth to a quarter of the way in from the ends of the top stone, to leave an overlap of about 8-12" (200-300mm) for a 4' (1.2m) slab. The slab can be fixed as necessary with epoxy adhesive (p102).

Seats in walls

A simple seat can be made by building a base which projects about 16" (400mm) for the length of the seat. Ideally the wall and seat should form an integrated unit, constructed as a series of corners. Alternatively, build the seat first and then construct the wall over it, making sure that the stones which butt up to the side of the seat extend well into the main body of the wall.

The stone slab or slabs for the top are held by the wall, so do not have to be as heavy as for a free-standing seat. Choose smooth comfortable stones for the 'backrest', and position them carefully.

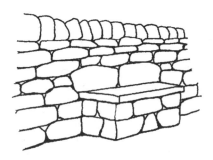

Building seats recessed into the main body of a free standing wall is not generally recommended, as there are problems, similar to those with niches (p118) in building the 'backrest' or rear side of the wall.

Recessed seats in retaining walls are easier to construct, the extra digging apart. Level off the wall at the required height and 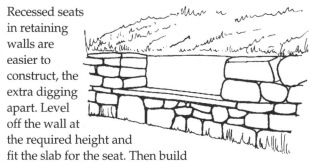 fit the slab for the seat. Then build corners lapped onto the end of the slab, and return them about 16" (400mm) in, across the back of the slab. In the example below, the back is also a slab, in this case of slate, set slightly angled and secured by the side wall overlapping it.

In taller retaining walls, a recessed seat with an arched top can form quite an impressive feature, similar to a giant niche.

Steps

Stone steps can be built in gardens, as part of dry stone walls or retaining walls on banks, and to reduce erosion on steep footpaths. The dimensions will depend on the gradient, but in general staircase-type steps on steep gradients should be avoided. The minimum dimensions should be as shown.

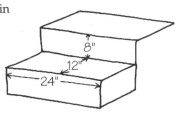

There are various ways of making stone steps, according to the type of stone available.

a   Massive heavy slabs can form the whole step.

b   The riser can be formed of a layer, or layers of dry stone work, capped by a single or two large slabs.

c   Smaller stone can be set lengthwise into the ground to form the tread, a process known as pitching. This is held by a large slab which forms the riser.

d   Rough or cut stone can be used to form the riser and front of the tread, with the rest of the tread of packed gravel or soil.

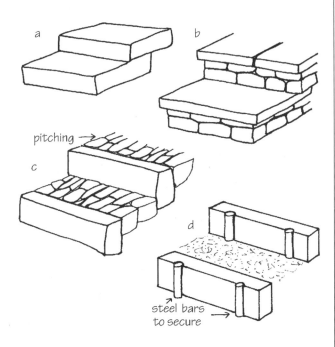

Construction of steps is further explained in *Footpaths* (BTCV, 1996).

Capping stone steps

Fields (1971) gives these rules for making flights of steps up retaining walls.

a   Choose slabs which are wide enough for foot room, long enough to tie into the faces of the wall on both sides, and thick enough to bear the weight of a man carrying a load.

b   Buttress each step from below with a foundation of smaller stones.

c   If building steps up through a retaining wall, build the wall to a head at either side of the steps.

Pens

Dry stone pens or enclosures for sheep are found in many upland areas, built to various patterns. Most consist of a single chamber, but others have interconnected 'rooms' for sorting out mixed flocks. Where the interconnecting pens are circular or rounded, they are sometimes called 'honeycomb' pens. These complex pens are found in areas which have a long and continuous tradition of upland grazing, such as the Carneddau range in North Wales, where over a dozen can be found. Some are well maintained and regularly used, whereas others have decayed to little more than piles of stones.

In Derbyshire and South Yorkshire the enclosures are often circular, while in Northumberland square pens are more common. In Scotland circles and ovals are found. Names also vary, from 'fanks' in the west Highlands to 'beilds' in south-eastern Scotland. In Yorkshire pens are called 'beelds' or 'stells'.

Pens are often designed for use as shelter, as well as for enclosure. This circular fank, about 42' (13m) in diameter is alongside the A708 near Grey Mare's Tail, about 9 miles north of Moffat. The walls are built to a Galloway Dyke pattern (p141), and include three radiating arms, mainly for shelter purposes.

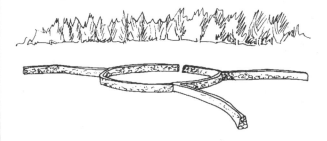

Other pens have additional 'catchment' walls splayed either side of the entrance, to ease the gathering of sheep.

Some pens found on exposed moorland were specifically constructed for stock shelter, rather than stock-handling. These were particularly widespread on the North York Moors, with many marked on Ordnance Survey maps.

Smaller pens are found on the edges of villages in parts of Derbyshire and Yorkshire. These pens, known as 'pounds' or 'pinfolds' were for the impounding of stray stock, under the charge of a 'pinder', who only released the animals on payment of a fine or duty.

Pens were also built as traps. In Eskdale, on the hillside above a property called Wha House, is a 10' (3m) diameter pen, with walls 7' (2.1m) high, which slope in towards the centre. There are no openings in the walls. This is purportedly a 'fox beild', which would have been used by balancing a plank over the opening, with a dead lamb or similar placed on the unsupported end. The hapless fox trying to reach the carrion would overbalance the plank and be trapped.

Pens are found in a huge variety of sizes and designs for all sorts of purposes, and make a subject of study for the historian or dry stone waller.

Butts

A shooting butt is a small enclosure or wall which provides shelter for the gun, and also partly conceals the gun from the quarry. The butt must be carefully sited with safety and clear sight lines in mind. Birds tend to fly downwind, so the butt is orientated relative to the prevailing wind, whilst also allowing shooting in other directions. The circular butt gives the most flexibility. The floor of the butt should be level for safety reasons.

A butt can also be used for a hide for watching birds and other wildlife.

DESIGN

The walls of the butt are normally about 4'6" (1.4m) high, for ease of shooting, with a similar height suitable for binocular use. The internal wall of an enclosed butt should have a batter close to vertical, as this is more comfortable for the gun to use, and avoids leaning to compensate for the batter. Likewise, a vertical wall is also more comfortable for bird watchers.

Enclosed butts

Enclosed butts with a small opening are found in various shapes including circles, squares and rectangles, of which circles are the most common. Dimensions vary, but they normally have an internal diameter in the range of 8-10' (2.4-3m), to give enough space for gun, loader/gillie and and a couple of dogs. The opening, called a 'haik' in parts of Scotland, is narrow in order to prevent cattle and sheep getting in and churning and fouling the ground. This example is about 2'6" (610mm) wide at the top, tapering to only 6" (150mm) at the bottom. A built-in seat may be included for the gillie, with a niche or small shelf for cartridges and possibly a bottle of whisky.

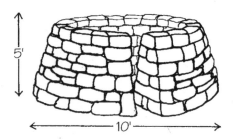

To accommodate more than one gun, a rectangular shape can be better, as it allows more guns to shoot in one direction. However on shooting estates, rather than increase the size of the individual butts to accommodate more guns, you will often see lines of five or more butts spaced at around 50m intervals. On land alongside the Egton Bridge road near Rosedale Abbey in the North York Moors there are over 20 butts.

In this example at West Tempar, Kinlock Rannock, Perthshire, a wall has been adapted by adding a circular butt at one end, and two semi-circular butts up against the wall. The semi-circular butts have lunkies in the wall to allow the dogs out when shooting across the wall.

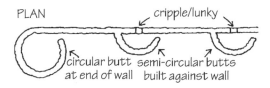

These two butts have extended openings to keep out the wind, and as a further deterrent to stock.

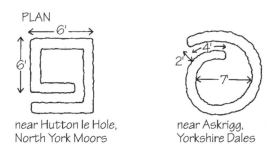

near Hutton le Hole, North York Moors

near Askrigg, Yorkshire Dales

Open butts

These include C, L and H shapes. The example shown below is one in a line of eight butts running south

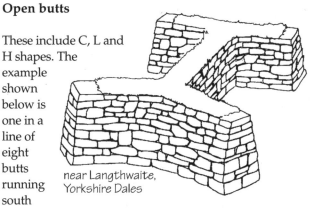

near Langthwaite, Yorkshire Dales

west from the road near Langthwaite, Arkengarthdale in the Yorkshire Dales.

Turf tops

Turf or heather tops are the norm for shooting butts, as they are better than stone for resting a gun, and provide camouflage, a quality also useful for observation hides. About 4' (1.2m) of stonework topped with two layers of turf is typical, but if stone is in short supply the stonework will be lower, with three layers of turf to finish.

As butts are usually in windy and exposed locations, it's a good idea to secure new turfs with twine or wire, either threaded through the wall, or tied around the thickness of the turfs so that the combined weight holds them. Metal or wooden pins are also sometimes used, driven down into the turf layers to secure them.

Some butts are also clad with turf on the outside as further camouflage. On rising ground, another variant is to build a C shaped butt by cutting into the slope, and using the spoil at the front of the stonework to camouflage it. This design also uses less stone.

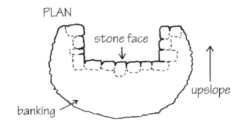

PLAN

stone face

upslope

banking

11   Variations in walling

The broad influence of geology has been looked at in chapter 1. A few areas with a fairly simple geology have similar walls throughout, such as the walls of the Cotswolds which are built almost entirely of oolitic limestone. The granite areas of south west England and Aberdeenshire each have their typical styles which make use of the large, rough granite boulders.

In other areas the geological picture is much more complex, and walls can vary from farm to farm, and from field to field. It can be misleading to take one style as being representative of a region or an area, when there is so much variation. Quite often you will find walling styles which are almost unique to a specific farm or estate. Frequently you will find an isolated style of wall which is far more widespread in an area hundreds of miles away. The influence of stone type, size and weight is always important, but there are many other influences at work, and it is almost impossible to define a typical style for a region or locality. There has probably always been much intermixing of styles, copying of techniques from other areas and movement of skilled workers, so that it is also difficult to attribute a particular style as originating in a particular locality.

The purpose of this chapter is to show some of the variations that are found in walling. The examples given illustrate styles which can be found in an area, but do not necessarily define what is 'typical' for an area. Subtle details and local traditions need to be considered before a wall is built or repaired, even if these are not necessarily followed.

The illustrations on the inside covers give further examples of variations in walling styles.

Dimensions

BATTER

Most walls are essentially 'A' shaped to aid stability, with their base equal to half their height, and the top width half that of their base (p58). Walls within an area may be built to an almost identical pattern, following the local specification made during the enclosure period. However, walls in very different areas can be remarkably similar, possibly because experience has led to a fairly universal wisdom.

The basic 'A' shape can vary either due to the function of the wall, or because of stone type. A wall built of large stone is necessarily wider than a wall built for the same purpose in an area of small stone.

Concave faces

Cornish hedges are normally built with concave faces (p81), as are many of the dry stone walls in the area. It seems likely that the hedge pattern has simply been copied in the local walling style. A concave batter aids stability, and may also be more of a deterrent to stock.

In the Rhossili area of the Gower peninsular, South Wales, many walls have a batter so concave that the top can be overhanging. This is achieved by careful selection of long stone, frequently with angled faces, set upside down compared to normal practice.

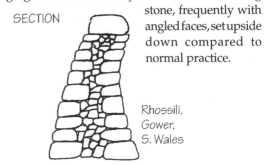

SECTION

Rhossili,
Gower,
S. Wales

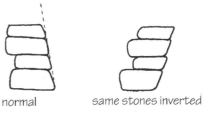

normal   same stones inverted

A spectacular retaining wall with a concave batter can be found in the disused slate quarry at the head of Cwm Ystradllyn, near Porthmadog, North Wales. The wall was built to support a waste heap and stop slates falling

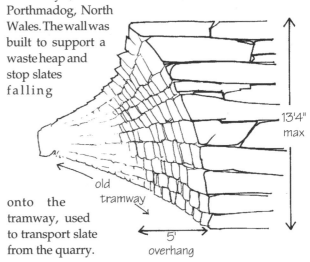

onto the tramway, used to transport slate from the quarry.

13'4" max

old tramway

5'
overhang

The concavity is achieved through the use of sloping faces, as on the Gower. Strength is achieved through the use of large stone, with the wall built of only 10-11 almost coursed layers. The capping stones are all about 6' (1.8m) in length, and the corner stones over 5' (1.5m) in length. Not a single stone appears to have moved since the wall was built.

Near-vertical batters

Walls of large stone frequently have a near-vertical batter, in order to fit the stone together without creating steps. If a stepped face is unavoidable, the step should be no more than a finger width, or only enough "to allow a mouse to creep along" (E. Hart, 1980). Many of the coursed granite walls of Aberdeenshire have stepped faces, but elsewhere it's often frowned upon as giving access to stock. Alternatively, large stones can be tilted to fit the batter.

Walls occasionally have one face more vertical than the other. Stones with flatter, larger faces are used on the vertical side, and smaller irregular rubble on the other. Such walls may be built where only the vertical side needs to be stockproof, or on roadside estate walls where the better stone is used for show on the outer face.

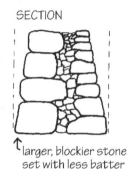

SECTION

↑ larger, blockier stone set with less batter

Technically these lopsided walls are likely to be weaker than symmetrical walls. Empirical evidence suggests that the walls are more likely to collapse towards the face with the smaller, less regular stone, probably due to uneven settlement between the two faces.

WIDTH

Large stone

The usual reason for walls being wider than normal is the size of building stone. If large boulders are being used, then the footings will often need to be wider than half the height of the wall. Many walls in North Wales, for example, are 30-36" (750-900mm) wide at the base, but under 5' (1.5m) high. In order to then maintain the correct batter, the top has to be wider than normal, that is, more than half the base width. The result is that the top is too wide to be crossed with top stones in the normal way, and a number of other coping styles are used (p136). Normally the top cannot be narrowed because the batter would fail to be stock proof, and larger stones would create steps in the wall face. This example shows how differences in style are directly related to the available stone.

Excess of stone

Other wide walls are the result of an excess of stone generated during field clearance, and are known as consumption walls. The example below is one of many in the coastal area south of Harlech, in North Wales.

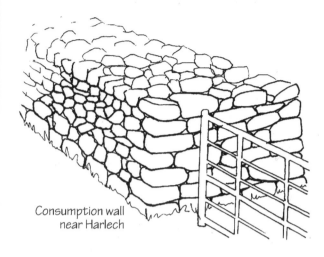

Consumption wall near Harlech

Perhaps the most massive and famous of these walls is the Kingswell West Dyke at Monymusk, Aberdeenshire. This wall is 27' (8.2m) wide at the top, 6' (1.8m) high and 500 yards (457m) long. Consumption walls generally have little more than a rough rubble top, although some care is taken with the stonework nearest the wall faces. Note that the Kingswell West Dyke has a line of carefully laid slabs which form a path along the top.

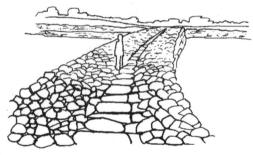

(after Rainsford-Hannay, 1972)

Clearance walls can be found in many areas, and are sometimes accompanied by the filling up and rounding off of corners, and the piling up of 'clearance cairns' in the middle of fields. A spectacular example of this practice can be seen at Wasdale Head in the Lake District. As you drive along the valley approaching the village you are confronted by what appears to be a sea of stone, and it is only as you get closer that individual walls can be identified. Many of the 'standard' field walls are about 6' (1.8m) high, and about 5' (1.5m) wide at the base, tapering to 3' (900mm) at the top. Large walls are over 8' (2.4m) high and wide, with other walls incorporating massive bulges. There are lozenge shaped mounds alongside tracks, and round consumption mounds in the middle of fields. These are perhaps 30' (10m) across, and built as a circular wall about 3' (1m) high, with the stone mounded inside.

HEIGHT

Walls can theoretically be any height, provided their bases are wide enough. As a general rule, the higher the wall, the longer and thicker the stone must be to build it. This is because with height, there is greater pressure on the lower stones, which are more likely to fracture or be forced out. However, some tall slate walls are built out of surprisingly thin stone, with walls taller than 20' (6m) built with few stones exceeding 6" (150mm) in thickness.

Low walls

Low walls, around 39" (1m) high, are common in areas where cattle or lowland sheep breeds predominate. Areas include the Cotswolds, and the parts of North Wales where lower cloddiau (p77) reflect the local tradition of cattle farming. The lower height of some internal boundaries within farms reflects the lower grazing pressures of earlier times. In many areas the boundary walls of farms, known as 'march dykes' in Scotland, are 12" (300mm) or more higher than the internal boundaries.

High walls

Walls may have been built higher than normal for enclosing deer, to form impressive estate boundaries, or to consume stone as described above. Some areas such as Glencoe had high walls reputedly to keep wolves at bay.

Sheep pens and smaller enclosures where stock are held in number need to have higher walls, of 6' (1.8m) height or more, to prevent stock escaping. Many animals will jump or scramble over a surprising height when trapped, and sheep can clamber over the backs of other sheep to escape.

Fields to enclose bulls may have higher than normal walls, but most have fallen into disuse. One such enclosure has recently been restored in the Piethorne Valley, Saddleworth Moor, Lancashire. Most of the wall is about 6' (1.8m) high including the top stones, reaching up to 8' (2.4m) in places, especially on sections at the base of slopes. The large coverband

below the top stones protrudes about 6" (150mm) from either side of the wall, and is secured by sizeable top stones. On the inner side this prevents the bull seeing out, or climbing over the wall. The size and weight of the coverstones, and the top stones, prevents the bull from nosing them off the wall.

Other rarer agricultural uses are also possible. For example at Rhoscolyn on Anglesey, there is a wall on the cliff top which is over 7' (2.1m) high, which was once part of a University experiment into crop protection. Sometimes high walls are found for which there is apparently no rhyme or reason.

Some of the most impressive dry stone structures are found around slate quarries. Almost certainly the largest free standing dry stone structure in Britain is Cei Mawr, which is located 1.25 miles east of Penrhyn Station on the Ffestiniog Railway in North Wales. This embankment supports the railway, and is effectively a dry stone wall with a railway on top. The embankment is 62' (18.6m) high, around 60' (18m) wide at the base, 16' (4.8m) wide on top, and runs for 110 yards (100m). The original structure was narrower with a very steep batter, but with increased loads on the railway it was buttressed in the 1880s to its existing dimensions, which has a batter of about 1:4.

FOUNDATIONS

Scarcement

A scarcement results when the wall is set in from the outside edge of the foundation. The resultant ledge can be any size, although it is usually 2-3" (50-75mm). This practice is most commonly seen in parts of Scotland. What appears to be a scarcement may not always be one. Large blocky stone may need to be set in slightly, in order to maintain the batter of the wall.

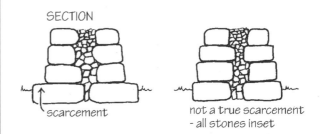

SECTION

scarcement

not a true scarcement - all stones inset

There are two main arguments for using a scarcement.

1 It provides good weight distribution, spreading the load of the wall over a larger area, and reducing the potential for settlement.

   This will hold true so long as the scarcement stones are large enough that they meet, or nearly meet, in the middle. If the gap is greater than for standard footings, there is more chance of the heartings being forced down by the weight of the wall above, resulting in the centre of the wall settling and possibly collapsing.

2 It ensures that stones do not slip off the footing as the wall settles.

This is difficult to evaluate, but seems unlikely, as the second layer of stones could still slip off the first.

The advantages probably outweigh the disadvantages on wet ground, where the scarcement helps spread the load.

Extended scarcements, of footings plus one or more layers of stone, are used in the Highlands of Scotland to even out undulations in the ground (p66). In parts of Aberdeenshire, where the large footing stones are irregular in shape, a type of scarcement is built to even out the footings with smaller stones, creating a level foundation for the walling stones.

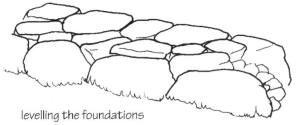

levelling the foundations

Shiners

Normally foundation stones are set with their largest face on the ground, but in some areas they are set upright. This is common practice in granite walls and stone hedges in South West England, where the stones are known as 'shiners'.

This method is not necessarily as unstable as it might appear, provided that the stone type used is heavy, and the stone sits on a good surface.

FRONT VIEW

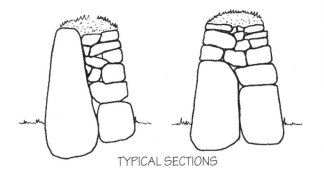

TYPICAL SECTIONS

When rebuilding, it's usually best to re-use shiners in the same way, as they are often difficult to use horizontally or 'dropped'. They may be too long if set across the wall, making a step. If not quite long enough, insufficient space is left to build a good foundation for the opposite face. They can occasionally be used higher up as throughs, but usually they are too heavy to lift this high. 'Dropping' a shiner also means finding enough extra face stones to replace that part of the face which the shiner would have filled. You may be able to use larger hearting as face stones, but the hearting isn't always suitable.

Away from South West England, shiners are rarer, although the bouldery walls and cloddiau of the Caernarfon-Bangor area of North Wales have sections containing shiners. Around Golan near Porthmadog there are several walls with extensive lengths of shiners, but generally thinner, 'slabbier' and less stable than the ideal.

Thinner shiners inevitably sit on a small surface, and are a potential weakness. However, if their use is unavoidable due to lack of other stone, or because this maintains a tradition, they can be used succesfully by building securely around them, as shown below. These techniques can be used to help secure any shiner, whatever its thickness, although blockier shiners with a good base need only be buried about 4" (100mm) deeper than normal foundations.

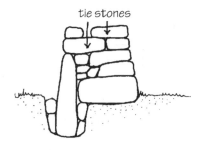

tie stones

Siting two thin shiners opposite each other is not recommended, as the hearting between will have nothing to bind to and will collapse, forcing the two shiners apart, unless very carefully constructed. If unavoidable, use large hearting, carefully placed.

Specialist building techniques

WATERSHOT

In some regions wallers stress the need to lay stones at a slight angle in order to shed water and prevent it running into the wall. This avoids water gathering in the stonework, where it could disrupt the stonework by freezing and swelling. This technique, called watershot or weathershot, works best with small, flat stones. It is common in the Cotswolds and in the Lake District around Ambleside, Grasmere and Keswick. A mortared version of this style is known as 'Lake District masonry'.

The stones only require a minimal tilt in order to shed water. If the stones are tilted too much they will themselves tend to slide.

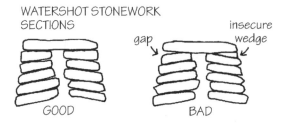

WATERSHOT STONEWORK SECTIONS

gap

insecure wedge

GOOD   BAD

Throughstones can be tricky to lay. Depending on the characteristics of the stone being used, you will need to decrease the tilt of the stones one or two layers before the throughs, to bring them up level enough for the throughs to be set securely. This is awkward to achieve with very regular stone.

TRACING

Whilst tracing is frowned upon for producing a weakened structure (p51), it is a common practice in some areas.

The basalt walls of Skye and many granite walls in Aberdeenshire and elsewhere contain stones too large to fit length into the wall, even given the wider than normal width of these walls. With some stone types you can break large stones in half, and use the two parts placed length into the wall. However, stones such as basalt and granite are too dense to easily break, and the weight and size of the stones means that they sit solidly even when traced. They should be placed so that the width of the traced stone into the wall is greater than the height.

Tracing is also commonplace in the Cotswolds. Here the stone is oolitic limestone, which is amongst the lightest 'walling' stone. Tracing tends to cause poor bonding between the stones, resulting in walls which flake away, course by course. The individual stones are small, regular and light, which tends to increase the problem. To counteract this, many Cotswold wallers refer to 'clapping' the stones in place, which means that rather than being placed gently, they are virtually dropped into position. This places extra force on the stones below, firming up the structure and showing up any weak stones, which are then reset.

If it is necessary to trace stones in order to maintain a local style, then it becomes increasingly important that the other basic principles of construction (p51) are closely followed. Good line, batter and crossing of joints are especially important, so that all stones are well bound and forces

evenly distributed. Avoid tracing very narrow stones, especially when placed low in the wall where they are a major cause of collapse. The style can be maintained while losing the worst traced stones.

JUMPERS

Jumpers are tall face stones which in coursed walls 'jump' through two or three courses. They are used where you have a number of large stones, but not enough to form a complete course. The term does not strictly apply to random walls in which a layer necessarily contains neighbouring stones which are of different height. However, some random walls are built of fairly regular stones, in which the taller stones can be termed jumpers.

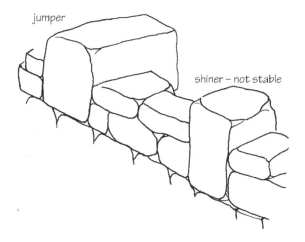

jumper

shiner – not stable

A jumper should be placed length into the wall to be secure. A jumper which is also traced will be inherently unstable. In extreme cases the face height of the jumper exceeds its length into the wall, being similar to, and sometimes referred to as 'shiners'. These stones are particularly unstable. Generally they are not part of any regional style, but are just the occasional stone badly placed to save time. However, they do occur more routinely in the granite walls of Aberdeen and the basalt walls of Skye, where true shiners are common. Here the nature of the stone limits the way in which it can be used, and the style may represent the best use of what is available.

GREEN FACES

Many wallers like to see gapping or rebuilding carried out using the stones with their weathered faces on the outside, a practice also called 'green', 'mossy' or 'lichen' side out. It's argued that this not only makes the gapping or rebuilding blend with the old, but also helps accelerate the greening of stones placed with a fresh side out.

In practice greening is partly dependent on stone type and climate. In the wetter west, particularly in the uplands, the greening process is relatively quick, and even new walls lose their fresh look within a couple of years. However, placing the stone green side out may have some merit with more friable stone, such as Cotswold limestone and some laminates such as mudstone, which can become crumbly and disintegrate with age. Here the mosses and lichens provide a protective skin, reducing the effects of weathering. In general though, other principles of building are much more important, and green side out should not be used as an excuse for the incorrect placing of stone.

PINNINGS

Pinnings or pins are wedge stones which are forced into gaps in the wall face, and are a traditional feature of walls in some areas, including much of Scotland. There are two main arguments in favour of pinning:

a It prevents snow from being blown into the heart of the wall, where it may melt and then re-freeze, slightly shifting the stones. This process of 'freeze-thaw' can seriously destabilise a wall over a period of years.

b Reducing the number of gaps in the face of a wall strengthens it by reducing the potential for settlement. Some pins may work loose under settlement and pop out, but others will be bound tighter, and it is these which will help extend the life of the wall.

In other areas pinnings are frowned upon, for the following reasons:

a You may disturb face stones or fillings when pushing in the pinnings.

b Pinnings, even if tapped with a hammer, may not be really secure, and often they are forced out as the wall settles or frost disturbs the face. Even with gentle tapping the pinnings often crack, allowing water to seep into them so they soon fragment.

c Pinnings are usually unnecessary as long as the face stones are properly placed and wedged from behind. Cracks and gaps are not a problem provided every stone sits tightly and the openings are too small for fillings to wash out. It is not essential to have every face stone snug against its neighbours if this might cause them to sit poorly.

Where pinnings are used, bear the following in mind:

a Use wedges and slivers, not rounded or square stones as these are more awkward to get tight, and more likely to pop out.

b Use one stone to one hole. Several small pins in a single hole are unlikely to stay tight.

c Preferably use freshly broken stone, as this tends to be rougher than weathered stone and will key better.

d Pins should be as long as possible to maximise stone to stone contact, but should not protrude beyond the face of the wall where they are likely to be knocked.

e Knock pinnings in with another stone or a wooden mallet as using a hammer tends to shatter them. Take care and don't knock too hard as this can force the stones apart. Hart (1980) suggests that they should be pushed in by hand rather than hammered in.

Many wallers pin as they work along a layer, rather than pinning a complete section of wall. It must be remembered though that pins are a supplement to a wall's strength, and should only be used to consolidate a stable structure. Resist the temptation to use pins to solve problems or to fill larger gaps which could be avoided with a little more patience.

Throughstones

The pattern of throughstones varies considerably between areas.

PROJECTING THROUGHS

One of the more noticeable variations is whether or not the throughs project. In many areas throughs project from both sides of the wall from 1" (25mm) up to 6" (150mm).

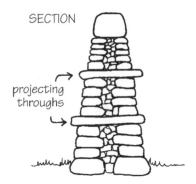

Beyond tradition, there are various explanations for this practice. In the Derbyshire High Peak, and in the slate areas of Wales and the Isle of Man, throughs which project 6" (150mm) or more are used to dissuade sheep from jumping. In sandstone areas, longer throughs may be used as they are, rather than trying to dress the ends and risk cracking them at inconvenient points.

Another possibility is that projecting throughs are used so that as the wall settles and widens, the throughs will still serve to bind the faces together.

Occasionally throughs project from one side of the wall only, being flush on the side adjoining tracks and paths. This may be to lessen the chance of them being knocked, or to discourage unwanted access and damage to the wall. On a slope, the projection is more likely to be on the downhill side. This may be because any settlement will be downslope, and thus the throughs will still bind the faces. Another reason is that if projections have to be made, putting them to the downhill side is less likely to give access to sheep than if they were put on the uphill side.

'Single projection' may also have been used to indicate ownership of a boundary wall, or for appearance on estate walls. Many walls around reservoirs in Northern England owe their distinctive appearance to projecting throughs and three-quarter throughs.

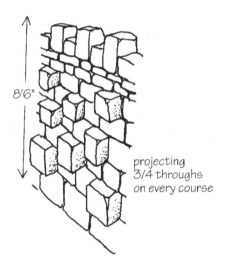

8'6"

projecting
3/4 throughs
on every course

ABSENCE OF THROUGHS

The use of throughstones in a wall is generally regarded as an essential part of their structure, but there are many long-standing walls which disprove this rule.

In the Craven district of Yorkshire throughstones are rare, but the blocky limestone binds firmly together without throughs, and settles into a more durable wall than many more regular types of stone. In Aberdeenshire throughs are normally absent, as stones of the available thickness which could span the wall would be too heavy to lift. Instead the size and weight of individual stones keeps the whole structure stable.

Similarly walls built of large bouldery stone rarely have a formalised pattern of throughs. Unlike walls built of smaller stone, which have two faces filled with hearting and joined by throughs, boulder walls have essentially two faces which join, with many boulders acting as three-quarter throughs.

Walls without throughs are often wider at the base and have a greater batter than would otherwise be the case. Whether this is a conscious design feature to aid stability, or has resulted from the need to fit very large stones in the base is a matter of conjecture.

FLUSH THROUGHS

Just because a wall does not appear to have throughs does not mean they are not there. Throughs are often built flush to stop cattle rubbing on them and loosening the wall, and are thus difficult to recognise. When rebuilding, flush throughs should be replaced flush, although with repairing gaps, this may mean replacing them lower than they were originally. This is because the stones of derelict walls, and especially the hearting, tends to 'disappear' through being trampled in or broken, and unless more stone is brought in, the wall will need to be built narrower than it was previously. To span the wall, the flush through will thus need to be placed lower.

Escaping sheep tend to 'run up' the face of a wall at an angle, rather than face on, and projecting throughs can act like steps to make escape easier. This tends to refute the argument that a consistent pattern of well-projecting throughs acts as a deterrent. Projecting stones probably only act as a deterrent when they are used in the coverband (p127), where they both look, and are, awkward to clamber over. Stockproofing depends on many factors, including the flatness of the face, the batter, the overall height of the wall, and most importantly, the nature of the sheep in question. The occasional projecting through will certainly aid a determined hill or mountain breed to scale a wall.

Flush throughs can follow any of the formal patterns outlined below, which require trimming individual throughs to fit. Trimming can be difficult with some types of stone, so formal patterns are more suited to slates, mudstones or thinner sandstones which are easier to trim.

Flush throughs can also be used without trimming, by fitting them at the appropriate height for individual lengths to span the wall exactly. This will not be as strong as fitting throughs at regular intervals along a course, but helps to strengthen the wall. Spread the throughs as evenly as possible along the length, staggered with height to fit. An even spread is important to ensure even settlement, as sections without throughs will settle differently from those with throughs, in extreme cases 'peeling away' and collapsing.

PATTERNS

For walls with throughs, one or two rows are normal, depending on the wall's height. Around the Derbyshire High Peak, both limestone and gritstone walls have three rows of throughs, as have many walls in North Yorkshire and Cumbria. In the Northern Pennines, on the north side of the A66 in Stainmore Pass, a few very tall limestone walls contain four rows of throughs.

The pattern of throughstones in an area can be remarkably consistent, usually because the spacings have been specified by an Enclosure Award.

In some areas walls contain a complete layer or layers of throughs, with the throughs butted up against each other in the layer. This is particularly noticeable around Langwathby in the Eden Valley, where large flat sandstone throughs bind two skins of small rounded stone. The efficacy of complete layers is open to question, as discussed below.

Complete layers may work better than spaced throughs as both sides are tied for their entire length. Also, the stonework above is less likely to settle unevenly, as it is built on a level bed of stone. However, some wallers maintain that the butted throughs effectively divide the wall into two or more independent layers of stonework, and if the wall settles unevenly across its width the throughs will tilt and shed the stonework above them.

There is also some evidence that the stones below a complete layer of throughs tend to work loose. This is because small stones get used for levelling up the stonework to make a base for the throughs to sit firmly, and these stones may settle unevenly. Where throughs are spaced, the wall becomes an integral structure for its entire height.

In many areas, particularly the sandstone areas of Northern England, many walls have complete rows of throughs below the coping, which are known as covers or coverbands (p135).

The availability and nearness of suitable stone is always a factor in the pattern of throughs. The walls immediately around Middletongue Quarry, a disused sandstone quarry near Greenhow Hill, North Yorkshire, have two rows of projecting throughs and a large projecting coverband. As distance from the quarry increases, the frequency of throughs decreases, until only a mile from the quarry, there are few visible.

OTHER POINTS

Throughs of different stone

In some areas, throughs of a different stone type are imported. This is noticeable on the borders of limestone and sandstone areas, such as the edges of the Craven fault, where sandstone throughs are common in limestone walls. Here sandstone is also often a component in the wall heads. If you look closely at these walls, you can find runnels in the faces of some limestone beneath sandstone, where rainwater dripping off the more acidic sandstone dissolves the limestone. These runnels indicate that the wall is probably several centuries old, as the process is very slow.

Slate throughs are also sometimes used with other stones. In parts of Wharfedale and much of Ribblesdale (Raistrick, 1966), throughs were split from large glacial erratics of Silurian slate, as the predominant local stone is too rounded to use for throughs. A similar practice occurs in the Duddon

Valley in the Lake District. However in areas where sandstone throughs are available, they tend to be used in preference to slate, which is more liable to fracture.

Great care needs to be taken when mixing flat throughs with rounded or irregular building stone, as it can be difficult to provide a firm, level bed for the throughs.

Mortar bands

In place of throughs, a layer of mortared stones is sometimes used, as in this example from Portesham, Dorset. Although this may seem a valid technique to use where throughs are not available, it's likely to cause the same problems as a complete layer of throughs, and is not generally recommended. The stonework beneath the mortared layer may also settle, leaving a gap as with mortared copes (p60). In this example a lime mortar has been used, which is more flexible than the normal cement mortar, and may be less likely to cause problems.

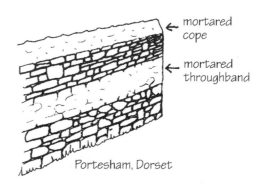

mortared cope

mortared throughband

Portesham, Dorset

Types of coping

Differences in patterns of coping provide the most obvious characteristics of different walling styles. This section deals with stone coping. Walls capped with turf are described on page 84.

UPRIGHT

The most common form of coping is the use of upright stones set to a relatively even height (p56), and is suitable for almost any stone type. Adjacent stones can vary in height, although the difference between the largest and smallest stones is rarely more than 2" (50mm), and the stones are ordered so there are no obvious dips or rises to the finished height of the wall. From a distance of 20 yards or so the overall effect is a very even line to the top of the wall.

Random

Random copings occur where the available stone varies by more than 1-2" (25-50mm). Even with random finishes, some wallers prefer to use a line to produce a relatively even top, by distributing shorter stones fairly evenly along the length, or by alternating taller and shorter stones. This is similar to 'buck and doe' (p134), but is less formal.

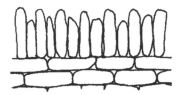

Many wallers simply judge the coping by eye, especially where the larger stones are of a similar height. Other wallers deliberately dispense with a line in order to create as jagged a finish as possible, in the belief that this deters sheep.

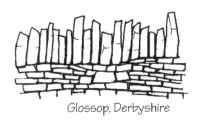

Glossop, Derbyshire

Occasional variations on this theme, not to be confused with formal buck and doe, include the use of much taller stone set at regular intervals amongst the more standard random stones. This example on Saddleworth Moor, Lancashire, has been used to effectively heighten a section of wall which goes over a rise, and where the height below the coping is only 20" (500mm) above ground level.

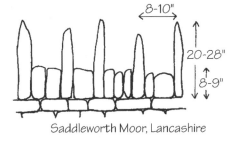

Saddleworth Moor, Lancashire

A similar method has been used to effectively increase the height of some walls near Blaenau Ffestiniog in North Wales. Thin slates, generally less than half an inch thick, and 6-8" (150-200mm) taller than the other copes are set every 12" (300mm) or so.

Level top

In this style great attention is placed on producing a level, even finish, and is suited to regularly shaped thin stone or blocky stone. Dressing of stone is usually necessary.

This method usually results in the individual stones being held more tightly than with other styles of coping. With thin stone there is good stone to stone contact, and any gaps between blocky stones are usually pinned.

Care must be taken that each stone merely brushes the line and does not displace it. Stones frequently have to be placed, removed and then dressed before being finally placed. Dips in the wall are used to accommodate larger copes, with very tall copes often fitted by removing a few stones from the top of the wall. To use smaller copes, some wallers prop up one or both faces of the stone until it brushes the line. For more detail on coping procedure, see page 56.

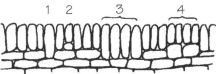

1 taller stone set into wall top
2 shorter stone propped up
3 section of wall built lower
4 section of wall built higher

Locked top

Rainsford-Hannay (1972) attributes this style to a John MacAdam of Craigengullich, even giving 1753 as the date of its invention, although this probably represents when it was first noted, as the general technique is not uncommon. In Rainsford-Hannay's description, the copings are usually of whinstone, about 10-12" (250-300mm) wide and tall, and seldom more than 2" (50mm) thick. Topstones, which normally need to be trimmed, are tightly placed along an entire section, and then specially selected thin pinnings are driven down between all the stones to lock them together.

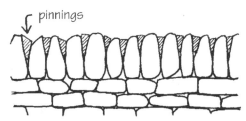

pinnings

By trimming irregular stone to produce regular copes and plenty of pinnings, this method produces a very tight top out of very irregular stone, and is particularly suited to the Galloway half dyke (p141). It is the predominant method of coping in South West Scotland, and is widely used elsewhere in Scotland, especially where the necessary trimming of unsuitable stone produces pinnings. The trimming and pinning makes this method fairly time consuming. Note the general principles of pinning (p130), taking care not to loosen the coping stones by forcing them apart.

This method is initially very strong, but as the pins work loose during settlement the coping tends to weaken with time.

Buck and doe

Buck-and-doe coping, sometimes known as 'cock-and-hen', alternates tall (buck) and short (doe) stones to give a castellated effect. Considerable trimming is usually necessary. It is most commonly found where a decorative finish is required on garden, roadside and estate walls. It may also have a practical use in dissuading animals to jump.

As the stone contact between neighbouring stones is less than with more even copings, buck-and-doe can be relatively weak. The taller the doe the more stable the coping. Where the doe is less than half the height of the buck, the bucks are fairly easily displaced, so many such copings are bedded on mortar.

The most common patterns use regular, relatively blocky stone, either alternating tall and short stone, or using stones of a similar size, but laying the alternate stones flat rather than upright. Generally the latter method is less stable, as the does are then usually less than half the height of the bucks. It should only be attempted with regular stone which gives good stone to stone contact..

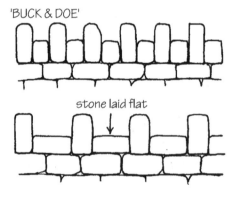

'BUCK & DOE'

stone laid flat

The decorative nature of this coping means that many variations are found, as in the example below. The triangular bucks are quaintly called 'Ben Vorlichs' by the locals, as they imitate the shape of a local mountain. The bucks and does sit centrally on a coverband, as they are not wide enough to span the wall.

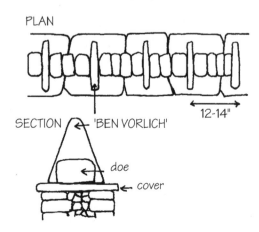

TRIANGULAR BUCK & DOE

PLAN

12-14"

SECTION   'BEN VORLICH'

doe

cover

The formalised nature of buck-and-doe copings makes repairs difficult, as the original stones are often broken or disappear with time. To maintain the pattern, specially trimmed stone may need to be imported, which will be expensive. Improvisation may be the answer, as in the Drummond Castle example, where the 'Ben Vorlichs' are spaced 24" (600mm) apart on repaired sections, instead of the original 12" (300mm) spacing.

TILTED OR SLOPING

Tilted copings vary from nearly flat to nearly upright, and are found constructed in many types of stone. Tilted copings tend to be found in areas of fairly regular stone, such as sandstone, as irregular stones are easier to fit upright than tilted.

Tilted copings require less stone than upright copings, but less height is gained. They can be stronger than upright copings, as each stone holds down its neighbour, making individual stones harder to dislodge. As the wall settles the coping tends to bind even tighter.

You should try to set all the stones at the same angle, although longer stones may need to be laid flatter if you are aiming for a fairly level top height. Try and correct the

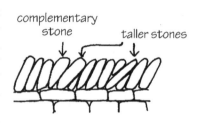

complementary stone   taller stones

angle with a complementary stone as shown, rather than by using small stones which are more likely to get dislodged.

In this example, the triangular stone and the sloping cope have been used as features to highlight the water trough below.

On slopes, a tilted coping is easier to build and more secure than other types (p64).

FLAT

Flat or slab coping is simply the use of slabs set flat on the wall top. In order to be stable, the slabs must be quite heavy, and consequently tend to be long slabs set along the wall. Take care when lifting and positioning the slabs (p22). This style is less stockproof than other copings, and is more often found on village or garden walls. However, it's not unknown on farm walls if the stone is suitably 'slabby' and more standard coping is hard to come by.

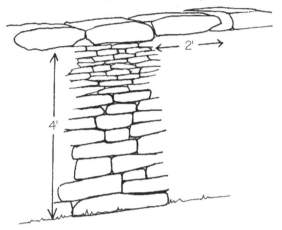

On this 4' (1.2m) upland farm wall, the slab coping varies in thickness from 2-8" (50-200mm). Most of the slabs are 2-3' (600-900mm) long, but there are numerous examples which are 6' (1.8m) and more in length.

As flat coping is lower than other types, the wall will need to be built higher than normal, and in total more stone will be required than for a wall with a standard cope. The simplest method of laying flat coping is to level off the wall and then set the slabs with their flatter side down, selecting and dressing the inside edges to ensure a good fit, and ensuring that all the levelling stones are firmly gripped, pinning if necessary.

Where the slabs vary in thickness, the wall may need to be finished to a different height for each slab.

For a more formal wall, the slabs are usually laid flatter side up for good appearance. The levelling stones need to be carefully chosen to accommodate the irregular surfaces of individual slabs.

Some wallers use a line to ensure a relatively level finish. The thickness of the individual slab can then be measured, and the wall levelled off accordingly. Each slab can then be lifted directly into position, without wasting effort on trial and error.

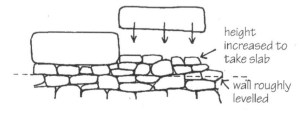

height increased to take slab

wall roughly levelled

If the slabs are easy to lift into position, or there are plenty of hands available, a different method can be used which gives a very even finish. With the line in place, set the slab in position, and then place building stones at the corners to give the required height. These are then set aside, the slab removed, and the stones replaced and levelled off between. Finally the slab is replaced to give a level finish.

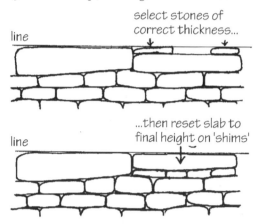

select stones of correct thickness...

line

...then reset slab to final height on 'shims'

line

Most slab coping is offset (p136). Often some of the slabs are 3-4" (75-100mm) narrower than the wall top, and are set to give an edge flush with one side of the wall. Care must be taken that the 'back' levelling stones are long enough to be gripped by the slabs.

COVERBANDS

Coverbands are a layer of slabs or 'covers' set like through-stones, immediately below the coping stones. The covers completely span the wall, greatly reducing the potential for water to get into the wall. The coverband also holds the top together, even if the coping becomes displaced.

The covers are much smaller than slab copes, as they are not reliant on 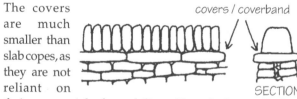 covers / coverband

SECTION

their own weight for stability, although they will often project from both sides of the wall. Covers must be set centrally, with an equal overlap on both sides, which will vary with the individual slabs. Coverbands are relatively common in sandstone areas with an abundance of thin flat stone, but are rarer elsewhere.

Construction procedure is similar to slab coping, although it's usual to level the wall off first, and 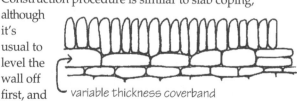 variable thickness coverband

then place the covers. This is done even when the covers vary in thickness, as these differences prove useful when fitting variable size cope stones to produce a level top.

Occasionally two thin covers are placed on top of each other where thicker covers are present, and there are insufficient tall cope stones to reach the required height. Alternatively, additional building stones can be placed on top of the cover, as this is quicker than building the section of wall higher.

Great care is taken to achieve complementary fits, although occasionally smaller stones are inserted in awkward 'V's where it is not possible to find a complementary stone, or dressing risks breaking the cover.

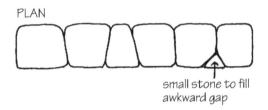

PLAN

small stone to fill
awkward gap

Some upland walls do not have a formal coverband, but have sections of walls with covers and small coping stones mixed in amongst larger coping stones.

This method is useful when rebuilding a wall of irregular stone which has a shortage of coping stone, and can use stone which would be too small for normal coping. It has been used, for example, on several in the Nant Ffrancon valley. Slabbier stone and longer, small faced building stones are set aside during the dismantling process to replace the missing coping. The wall is levelled as usual, and a section of taller coping is rebuilt. Using the saved stone, a section of irregular covers is laid with smaller copes above. This is repeated, maintaining a fairly level top throughout.

The resulting wall is slightly lower than the original, but looks as high because it has a regular, even top. It's also possible to achieve a very tight finish, as the taller copes are held at their base by the covers at each end of the section. The irregularity of the covers is an advantage, as it provides a good key for the smaller copes, which are wedged firmly between the taller copes.

OFFSET COPING

Coping is not always set centrally on the wall, but may be offset to one side. This is generally the case in much of North Wales and parts of the Lake District, where the nature of the local stone often results in walls being too wide at the top for the available coping stone. Rather than set the stone centrally which would leave a pronounced lip on either side, the stone is offset with the space at the back

filled with the poorer stone left over from the building process.

In these areas the ground level often differs on either side of the wall, notably on the 'mountain walls' which separate the summer hill grazing from the lower winter grazing. The ground level is often about 12" (300mm) higher on the uphill side, making the wall vulnerable from that side, which is subject to pressure from sheep trying to get from the poorer hill grazing in summer to the better lower pastures. The coping is therefore set to the uphill side, in order to effectively increase the height of the wall from that side.

Procedure

1 When levelling the wall, use the longest stones first along the back of the wall, so they will be overlapped by the copes.

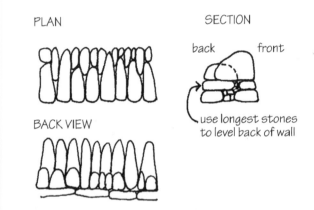

PLAN

SECTION

back   front

use longest stones
to level back of wall

BACK VIEW

2 In North Wales the 'best' or squarest faces of the copes are set to the same side, which limits the options to get good complementary fits between the stones. It's easier if stones are positioned as for a clawdd (p80), placing stones where they best fit, rather than working in a sequence. The resulting clusters of copes should then be firmly wedged with a stone hammered into each gap.

3 Any longer copes which straddle the wall should be spaced at intervals to help the back stones key together.

4 Wedge rubble along the back, carefully matching it with the gaps.

5 Once the back has been completely wedged, any gaps at the front and then between the tops are wedged as for standard coping (p57).

In the southern part of the Lake District triangular copes are used, set with the tops slightly overhanging as a further deterrent to stock. Occasionally the back of the wall is levelled off around an inch (25mm) higher than the front, to help achieve this overhang.

SECTION

Offset coping also occurs on many estate and other walls where an even edge is required on the 'show' side of the wall. Offset coping is not as secure as standard coping, as there are more smaller stones which can work loose. It also places an uneven load on the wall, which may affect its long term stability.

DOUBLE

Double coping consists of a row of coping along either side of the wall top, and is generally only found where the wall top is too wide to be straddled by a single row of copes. It is particularly common on the basalt walls of Skye, where the blocky stone results in wide walls. Basalt is amongst the heaviest rock found in Britain, and to be straddled by a single cope would require stones too heavy to lift.

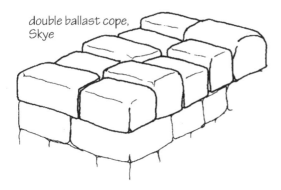

double ballast cope, Skye

The stones tend to have relatively square faces, about 6-8" (150-200mm) square. They project slightly, but given their weight and good bases, are very solid. Sometimes rubble is set on top to increase the height. This method can also be found in areas of blocky sandstone, particularly in parts of South Wales.

Occasionally thinner stone is used to create a double upright cope on wider walls. Stagger the joins, as shown, to increase stability.

PLAN

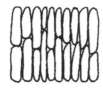

This method is generally satisfactory provided the stones, when in position, are fairly 'short'. Any stones which are taller than they are long tend to be easily displaced. They can't be used the other way up, with their long axis across the wall, as this then leaves insufficient space to fit another stone. The normal rule is that stones for double coping must not be taller than half the width of the top of the wall, or otherwise they will be taller than they are long.

However, this example, from Tintagel, Cornwall, uses a slate cope on one side, with slates 12-20" (300-500mm) high

and 12" (300mm) deep very tightly jammed with thinner wedges. The other side, which is higher relative to ground level, has a less intimidating cope of squarer stones, 10-12" (250-300mm) high.

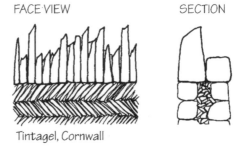

FACE VIEW   SECTION

Tintagel, Cornwall

SHAPED COPING

Shaped coping, usually of sandstone, is common on garden and estate walls, and is normally mortared or set on a bed of mortar. The most common shapes are semicircular or saddleback, followed by triangular, with half-octagon and extended semicircles sometimes found.

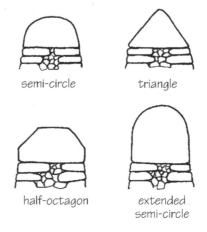

semi-circle   triangle

half-octagon   extended
                      semi-circle

'Buck and doe' variations can also be found, with alternating taller and shorter versions of particular shapes. Shaped coping is normally set on a level top, with slight variations accommodated by the use of a mortar bed.

Sandstone is the usual material for shaped stones because it can be easily sawn, but many other types of stone walls have copes roughly dressed to a semicircle. These roughly shaped copes tend to be found nearer farmhouses or settlements, and are sporadic rather than widespread. However there are exceptions, with virtually every wall on the Isle of Bute having a rounded cope, of either sandstone, slate or whin. Even the rougher copes on some coastal walls mix the stone cleverly to give an overall rounded effect.

Occasionally other methods are used to achieve a shaped top. One example from the Cotswolds is described on page 139, and another near Seend, between Melksham and Devizes, uses small stones mortared into a semicircle. The wall in Portesham, Dorset (p132), has a similar mortared cope in a triangular shape.

RUBBLE FINISH

Rubble or rough-stone copings use any size and type of stone, arranged loosely according to circumstances. Many rubble-finished walls predate the Parliamentary Enclosure era, or form less important subdivision walls within more neatly coped boundaries.

On wider wall tops the cope may be little more than a pile of rubble. On more normal size wall tops each stone may span the top, but is merely set on a firm base with little attempt to make a good fit to adjacent stones.

rubble cope on wide wall

rubble cope on normal-width wall

Rubble coping tends to be used on walls of less regular stone which have little good coping stone, and uses up the poorer stone left over during building. It is relatively quick and easy to build, but is not as solid as a more formal cope.

With care, it's possible to create a more durable rubble cope where the stones do not span the wall top. The technique involves cladding the wall top with closely fitting rubble, rather similar to the random coursing of a clawdd (p78), only in the horizontal plane. Start by placing the best stones length in to make a cope along both edges of the wall top, fitting them as tightly as possible. Then carefully fill the gap between with smaller rubble, fitting complementary shapes together and hammering the smallest pieces into any small gaps. Choose larger stones for any dips so that the top is relatively level.

PLAN

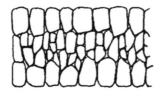

This technique is made easier if you can narrow the wall slightly from its original width, as these type of walls tend to be wide and contain a lot of hearting. This will provide a greater selection of stone from which complementary shapes can be chosen. The finished cope will be stronger and much more attractive than the traditional pile of rubble. Don't narrow the wall too much though, or there will only be room for a double coping.

MORTARED COPINGS

Formal patterns of coping are often mortared to help achieve a neat finish, secure a less stable design, or simply to prevent theft of expensive shaped stones. Mortared copes are often found around car-parks or other easily accessible places where damage and theft is more likely.

In the Cotswolds many of the random copes on standard walls are mortared, partly to deter thieves, but also because the stones are usually too small and light to anchor the courses below, with many small and traced stones.

Procedure

Use a lime mortar rather than a cement mortar, as it is more flexible. The colour of the mortar is important, especially if you are doing a repair to match with existing mortar. The colour will depend on the colour of the sand, and on any colourant added, and is largely a matter of trial and error. Obtain sand from a consistent source, so that you get to know the colour of the mortar. As necessary use a colourant such as Cementone, in black or brown, and use less than recommended by the manufacturer. A suggested measure is a large coffee jar lid of colourant to a mixer load of mortar!

1 Mix up mortar in a proportion of 1:3 lime to sand by volume. Where extra strength is required a small amount of cement should be added to the dry lime-sand mixture in a proportion of 1:6. If you must use all cement instead of lime, make the mixture 1:4 cement to sand if mixing by hand, or 1:6 if mixing by machine.

2 Add water slowly to the dry mortar until it becomes workable. The mortar should be stiff enough to stay on the trowel.

3 Spread a bed of mortar about 1" (25mm) deep along about 24" (600mm) of the wall's top, set in about 1" (25mm) from the edge of the wall.

4 Position the first coping stone on the wall and bed it down. Then mortar the edge against which the second stone will be placed.

5 Push the second stone tightly against the first, making sure there are no air pockets between the two. Then mortar the edge against which the third stone will be placed.

6 Continue in the same way. Add mortar as necessary so the stones sit upright.

right

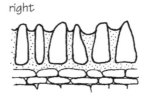

wrong

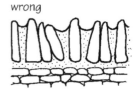

7 Add additional mortar to any places where it is uneven, a process called pointing.

8 Frequently the mortar is left rough, but if a neater finish is required you can smooth between the stones using a wet sack or rag, or a small brush. This works best if the mortar has gone off a little.

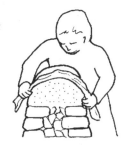

The overall effect is better if the bed of mortar between and below the stones is about the same thickness.

In parts of the Cotswolds where full sized stones are infrequent, smaller stones are paired as shown. For strength it is best to have at least one full sized stone between every

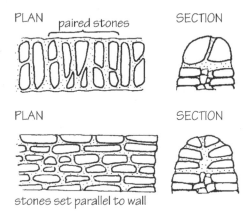

PLAN paired stones

SECTION

PLAN

SECTION

stones set parallel to wall

four or five pairs.

Where better coping stones are available, they are often only set on a bed of mortar. The general principles of coping should still be followed, including any pinning and wedging, as the mortar is only a supplement to the strength of the coping.

The use of mortar may be considered unsightly, and a hidden, but less secure method can be used. A 1" (25mm) deep bead of mortar 4-6" (100-150mm) wide is laid along the centre of the wall top, and the stones are then positioned. Any visible mortar can be removed or masked with a pin.

Single walls or dykes

Walls partly or completely of stonework one stone thick can be found in most areas where large building stone predominates, notably in Scotland and South West England. Single walls are nearly always built of field clearance stone, as opposed to quarried stone, and the rock type is usually igneous, with granite the most common type. Because of the size of the larger boulders, a team of two wallers is usually needed. Take great care with moving large stones (p22).

There are two main styles of single walling. The 'single' has single stonework throughout. The 'half-single' is built double in the lower part, with the upper part single, and is widespread across much of Scotland. The half-single probably developed as a way of using both large and smaller stones in the same wall. For the same reason, sections of single wall are sometimes mixed in with double, a style known as 'butt and hudd' (p144).

Singles are rarer than half-singles in Scotland, being mainly associated with granite areas such as the South West and parts of the North. In Aberdeenshire granite double walls predominate. As single walling is characteristic of Scotland, the following information concentrates on Scottish methods and terms. To distinguish between single dykes and 'standard' walls the Scots refer to the latter type of stonework as 'double' or 'doubling', as it has two skins of stone. A half-dyke is often termed a Galloway dyke, the history of which is discussed in Rainsford-Hannay (1972) and Prevost (1957).

Single dyking has several advantages over double. It is simpler and faster to build and repair, and generally uses less stone for a given height. It requires tough coarse-grained stone such as granite in order to bind properly, and the style is a good use of this type of stone. Single dyking is surprisingly stable, but looks so unsteady that all stock, including the notoriously adventurous black-faced sheep, are supposed to be deterred from climbing it. Single and half-dyking require less hearting than a double wall, and regular topstones are not required. Single dyking does not however give as much shelter as double stonework, because of the gaps between the stones.

DYKING PROCEDURE

Dismantling

Generally the dyke is dismantled to one side only, leaving a working space of about 3' (900mm), although larger stones might be spread on both sides. Stones should be reasonably well spread to give good access to individual stones, especially larger boulders. Set any pins or wedges to one side.

Foundation

The foundation of single dykes can either be double stones as for 'standard' double walls, single stones or a mixture of the two. A double foundation provides a good level start to the wall and disperses weight well, sometimes aided by a small scarcement (p127), and is preferred by many single dykers. It also uses up some of the stone which, in single walling terms, is rather small.

For a double foundation follow the procedure given on page 48. For a single foundation, dig the trench to an accurate line, and then set the stones centrally by eye. Occasional long stones should be accommodated by widening the trench at that point, and setting the stone so that it extends equally on both sides. It's permissible to 'trace' stones (p51), provided that they completely span the wall, or half span it. A three-quarter span is no good, as it leaves a gap too narrow to place a secure stone.

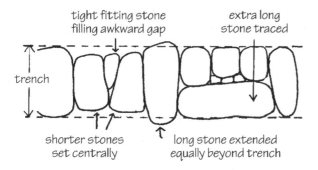

tight fitting stone filling awkward gap

extra long stone traced

trench

shorter stones set centrally

long stone extended equally beyond trench

Profile

Whilst the profile of single walls is 'A' shaped, as with double walls, the width of the single stones in any layer varies, and consequently the face is not flat and frames are not appropriate.

Building

Stones are set 'upright', like coping.

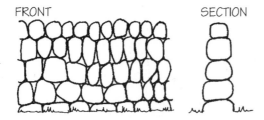

FRONT

SECTION

The pattern is generally determined by the need to maintain very good contact between stones. Fairly regular stones can be layered and resemble coursing. Where the stone is less regular the pattern is more random, but the stones are still set upright.

Generally the size of stone decreases higher up the wall, but the location of any individual stone is determined more by its fit across the wall than its height, as care needs to be taken to maintain the overall 'A' shaped profile. 'Taller' stones are thus often placed on top of 'shorter' ones.

As with a doubled wall, work should be sequential, completing one layer before starting on the next. The techniques are in many respects similar to those of clawdd construction (p78), with the stones set vertically on edge and jammed together, or like setting rows of topstones on top of each other.

Essentially the technique is 'upside down' compared to doubled walling, where the rule for each stone is generally 'flat side down, irregular side up'. Single walling is stronger if the irregular side is down, fitting into gaps and dips, with

the weight of the wall forcing the stones down and tightening the structure. With the use of fewer, larger stones, there is less flexibility to build over and around problems compared to doubled walling.

Keep the following in mind when placing each stone:

a The longest face of the stone should be set across the wall. This rule should only be broken for very long stones which still span the width of the wall, as in the example from the Isle of Bute (p143).

b Ensure that each stone is centralised.

PLAN

c Ideally each stone should sit securely without wedging or pinning from the face. Wedging an inside edge is acceptable, but best avoided. If a stone will not sit without front pinning try to find somewhere else to use it. Pins can fairly easily 'pop' and should ideally be used only to consolidate a stable stone, and not to wedge one into position.

d Try to provide as level a surface as possible for the next layer, as steps between stones will be difficult to build on. Occasionally the tops of larger bouldery stone are 'scalloped' with a hammer to provide a better bed for the next layer.

e Minimise the gaps. Any grooves that are formed between stones should be filled by the stone above.

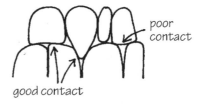

poor contact

good contact

f Domed and rounded stones are awkward to use and should not be placed 'dome' up. If the dome cannot be dressed, it should be jammed into a suitable dip, preferably without pinning.

g Ridged stones should be placed with the ridges across the wall. If placed with ridges along the wall they are almost impossible to build on.

Pinning

Pinning of single walls is subject to some debate. Most old single walls have many gaps which are not pinned. Some wallers claim this was deliberate, in order to create a 'fragile and tottering appearance' (Rainsford-Hannay, 1972) that would discourage sheep from jumping. It's claimed that sheep won't try to jump a wall which they can see through. Other wallers maintain that there would have been extensive pinning originally, but that much has worked loose during settlement.

The 'belt and braces' approach is favoured by some wallers today, arguing that as the wall settles it will grip more tightly the pins that are needed, and the others will slip out anyway. Others claim that the real skill lies in building a strong but fragile-looking structure, without too much pinning.

Pinning is carried out as for other walls (p130), usually pinning each section as you build.

Coping

Coping is nearly always the level top type (p133).

The line for the top of the coping (p56) is normally set up before the layer preceding the coping stones is laid on the wall. This allows the stones in this layer to be chosen to give the right height for the available coping stones to fit. Normally a level finish should be avoided for the layer below the coping, unless the coping stones are of unusually uniform size.

Any taller coping should be used in gaps or dips, and occasionally very large stones are used to 'jump' from the preceding layer to the top of the cope. This helps to promote a tighter cope, as it provides a solid stone against which the others can key.

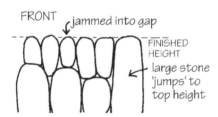

Avoid sloping taller coping to achieve the correct finished height, unless it is held by a complementary stone.

Nearly all wallers agree that every nook and cranny between the coping stones, and between the cope and the preceding layer, should be pinned, as the cope stones rarely sit as well as they would on a doubled wall top. Regardless of the care taken though, the coping is relatively fragile, and so 'scare' fences of one or two strands of barbed wire alongside the coping are common in cattle areas.

Further considerations

Whilst most stones are set vertically, awkward shapes can be sloped provided this is done to make them sit solidly, and that good contact is maintained with neighbouring stones. Large stones are sometimes set horizontally, although there is a tendency for them to wobble on any slight irregularity. They need to be matched carefully to the layer below, either 'very flat on very flat', or of a suitable shape to fit any irregularities.

Although it's preferable to avoid running joints between layers, it's more important to ensure that each stone sits solidly and has good contact with its neighbours. The principles are similar to those for cloddiau (p79).

For other considerations see 'general points' below (p142).

Galloway dykes

The Galloway or half-dyke probably developed as the best way to use supplies of stone that were mainly large and medium size, with little hearting. The large stones used in the upper single part would make a very wide wall if used double. It is an efficient walling style, using less stone at any given height than a double wall.

The lower half of a Galloway dyke is built as a standard 'doubled' wall, although the stone is often smaller than would occur at this height in other walls, as it comprises all those stones not large enough to build the single.

The single must consist of at least three layers of single to be a true half-dyke. Many Scottish dykes have a thick irregular cover plus level coping, but these are not half-dykes.

DIMENSIONS

According to Rainsford-Hannay (1972) and Prevost (1957), the true Galloway dyke was of the dimensions shown. Prevost gives the finished height as between 5'3" (1.6m) and 6' (1.8m), and specifies throughs at 1'9" (530mm). He contrasts the Galloway dyke with the normal half-dyke, where the doubled section extends to half the wall height.

In practice the Galloway dyke or half-dyke varies in dimension and detail from area to area. The cover-band usually

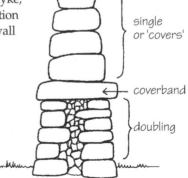

projects by up to 2" (50mm), with larger projections avoided as cattle rub on them, and any stones of this length should be used as throughs, lower in the wall. A useful rule of thumb is to use the size of the coverband stones to determine the height and width of the double. The double is battered about the same as a standard dry stone wall, at 1:6 to 1:7, or 1" of batter for every 6-7" (1cm for every 6-7cm).

The building of the single follows the same principles given above, with a few refinements. Many dykers refer to all of the stones of the single as 'covers'.

PROCEDURE

Dismantling

The doubling stone is set out on both sides as for a standard wall, and the covers and single stones are set out on one side only. If the double contains throughs it's usually best to set these out on the opposite side of the wall to the covers and singles, so you don't muddle them up.

Foundation

Unlike standard walls, the largest stones do not necessarily form the foundation, but are used instead in the single section of the wall, so the foundation stones are often much smaller than normal. Occasionally stones which are too large to be lifted up to the single section are used in the foundation, but if you are rebuilding, all the single stones have to be saved for re-use as singles, unless additional stone is available.

Short line bars are often used for the double, although the irregularity of the single makes them less appropriate higher up.

Hearting and pins

Having sufficient hearting and pins is often a problem with rebuilds, and it's all too easy to use up all the pins as hearting. Dressing of the singling and coping may produce some usable pins, though rarely enough. It's not advisable to skimp on hearting, so you are likely to need to bring in some more.

Throughs

Throughs are necessary for higher doubles, and advisable for lower doubles, as the building stones are relatively small for their position in the wall, and anything that helps resist bulging or uneven settlement is helpful.

If the double is over about 20" (500mm) high, it usually contains projecting throughstones at 36" (900mm) centres. The double is capped by a coverband on which the single is built.

GENERAL POINTS

These points apply to single dykes, half-dykes and Galloway dykes.

Heads

The construction of heads to single walls can be a problem. Care has to be taken to ensure that joints are crossed, although it is often difficult to achieve more than minimal overlapping.

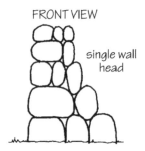

FRONT VIEW

single wall head

With a Galloway dyke, it may be advisable to sacrifice one or two of the stones from the first layer of covers and use them in the head. Although you may then have to use less suitable stone for one or two covers, it's more important that the head is really solid.

Another method found in some Galloway dykes is to build a standard wall head, merging this with the rest of the dyke.

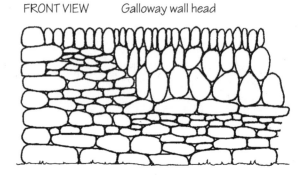

FRONT VIEW   Galloway wall head

Curves

Curves present a problem on single walls. Care must be taken to avoid 'fanning' (p68) by using complementary shapes, which is easier with more irregular stone. Level bedded stone, such as many sandstones, are too regular and difficult to build to a curve.

Turf top

In areas where turf tops are common, these can be used on single walls. There is no need to level the final layer, but it must be wide enough to take the turf. Some dykers cut the turf about twice the width of the wall top, and then drape the turf over, as this helps prevent drying out and provides a more secure and substantial finish.

Rosehall, near Lairg

Turf tops may need maintenance, as if the turves dry out they will get displaced. Many single walls look as if they are disintegrating, but it is merely that the rough top has become exposed because the turf has gone.

Clashing

The single sections of some Galloway walls in South West Scotland are pointed with mortar or 'clashed' after completion, to help prevent cattle damage.

Theoretically the dyke should be left to settle for a year after completion, before the singling is roughly pointed with a 5:1 mix of coarse sand:cement. Tacky mortar is literally thrown into all the gaps and joints, left for half an hour or so until it is just going off, then pushed in and finished with a soft brush.

This can look unsightly at first, although the damp climate means it weathers quickly and has a softer look after 4-5 years.

REGIONAL VARIATIONS

As with all types of wall, the pattern of singles and Galloways varies from place to place, and the following are just some of the examples which can be found.

Scotland

Ardmaleish Farm, Isle of Bute

Here the single is a mix of irregular sandstone lumps and slate, with the use of long slates to help bind the smaller slates. The longer slates would normally be placed first and their bases secured, with subsequent stones forced down into the gaps between them. The use of rounded stone in

the upper layers does not work well, as it does not bind with the slate. The single footing is unusual in that most of the stones are set vertically rather than flat.

Braentra, Srathrusdale

A very random single, in terms of layers, and also mixes vertical, flat and angled stones. The singles of Strathrusdale contain some impressive boulders, but unfortunately many of the roadside walls are falling into serious disrepair, damaged by snow ploughs piling snow against them, and the raising of the road surface causing drainage problems along the base of the wall.

Laid, Loch Erboll

This single at Laid, Loch Erboll, contains small 'pockets' of doubling, with foundations a mixture of standard double, single and shiners (p128).

Glen Too, Dumfries & Galloway

This half-dyke in Glen Too has a thin, flat coverband, with a very random single of angular stone.

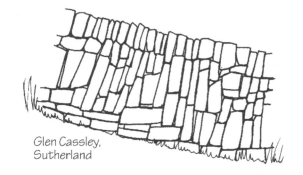

Glen Cassley, Sutherland

Incorporating stones from the remains of a broch (p97), this half-dyke in Glen Cassley is thought to be over 150 years old, but the singling is still very solid. The doubling is only 12" (300mm) high, topped with singling of upright sandstone laid perpendicular to the slope. The half-dyke has very solid heads at the bottom of the slope, built as for standard walls.

Borgue, Dumfries & Galloway

A Galloway dyke of whin, with random, angular singling and tilted coping.

'BUTT & HUDD'

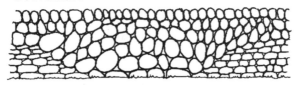

Murray-Usher Estate, Dumfries & Galloway

The 'butt and hudd' style mixes single and double walling in fairly random sections along the wall, according to the stone available.

Rest of Britain

In the rest of Britain, occasional single walls of the type described above can be found in areas where the walling stone tends to boulders. More commonly though, single walls are built with the stone predominantly laid flat, a

Westerdale, North York Moors

style which is only rarely found in Scotland.

The problems of sitting 'flat' stones solidly in a single are outlined on page 141. The coping is also often weak, as being laid flat, there is no cohesion between the stones.

Singles of large flat stones can be very secure, as seen in the walls on Dartmoor, which has the most extensive area of single walling outside Scotland.

near Helltoe Rock, Dartmoor

Most of the Dartmoor singles are only three or four stones high, even when 4' (1.2m) high. Wedges are often used, with the weight of the granite holding them very securely. The cope is less secure, especially where smaller stones are used.

The example below demonstrates amazing craftsmanship, being built of large blocks expertly fitted together and finished to a level top. The largest block, in the top centre, is 5'2" (1.55m) long, 1'10" (550mm) high, and 1'5" (420mm) wide, and must weigh almost a tonne. A characteristic of these granite singles is that all the stones are set to give an even face on one side of the wall, with an undulating back face, rather than being set centrally as in the Scottish singles.

near Princetown, Dartmoor

Rarely, half-singles are built to a herringbone pattern.

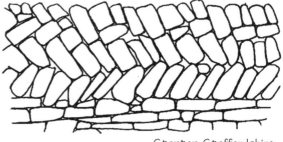

Stanton, Staffordshire

Stone fences

Stone fences, also known as flag fences or walls, slate fences or tombstone walls, consist of a single line of stones set vertically on edge. Most walling areas with suitable large slabs have the occasional example. These may represent the remnants of a more extensive system which was mainly replaced because, at only about 30" (750mm) high, the fences were too low to contain modern breeds of cattle and sheep. In a few areas stone fences still form a significant part of the boundary system.

Generally stone fences are quicker to build and repair than dry stone walls. Very heavy slabs can be a problem, and a winch or other machinery may be needed to get them upright. Where long lengths of stone fence have assumed a 'drunken' appearance from years of neglect, the time advantage over dry stone walls is minimal, as it takes a long time to remove and re-site all the stones.

Sometimes a stone fence has a hedge planted alongside it, particularly alongside roads. This serves the same function as a 'Galloway hedge' (p85), with the stone fence protecting the base of the hedge, and the hedge adding to the height of the boundary. However, the roots inevitably tilt the flags so this is not usually a very durable combination.

CAITHNESS FLAGS

The flag fences of Caithness comprise the most extensive stone fence system in Britain. The flags are old red sandstone, usually 1.25-2" (30-50mm) thick, and about 30" (750mm) out of the ground. Unlike many other stone fences, the individual stones are overlapped and the top is very level. The overlaps vary considerably from 2-9" (50-230mm), with about the middle of this range being the norm. The regularity of the stone makes this overlapping method relatively easy to build, and the overlaps provide mutual support for the flags.

The flags are set in a narrow trench about 12" (450mm) deep, and then the soil is compacted back in thin layers. Shorter slabs are packed higher to give a level top. Slabs with less than 12" (300mm) in the ground are not particularly stable, and are best sited between solid neighbours. Fences constructed entirely of shorter slabs are not recommended, as they soon tilt out of position.

Many Caithness flags have had fences added, either to aid stockproofing or to protect the flags from cattle damage. Square fence posts are driven in at about 10-17' (3-5m) intervals on alternate sides of the flags, projecting about 6-8" (150-200mm) above them, and supporting one or two strands of barbed wire.

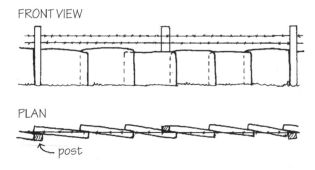

FRONT VIEW

PLAN

post

LAKELAND SLATE FENCES

Stone fences are also relatively common in parts of the Lake District along the boundary of the Silurian slates and the

Borrowdale volcanics, where the Coniston and Brathay flags occur.

Some are simply overlapped using the angle of the edges, as shown.

PLAN

Others have been carefully shaped so that the slabs interlock. This forms a stronger structure than the overlapping Caithness style, as the slabs cannot move in either direction. This interlocking is more prevalent on the older stone fences, presumably because of the time and skill required to shape the flags. More modern stone fences and repaired sections tend to have the simpler overlap. The tops show variation in level, from as low as 18" (450mm) to over 30" (750mm).

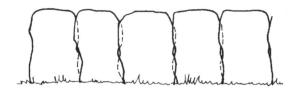

OTHER STONE FENCES

In more urban settings thin sandstone flags can sometimes be found fastened with iron plates bolted on either side. Beddall (1950) describes such fences in the area of Rochdale and Todmorden, made of thin gritstone flags about 6' (1.8m) high, 2' (600mm) wide and 3-4" (75-100mm) thick.

Isolated examples of stone fences are found where thick sandstone slabs occur.

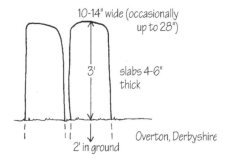

10-14" wide (occasionally up to 28")

3'

slabs 4-6" thick

2' in ground

Overton, Derbyshire

This fence (above) stretches for about 450 yards (400m), although there are extensive gaps.

Stanton, Derbyshire

The fence at Stanton, Derbyshire is an unusually high stone fence, with the stones butted together, and the height maintained by balancing stones lengthways on the shorter uprights. This fence partly encloses a ridge and furrow field, indicating its age.

At Wycoller Country Park, near Colne, Lancashire, there are several stone fences which are thought to be the remains of 13th century 'vaccary' or cattle enclosures. Generally the slabs are of similar dimension to those at Overton, but there are a few very large slabs, 5" (130mm) thick, 6' (1.8m) wide, and about 36" (900mm) out of the ground.

In North Wales many areas of slate, shale or mudstones have remnants of stone fences of varying height, with 2-6" (50-150mm) gaps between stones, and frequently mixed in with sections of standard walling. The most common form though are the slate fences found in the slate mining areas of Bethesda and Corris. These comprise narrow slates spaced about 2-3" (50-75mm) apart, and wired together at the top.

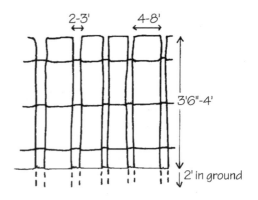

Originally the wires were fitted by twisting them together and then passing them around the next slate. For repairs, it's easier to run two wires the whole length of the fence, and then twist them together between the fence with a stout piece of wood or similar, like a windlass. Occasionally the wires are simply woven between the slates, but the twisted method is stronger.

Conservation and the volunteer worker

BTCV is the largest practical conservation organisation in the UK. It supports more than 85,000 volunteers from all sections of the community in activities to protect and improve the environment. With more than 110 offices around the UK, BTCV is able to work in a range of areas carrying out different activities. The Practical Handbooks series is one of the ways of helping to ensure that work undertaken by BTCV, volunteers and other conservationists is to the highest standard.

To ensure the success of any conservation project, it is important to establish:

* Whether it is a worthwhile conservation project. Any work to be carried out should respond to a real need which is directly related to a broad framework of development. In terms of conservation, this means that projects should be undertaken as integral parts of site management plans, not as isolated exercises. The prime purpose of the work should also be made clear. For instance is it to improve local wildlife habitats or to improve access to the countryside?

* That the work is suitable for volunteers. Volunteers cannot successfully tackle all types of work and they should not be involved where there is a risk of serious accident or injury, where machines can do the same job more effectively and for a lower cost, or where the skills required are beyond their capabilities. The latter can be overcome if professional training is provided so that a situation can be avoided where volunteers become dispirited or the work is not done to a high standard.

* Where the project will take place and how much time it will take to complete. Once this has been done it is necessary to establish whether there are any hazards and risks associated with the site.

* Whether the work should be done by paid staff. Voluntary service should not replace paid, local labour but complement it. Employers should make sure in advance that the position of volunteers and paid workers is clear with respect to any relevant labour unions.

Volunteers should not be regarded as providing 'free labour'. Someone has to pay for transport, materials, tools, insurance, refreshments and any accommodation charges. Before each party makes a commitment to a project it should be clear who is to pay for what. While volunteers may willingly fund their own work, clients should be prepared to contribute and should not assume that all volunteers, who are already giving their time and effort, will be able to meet other expenses out of their own pockets. Several grant-aiding bodies may help pay the cost of environmental and conservation projects. For details of grants and awards, contact BTCV at the address below. Comprehensive information is available in publications by the Charities Aid Foundation (see page 148).

It is important that volunteer workers are covered by public liability insurance for any damage or injury they may cause to third party property or to the public. Cover of at least two million pounds is recommended. Additional insurance to compensate the volunteer for injury to him or herself or to other volunteers on a project should also be considered. Specially tailored insurance is available through BTCV's own Group Membership Scheme. Contact the Local Groups Unit at the address below.

The volunteer group organiser should visit the work site well before the project to check that it is suitable and that volunteers will not be exploited, and to plan the best size of working party and the proper tools and equipment. Volunteers should be advised in advance on suitable clothing for the expected conditions, they should be physically fit and come prepared for work. Above all, individuals should genuinely want to volunteer – those 'press-ganged' into volunteering may do more harm than good and will not enjoy the benefits associated with volunteering. Young volunteers need more supervision and are best suited to less strenuous jobs, and it is recommended that where they are involved, the project should emphasise education. Recent legislation, including The Children Act, gives comprehensive guidance on supervisory ratios and other means to safeguard the welfare of young people. The recommendations of the Home Office report *Safe from harm*, should also be followed, and for any activities in remote areas, organisers should also be fully aware of the Adventure Activities Licensing Regulations.

Volunteer group organisers and clients should keep records of the work undertaken: the date of the project, jobs done, techniques used, number of volunteers and details of any notable events including accidents, unusual 'finds', publicity etc. Such information makes it easier to handle problems or queries which may arise after the project. It also provides a background on the project site for future visits, supplies practical data by which the site management plan can be evaluated and allows an assessment to be made of the volunteer effort.

As well as directly managing project work, whether for a day or more, BTCV supports volunteers indirectly through the local group service, runs a year round programme of training courses and organises hundreds of conservation working holidays in the UK and abroad. To find out more about what opportunities are available please contact BTCV (address on page ii).

Contacts

This is a list of some of the organisations and websites in the UK which are involved with conservation, countryside management and wider environmental concerns. The BTCV web site (www.btcv.org) provides links to a very large number of environmental organisations throughout the world.

Arboricultural Association
Ampfield House, Romsey, Hants SO51 9PA
Tel:01794 368717
www.trees.org.uk

Association for the Protection of Rural Scotland
Gladstone's Land (3rd floor), 483 Lawnmarket,
Edinburgh EH1 2NT
Tel: 0131 225 7012
www.aprs.org.uk

Brogdale Horticultural Trust
Brogdale Road, Faversham, Kent ME13 8XZ
Tel: 01795 535286
www.brogdale.org.uk

Common Ground
Gold Hill House, 21 High Street, Shaftesbury
Dorset SP7 8JE
Tel: 01747 850820
www.commonground.org.uk

Conservation Volunteers Northern Ireland (CVNI)
159 Ravenhill Road, Belfast BT6 0BP
Tel: 028 9064 5169
www.cvni.org.uk

Council for the Protection of Rural England (CPRE)
128 Southwark Street,
London SE1 0SW
Tel: 020 7981 2800
www.cpre.org.uk

Council for the Protection of Rural Wales
Ty Gwyn , 31 High St, Welshpool, Powys SY21 7YD
Tel: 01938 552525
www.cprw.org.uk

Countryside Agency (England)
John Dower House, Crescent Place, Cheltenham
Gloucester GL50 3RA
Tel: 01242 521381
www.countryside.gov.uk

Countryside Council for Wales
Maes y Ffynnon, Penrhosgarnedd, Bangor,
Gwynedd LL57 2DW
Tel: 0845 1306229
www.ccw.gov.uk

Countryside Management Association
Writtle College, Lordship Road, Writtle, Chelmsford,
Essex CM1 3RR
Tel: 01245 424116
www.countrysidemanagement.org.uk

Dep. for Environment, Food & Rural Affairs (Defra)
Information Resource Centre, Lower Ground Floor,
Ergon House, c/o Nobel House, 17 Smith Square,
London SW1P 3JR
Tel: 020 7238 6000
Helpline: 08459 335577
www.defra.gov.uk

Department of Agriculture and Rural Development for Northern Ireland
Dundonald House, Upper Newtownards Road,
Belfast BT4 3SB
Tel: 028 9052 4999
www.dardni.gov.uk

Dry Stone Walling Association
Westmorland County Showground, Lane Farm,
Crooklands, Milnthorpe, Cumbria LA7 7NH
Tel: 01539 567953
www.dswa.org.uk

English Heritage
Fortress House, 23 Savile Row, London W1X 1AB
Tel: 020 7973 3000

English Nature
Northminster House, Peterborough PE1 1UA
Tel: 01733 455000
www.english-nature.org.uk

Environment Council
212 High Holborn, London WC1V 7BF
Tel: 020 7836 2626
www.the-environment-council.org.uk

Farming and Wildlife Advisory Group
National Agricultural Centre, Stoneleigh, Kenilworth,
Warwickshire CV8 2RX
Tel: 024 7669 6699
www.fwag.org.uk

Fieldfare Trust
67a The Wicker, Sheffield, South Yorkshire S3 8HT
Tel: 0114 270 1668
www.fieldfare.org.uk

Flora locale
www.floralocale.org

Forestry Commission
231 Corstorphine Road, Edinburgh EH12 7AT
Tel: 0131 334 0303
www.forestry.gov.uk

Game Conservancy Trust
Fordingbridge, Hampshire SP6 1EF
Tel: 01425 652381
www.gct.org.uk

The Green Wood Trust
Station Road, Coalbrookdale, Telford,
Shropshire TF8 7DR
Tel: 01952 432769
www.greenwoodtrust.org.uk

Henry Doubleday Research Association
Ryton Organic Gardens, Coventry CV8 3LG
Tel: 024 7630 3517
www.hdra.org.uk

Lantra (National training organisation for the
land based sector)
National Agricultural Centre, Kenilworth,
Warwickshire CV8 2LG
Tel: 024 7669 6996
www.lantra.co.uk

Landlife
National Wildflower Centre, Court Hey Park,
Liverpool L16 3NA
Tel: 0151 737 1819
www.landlife.org.uk

National Hedgelaying Society
Hon Secretary: Bruce Maley, Waypost, Vines Cross,
East Sussex TN21 9EG
Tel: 01959 565678
www.**hedgelaying.org**.uk

National Proficiency Tests Council
Avenue J, National Agricultural Centre, Stoneleigh,
Warwickshire CV8 2LG
Tel: 024 768 57300
www.nptc.org.uk

National Stone Centre
Porter Lane, Middleton, Wirksworth,
Derbyshire DE4 4LS
Tel: 01629 824833
www.nationalstonecentre.org.uk

National Urban Forestry Unit
The Science Park, Stafford Road,
Wolverhampton WV10 9RT
Tel: 01902 828600
www.nufu.org.uk

Ramblers Association
2nd Floor, Camelford House,
87-90 Albert Embankment, London SE1 7TW
Tel: 020 7339 8500
www.ramblers.org.uk

**Royal Forestry Society of England, Wales and
Northern Ireland**
102 High Street, Tring, Herts HP23 4AF
Tel: 01442 822028
www.rfs.org.uk

Royal Society for the Protection of Birds (RSPB)
The Lodge, Sandy, Bedfordshire SG19 2DL
Tel: 01767 680551
www.rspb.org.uk

Scottish Natural Heritage
12 Hope Terrace, Edinburgh EH9 2AS
Tel: 0131 447 4784
www.snh.org.uk

Scottish Wildlife Trust
Cramond House, Cramond Glebe Road,
Edinburgh EH4 6NS
Tel: 0131 312 7765
www.swt.org.uk

Small Woods Association
The Old Bakery, Pontesbury, Shropshire SY5 0RR
Tel: 01743 792644
www.smallwoods.org.uk

Sustrans Ltd
35 King Street, Bristol BS1 4DZ
Tel: 0117 926 8893 www.sustrans.org.uk

Thrive
Geoffrey Udall Centre, Beech Hill, Reading RG7 2AT
Tel: 01189 885688
www.thrive.org.uk

The Tree Advice Trust
Arboricultural Advisory and Information Service,
Alice Holt Lodge, Wrecclesham, Farnham,
Surrey GU10 4LH
Tree Helpline: 09065 161147
www.treehelp.info

Tree Council
71 Newcomen Street, London SE1 1YT
Tel: 020 7828 9928
www.treecouncil.org.uk

Woodland Trust
Autumn Park, Grantham, Lincolnshire NG31 6LL
Tel: 01476 581111
www.woodland-trust.org.uk

Associations, training and grants

The Dry Stone Walling Association

In 1938 the late Colonel F Rainsford-Hannay formed the Stewartry of Kirkcudbright Drystane Dyking Committee to further the knowledge of and enthusiasm for the walling craft. In 1968 the Committee founded a national organisation called the Dry Stone Walling Association of Great Britain. The DSWA, now a registered charity and based at the National Agricultural Centre at Kenilworth, Warwickshire, is a thriving organisation with a growing membership, reflecting the upsurge of interest in walling in recent years.

The Association offers four levels of membership:

Open – for those with a general interest in walling

Junior – for those under 16

Professional – for the working waller or dyker

Corporate – for companies and organisations wishing to support DSWA work.

Members receive the magazine Waller and Dyker three times a year, which contains general articles, information about branch activities, practice meets, courses and other information. In 2002 there were 18 local branches, covering most of the major walling areas of Great Britain. The branches organise their own competitions, courses and other activities.

The DSWA produces the Register of Professional Wallers and Sources of Stone, to advertise professional members and those corporate members supplying stone. The DSWA also publishes a range of leaflets and booklets on all aspects of the walling craft. Visit the DSWA website (www.dswa.org.uk) for further information.

Training and certification

Training courses on dry stone walling are run by BTCV and by local branches of the DSWA. Branches of the DSWA also hold practice meets, which are informal sessions open to all.

The DSWA operates the Craftsman Certification Scheme, which is a series of progressive, practical tests designed to ensure that dry stone wallers and dykers achieve the highest standards of craftsmanship. The tests are available at Initial, Intermediate, Advanced and Master Craftsman levels, and have been developed over a number of years to provide wallers/dykers with nationally recognised accreditation.

Many agricultural colleges run courses in dry stone walling. Some courses are designed to prepare and examine students according to the Farm Maintenance test of the National Proficiency Test Council. Further details are available from the NPTC Secretary for your area, who can be contacted either through your local agricultural college, or through the head office of the NPTC. Details are given on the NPTC website (www.nptc.org.uk).

National Vocational Qualifications/Scottish Vocational Qualifications

National Vocational Qualifications (NVQs) and Scottish Vocational Qualifications (SVQs) are work-related, competence based qualifications, which are available to anyone at any age or stage of their career. Candidates do not have to follow a course, but need to have evidence that they have the competence to meet the NVQ/SVQ standards.

The NVQ in Environmental Conservation includes competence in dry stone walling and other practical conservation techniques. Over 50% of the NVQs in Environmental Conservation are gained by trainees and others working with BTCV. Contact your local BTCV office for further information.

DSWA Certificates are accepted as evidence of competence towards the Environmental Conservation NVQ.

Competitions and awards

Branches of BTCV and the DSWA organise local competitions, and the DSWA promotes the 'Grand Prix' circuit of walling competitions. BTCV and DSWA also stage exhibits and demonstrations of walling at agricultural shows and other events.

DWSA runs the Pinnacle Award Scheme to commend dry stone walling projects of outstanding quality and merit, or other noteworthy projects of which dry stone walling comprises the most prominent feature. This award, while still recognising the importance of dry stone walling for stock management, is a reflection of the growing use of dry stone walling skills in pubic works, sculptures, garden features and historical restoration projects.

The Ronnie Ball Award of the DSWA recognises and rewards the achievements of individual young people in the craft of dry stone walling and dyking.

Grants

DSWA publish a leaflet on grants for dry stone walling and dyking, which gives outline details and contact addresses. There is no single system of grants for walling, and the availability of grants depends mainly on the area in question. Grants may be available as part of farm agreements for farms within Environmentally Sensitive Areas, National Parks or for Sites of Special Scientific Interest. Funding for land managers may be available through the Countryside Stewardship Scheme (England), which is operated through the Department for Environment, Food and Rural Affairs (DEFRA).

In Wales, the Countryside Council for Wales operates Tir Cymen, which is a whole-farm scheme under which dry stone walls and cloddiau may qualify for grant aid.

In Scotland, the Scottish Executive and Scottish Natural Heritage should be contacted for current information regarding grants.

Grants for dry stone work other than farm walling may also be available. For example, dry stone features in community gardens, in restoration schemes, alongside cycle paths or other projects which benefit the community may attract other sources of funding from organisations which sponsor the arts, community action, urban renewal and so on.

For most projects, initial contact should be made with the conservation officer of similar of the local authority, who should be able to give further advice relating to your area and project. BTCV publish the *Grants and Awards Factsheet*, updated every six months, and which is available to associated groups of BTCV. Contact BTCV for further advice.

The Millennium Wall

The Millennium Wall is a permanent exhibit of regional and local styles of dry stone walling. In April 2000, wallers gathered at the National Stone Centre at Wirksworth in Derbyshire and constructed the wall, using stone brought from all the major walling areas of Britain. A series of interpretative display boards provides information to visitors, and a video and book about the wall are available from the DSWA. For further information visit the DSWA website.

Site studies and surveys

Dry stone walls have great value for field study. Aspects of geology, local history, land-use, social history and wildlife can all be studied by research and observation of local walls. Whilst being of intrinsic educational value, studies and surveys are also important to further the understanding of walls, and to provide a base line from which changes can be measured and comparisons made. When co-ordinated nationally, survey information is very helpful for organisations involved in formulating policies which may affect the maintenance, repair and rebuilding of dry stone walls.

DSWA wall surveys

To encourage a co-ordinated approach to wall surveys, the Dry Stone Walling Association (DSWA) has drawn up a set of guidelines and survey forms which can be used by any group or individual wanting to do wall studies. There are three different categories of survey, A, B, and C, as described below.

Studies can be done of a farm, valley, parish or larger area. Permission must be sought to go on any land other than a public right of way, and it is sensible to gain the co-operation of all landowners in the area in question. Copies of the completed survey information should be sent to the DSWA, and to any local co-ordinator or sponsoring organisation, and to the landowner if requested.

A: LENGTH AND CONDITION

Normally this category should be covered first, to provide the baseline for categories B and C.

Walls are measured from the map or on the ground in convenient sections, for example from field corner to gate. The land use on either side is recorded, together with any furniture such as lunky holes, stiles or water smoots. Any fencing is also noted.

The condition is assessed as being in one of six condition classes, from A to F. As described in chapter 2, these condition classes were used in a survey of walls in England in 1994, which covered 700 one-kilometre squares. The results of the survey are detailed in *The condition of England's dry stone walls* (Countryside Commission, 1996), which is available online at dswa.org.uk

B: STYLE, REGIONAL VARIATIONS AND FEATURES

The same wall sections as identified in the length and condition survey can be surveyed for walling style and features. The height and width of the wall are noted first. The style can be recorded as double, single, single above double, retaining, stone-faced bank or slab wall, with banks and ditches also noted. Style details include throughbands, coverband, coursing, the use of dressed stone, the stone shape and the type of coping. The survey notes includes diagrams to help identify the different styles and features.

Features which can be noted include smoots, wall heads, stiles, gates, bridges, arches, niches, bee-boles and inscriptions. Finally the type of stone is noted as slate, granite, limestone, sandstone or other.

C: HISTORY AND NATURAL HISTORY

The type of information gathered will depend very much on the expertise and interests of the surveyor, and the resources available.

The local history of walls can be researched initially by talking with landowners and other local people with knowledge of the area, and then by research through the county records office and other local sources.

For natural history surveys, the DSWA recommend following the methodology and codes described in the booklet 'What's on a Wall' (South Court Environmental Ltd, 1994), which is available from the DSWA. Species lists are included for algae, ferns, galls, grasses, lichens, liverworts, mosses, trees and shrubs, vascular plants (wild) and vascular plants (garden escapes). For wall fauna, lists are included for birds, butterflies and moths, snails, spiders, woodlice and other animals. Specialist knowledge is required for the identification of many of these organisms.

Churchyard walls

The Living Churchyard and Cemetery Project, in conjunction with the DSWA, have drawn up a survey form for dry stone walls enclosing churchyards. This survey concentrates on the type of stone, the style of building, the amount of dressed stone, and features within the wall.

Copies of the survey form are available online or by post from the DSWA.

Bee boles

Until the late 1800s, bees were kept in straw skeps. In windy or wet areas the skeps were placed in specially constructed niches, called boles, set into stone or brick walls (Chapter 10, Niches and boles). South and south-east facing locations were usually chosen, to provide maximum warmth and shelter from wind and rain. Together with the International Bee Research Association, the DSWA have produced a form for the recording of bee boles. To date, about 1000 sets of boles have been recorded.

Bibliography

This bibliography includes those publications referred to in the text, as well as others relevant to the subject of dry stone walling.

Many of the older titles are out of print, but should be available through libraries. Over the years, proceedings of local historical societies and other similar local publications have included articles on the history, wildlife and other aspects of local walls. Research in county record offices, libraries, museums and other local sources should be rewarding for those interested in the walls in their area.

Not listed here are the leaflets and booklets available from the Dry Stone Walling Association, which are of interest to the working waller and dyker, as well as to those with a more general interest in the craft. Details are available from the Dry Stone Walling Association (p149)

Beddall, J L (1950)
Hedges for Farm and Garden
Faber and Faber

Bennison, George M and Wright, Alan E (1969)
The Geological History of the British Isles
Edward Arnold

Blandford, Percy (1974)
Country Craft Tools
David and Charles

Brooks, Margaret A (1973)
Dry Stone Walls and Wall Building in West Yorkshire
University of Leeds, unpublished dissertation

Callender, R (1986)
Drystane Dyking in Deeside
Private publication

Countryside Commission (1996)
The condition of England's dry stone walls
Countryside Commission

Countryside Commission (1998)
Limestone Pavement
Countryside Commission

Cramb, I (1992)
The Art of the Stonemason
Betterway Books, Ohio

Darlington, A (1981)
The Ecology of Walls
Heinemann

Dry Stone Walling Association (2002)
Dry Stone Walls – The National Collection
DSWA

Evans, E Estyn (1957)
Irish Folk Ways
Routledge and Kegan Paul

Fields, Curtis P (1971)
The Forgotten Art of Building a Stone Wall
Yankee, Dublin, New Hampshire, USA

Garner, Lawrence
Dry Stone Walls
Shire Publications

Goldsworthy, Andy (1994)
Stone
Viking

Griffiths, David (1999)
In There Somewhere
Dry Stone Walling Association

Hart, E (1980)
The Dry Stone Wall Handbook
Thorsons

Hawkes, Jacquetta (1951)
A Land
Penguin

Health and Safety Executive (1992)
Manual Handling Regulations 1992
HMSO

Health and Safety Executive (1996)
Construction (Design and Management) Regs. 1994
HMSO

Health and Safety Executive (1996)
Safety at street works and road works: a code of practice
HMSO

Jenkins, J Geraint (1965)
Traditional Country Craftsmen
Routledge and Kegan Paul

McAfee, P (1997)
Irish Stone Walls
O'Brien Press, Dublin

McRaven, C (1989)
Building with Stone
Storey Books, Vermont

Menneer, R (1994)
Wildlife Revival in Cornish Hedges
Rowe Printers, Cornwall

Mitchell, W R (1992)
Drystone Walls of the Yorkshire Dales
Castelberg, N. Yorks

Ogilivie, E (1996)
An Illustrated Guide to Stone Antiquities on the North Yorkshire Moors
Muddy Boots, N. Yorks

Prevost, W A J (1957)
The Dry Stone Dykes of Upper Annandale
Transactions of the Dumfriesshire and Galloway Natural History and Antiquarian Society

Rainsford-Hannay, F (1972)
Dry Stone Walling
Grieve, Dumfries

Raistrick, Arthur (1966)
Pennine Walls
Dalesman Publishing Co.

Rollinson, Arthur (1972)
Lakeland Walls
Dalesman Publishing Co.

Rule, Ann Louise (1974)
Hedge Building in Mid and West Cornwall
University of Leeds, unpublished dissertation

Segal, S (1969)
Ecological Notes on Wall Vegetation
Junk, The Hague, Netherlands

Stow, Dan (2001)
In the Company of Stone
Artisan, New York

Wood, Eric S (1973)
Field Guide to Archaeology
Collins

BTCV publications

The BTCV Practical Handbook series was started in the 1970s, with most of the original titles remaining in print throughout and new titles being added over the years. There is a rolling programme of revision with most Handbooks now in their second edition. BTCV welcomes feedback at any time on any aspect of the Handbooks, whether the comments are general or detailed, practical or academic, complimentary or critical. Please contact:

Handbooks Editor, BTCV, Howbery Park, Wallingford, Oxfordshire OX10 8BA.
Tel: 01491 821605   Fax 01491 839646
E-mail: information@btcv.org.uk

...or comment online at www.btcv.org/handbooks

The Handbook series comprises:

Fencing
Sand Dunes
Woodlands
Toolcare
Tree Planting & Aftercare
Footpaths
Waterways and Wetlands
Hedging
The Urban Handbook
Dry Stone Walling

To order any of the Handbooks, or for details of other BTCV publications and merchandise, please contact:

BTCV,
Conservation Centre, Balby Road,
Doncaster DN4 0RH
Tel: 01302 572200

Individual members and affiliated groups of BTCV receive the Conserver magazine, and have access to advice on many aspects of conservation volunteering, including organising a local group, health and safety advice, grants and insurance.

For further details please contact The Information Office at the address above.

Glossary

Batter
The slope (taper) of a wall or hedge, expressed as an angle or as a ratio of horizontal to vertical dimensions.

Batter frame
A wooden or metal frame used as a guide to the correct batter and to the heights of throughs and topstones when building a wall or hedge. Also known as a pattern (South West), template or wall gauge (Cotswolds) or walling or dyke frame (Scotland).

Bed
Deposition layer in sedimentary rock. In walling, the flattish base of a stone or any plane along which it splits readily.

Bee bole
A niche in a wall built to store straw bee skeps.

Breccia
Rock composed of sharp-angled fragments cemented in a fine matrix.

Broch
An Iron Age round tower built of dry stonework as a citadel against raiders. Found especially in the Orkneys and Shetlands.

Buck-and-doe
A form of coping alternating large and small upright topstones. Also known as cock-and-hen (Cotswolds).

Chain
A traditional unit of measurement, 22 yards (20m).

Chip and block
A type of stone hedging in which small stones (chips) and large stones (blocks) are intermixed within each course (Devon).

Clearance wall
A wall built largely from stones cleared from the surface of adjacent land. When the wall is made extra wide to accommodate the stones it is also known as an accretion wall or consumption dyke (Scotland).

Cleavage
The structure by which certain metamorphic rocks, such as slate, split most readily, often at an angle to the original bedding plane.

Coping
The line of stones along the top of the wall which protects the structure beneath. Also known as the cap, comb (Cotswolds and South West), cope or topping.

Course
A layer of stones in the face of a wall or hedge.

Coverband
A layer of throughstones placed on top of the double dyking to anchor it and form a base for the coping (Scotland).

Cripple hole
A rectangular opening at the base of a wall built to permit the passage of sheep. Also known as a hogg hole, lonky or lunky hole, sheep run, sheep smoose, smout hole, thawl or thirl hole.

Crown
The top of a bank or hedge. Also known as a comb (Devon).

Ditch
A long narrow trench dug as a boundary, barrier or drain. In Ireland and parts of Wales, a bank or other raised barrier.

Double dyking
The part of a normal dry stone wall which has two rows of face stones packed between with fillings. Also known as doubling (Galloway). Distinguished from single dyking in which only one thickness of stones is used with no fillings.

Dry stone wall
A wall built without mortar. Also known as a drystane dyke (Scot.) or dry stone hedge (Cornwall).

Dyke
A wall (Scotland). Also spelled dike.

Elvan
See Whinstone.

Face
An exposed side of a wall, hedge or bank.

Face stone
A stone whose outer surface forms part of the face of the wall.

Fence
A structure serving as an enclosure, barrier or boundary, loosely used to include walls, hedges, banks, ditches and dykes.

Fillings
Small, irregular stones placed between the two faces of a wall to pack the space between them. Also known as hearting (Scotland).

Fissile
Rock characterised by a tendency to split readily along planes of bedding or cleavage.

Flag
A thin-bedded sandstone which breaks up readily into flat slabs. Loosely used for a flat slab of any type.

Foliation
The structure, similar to but less regular and perfect than cleavage, by which the minerals in rocks such as schist and gneiss are arranged in parallel planes due to metamorphism.

Footing
A stone at the base of a wall, or the foundation of a wall in general. Also known as a found.

Freestone
Stone which has no tendency to split in any particular direction.

Galloway hedge
A combination dry stone wall and thorn hedge which is constructed along a hillside so that the hedge shrubs root through the wall and are protected by it from livestock on the uphill side.

Gap
A breach in a wall due to defect or damage. (v) To fall, leaving a breach; to repair a breach.

Grit
Any hard sandstone, especially one in which small pebbles are mixed with the sand to give a rough texture suitable for millstones. Also known as gritstone.

Head
The smooth, vertical end of a wall or section of wall. Also known as a cheek (Scotland).

Hedge
A line of closely planted shrubs or low-growing trees. In Devon, an earth-filled bank used as a barrier or boundary and faced with stones or turf. In Cornwall, any earth or stone barrier.

Herringbone
A type of stone facing in which alternate courses of stones are angled in opposite directions.

Joint
In walling, the crack between two adjacent stones in a course.

Lamination
A structure of fine, closely spaced layering along the bedding planes in certain sedimentary rocks.

Lintel
A stone slab or wood or metal beam placed over an opening to bridge it and support the structure above.

Locked top
A type of coping in which the topstones are pinned into a solid unit using long thin wedge stones. Mainly Scotland.

March dyke
A major enclosure wall running between estates (Scotland).

Masonry
Stonework characterised by the use of cut and trimmed stone.

Oolite
Rock, usually limestone, composed of small, round calcareous grains.

Pein
The striking surface of a hammer head.

Pinnings
Small stones wedged into spaces in a wall face.

Quartzite
Sandstone consisting mainly of quartz grains cemented into a hard continuous mass by silica.

Rag
Any of several kinds of hard coarse rock, mainly limestones, which break irregularly. Also known as ragstone.

Retaining wall
A wall built across the face of a bank or slope to keep the soil from slipping.

Rhyolite
A volcanic rock similar in composition to granite and usually exhibiting flow lines.

Rood

The traditional unit of wall measurement, 6 yards (5.5m) in granite districts in Scotland and 7 yards (6.4m) in limestone districts and through most of Yorkshire.

Rubble

Rough, mainly untrimmed, walling stone; walls or copings characterised by such stone.

Runner

A long face stone used in a wall head (Scotland).

Scarcement

The in-set between the outer edge of the footings and the first course of face stones (Scotland).

Shooting butt

A small, usually circular enclosure built to shelter grouse shooters.

Smoot

A small rectangular opening in the base of a wall. Rabbit smoots (Scotland: pen hole; Mendips: pop hole) are designed to permit the passage of hares and rabbits. Water smoots (Scotland: double water pen) are designed to permit the passage of water.

Spar

Any of various non-metallic, lustrous and readily cleaved minerals, such as felspar.

Stile

A set of steps over, or an opening through, a wall, hedge or other fence designed to allow passage to pedestrians but not livestock.

Stoop

An upright monolith set into the ground against the wall head of a gate or stile. Also spelled stoup.

Subdivision wall

A wall built to divide a major enclosure into smaller sections, often somewhat lower and less well constructed than the boundary wall.

Through

A large stone placed across the width of a wall to tie the sides together. Also known as a throughstone or a throughband or tieband (Scotland).

Tie

A throughstone used in a wall head.

Topstone

A stone used in a wall's coping. Also known as a cope stone, topper or topping.

Wedge

A small stone placed under or behind a face stone to position it securely.

Whinstone

Any hard dark-coloured rock such as greenstone, basalt, chert or quartzose sandstone. Also known as elvan or elvin (Cornwall).

Index

A

amounts of stone, estimating   38-39
apertures, in walls   118-120
arches   114-117
asymmetrical batter   66

B

batter   125-126
batter frames   32-33, 49-50
bed, of sedimentary stone   36
bedrock, building on   68-70
bee boles   118, 153
boulders, in line of wall   70-71
breaking stone   40-43
broken ties   91
building, principles of   51
bull's eyes   118
butt and hudd   144
butts   122-123

C

cairns   112-113
Caithness flags   145
cantilever lintels   97
carrying stone   22-25
cattle grid   87
cement & lime, safety precautions   26
chip and block   82
clamp, for line bars   33
clashing   143
clawdd   77-81
clearance walls/dykes   126
cloddiau   77-81
clothing   28
concave faces   125
concrete   59-60
condition of walls   13
coping   56-57
   - styles of   132-139
   - across boulders   70-71
   - mortared   138-139
   - on slopes   64-65
   - procedure   57
corners
   - in walls   92-93
   - in stone hedges   86
Cornish stone hedge   4, 81-83
coverbands   135-136
cripple holes   93-95
curves   67-68

D

dating of walls   10-11
decay of stonework, preventing   35
dehydration   27
density of stone   38-39
dimensions of walls   58-59
dismantling walls   47-48
   - on slopes   61
domes   114
double dykes   5-6
Dry Stone Walling Association
   15, 34, 150-151

E

Enclosure Era   1, 9-10
epoxy resin glue   102
exposure   27

F

fauna of walls   15
fences, of stone   144-146
fences with walls   104-106

filling   54-55
first aid kits   28
flag fences   144-146
flora of walls   14-15
footings   48-49
formers for arches   115
foundations   48-49
   - assessing existing   57
   - new   59
   - across slopes   67
   - up slopes   63

G

Galloway dyke   6, 141-144
Galloway hedge   85-86
gapping   57
gate hanging   111
gates   101-103
geological column   1
gneiss, splitting   42-43
green faces   129
group work, organising   34

H

half-dyke   6, 141-144
hammering stone   25
hammers   30-32
handling stone   22-25
harrhanging   102
heads of walls   89-92
   - non-standard   91-92
   - on slopes   62
   - stone hedges   86
hearting   54-55
heather, wall top   85
hedges, stone   76-88
height, variations in   127
herringbone   5, 83
history of walls   8-10
hyperthermia   27
hypothermia   27-28

I

Ireland   7-8
Isle of Man   6

J

joints   54
jumpers   129

L

Lake District slate fences   145
large stones, moving   24
layering   51
   - on slopes   63
locked top   133
lifting stone   22-25, 30
lime mortar   138
limestone   36
limestone pavements   3
line bars   33-34, 50
lines, building   33
lining out   48
lintels, strengthening   96-97
lips, in bedrock   69
lunky holes   6, 93-95

M

maintenance of walls,
legal aspects   17-18
manoeuvring large stones   24
Manual Handling Regulations   25
mortar   59-60

N

new walls   58-59
niches   117-118

O

obligation to fence   18

ordering stone   38-39

P

pens   121-122
phantom gates   7
pillars   107-112
pine cone cairns   113
pinnings   130

Q

quoins   108-110

R

retaining walls   73-76
roadside working   26
running joints   54

S

safety considerations   22
seats   120
sedimentary stone   35-36
scarcement   66, 127
schists, splitting   42-43
shale   36-37
shaping stone   40-43
shiners   128
single dykes   6, 139-141
site risk assessment   21
slate, cleaving   40-41
slopes, walls on   61-67
smoots   93-97
sources of stone   37-38
South Western rung stiles   87
spherical cairns   114
stiles
   - in stone hedges   86
   - step stiles   98-99
   - step-through stiles   100
   - squeeze stiles   99-100
stone fences   144-146
stoops   101
sunburn   26-27

T

T-junctions   93
three-quarter throughs   55
three-way stiles   101
throughs   55-56
   - absence of   131
   - flush   131
   - in new walls   59
   - patterns of   130-132
   - projecting   130-131
tools   28-32
traced stones   51, 129
transporting stone   30
triangular lintels   96-97
treasure trove   19
trees   71-72
turf dykes   83-84
turf tops   84-85

U

undulating ground, walls on   65-66

V

vertical random stone hedges   82-83

W

wall heads   89-92
   - on slopes   62
water gates   103-104
water smoots   96
watershot   128-129
weather precautions   26-28
wedging   53
whinstone   36
width, variations in   126
work season   26